Applied Charged Particle Optics

PART A

Advances in Electronics and Electron Physics

Edited by

L. MARTON   CLAIRE MARTON

Smithsonian Institution
Washington, D.C.

SUPPLEMENTS

Applied Charged Particle Optics

Edited by
A. SEPTIER

CONSERVATOIRE NATIONAL DES ARTS ET MÉTIERS
PARIS, FRANCE

PART A

1980

ACADEMIC PRESS

A Subsidiary of Harcourt Brace Jovanovich, Publishers

New York   London   Toronto   Sydney   San Francisco

ACADEMIC PRESS, INC.
111 Fifth Avenue, New York, New York 10003

United Kingdom Edition published by
ACADEMIC PRESS, INC. (LONDON) LTD.
24/28 Oval Road, London NW1 7DX

LIBRARY OF CONGRESS CATALOG CARD NUMBER: 63–12814

ISBN 0–12–014573–1

PRINTED IN THE UNITED STATES OF AMERICA

80 81 82 83   9 8 7 6 5 4 3 2 1

Contents

Numerical Methods for Computing Electrostatic and Magnetic Fields

P. BONJOUR

Methods of Computing Optical Properties and Combating Aberrations for Low-Intensity Beams

P. W. HAWKES

Emittance and Brightness: Definitions and Measurements

CLAUDE LEJEUNE AND JEAN AUBERT

High-Resolution Scanning Transmission Low-Energy Ion Microscopes and Microanalyzers

RICCARDO LEVI-SETTI

High-Energy Ion Microprobes

BERND MARTIN AND RAINER NOBILING

List of Contributors

Numbers in parentheses indicate the pages on which the authors' contributions begin.

JEAN AUBERT (159), *Institut d'Electronique Fondamentale, Université Paris, Orsay, France*

P. BONJOUR (1), *Institut d'Electronique Fondamentale, Université Paris, Orsay, France*

P. W. HAWKES (45), *Laboratoire d'Optique Electronique, Centre National de la Recherche Scientifique, Toulouse, France*

CLAUDE LEJEUNE (159), *Institut d'Electronique Fondamentale, Université Paris, Orsay, France*

RICCARDO LEVI-SETTI (261), *Enrico Fermi Institute and Department of Physics, The University of Chicago, Chicago, Illinois 60637*

BERND MARTIN (321), *Max-Planck-Institut für Kernphysik, Physikalisches Institut der Universität Heidelberg, Heidelberg, West Germany*

RAINER NOBILING (321), *Max-Planck-Institut für Kernphysik, Physikalisches Institut der Universität Heidelberg, Heidelberg, West Germany*

Foreword

We are most pleased to have as a supplement to *Advances in Electronics and Electron Physics* these volumes edited by Professor A. Septier on *Applied Charged Particle Optics*. No subject better represents the value of electron physics to modern technology. This point is well elaborated in Professor Septier's own preface. We, therefore, can only add our best wishes and our thanks to the Editor and contributors for their efforts in producing so valuable a reference work.

L. MARTON
C. MARTON

Preface

Charged particle optics is a relatively young subject, for it was in 1926 that Busch showed that an inhomogeneous axial magnetic field exerts a focusing action on an electron beam and is thus capable of bringing electrons from an "object" point together at an "image" point. Electrostatic "lenses" appeared on the scene a few years later, around 1931–1932, barely 50 years ago.

This discovery, that lenses for charged particles are in some sense analogous to the glass lenses used to focus light, stimulated the development of this new branch of optics. Within a few years, spectacular progress had been made, both in the theory and in practical applications, particularly in the design of cathode-ray tubes, mass spectrometers, and electron microscopes.

It is surprising that so many decades should have separated the period during which the free electron was discovered and that in which the first devices for focusing and analyzing beams of charged particles appeared, for the laws governing the action of electromagnetic fields on charged particles had been known since the nineteenth century. It was doubtless the work of Louis de Broglie in 1924–1925 on the wavelike nature of particles that attracted the attention of numerous physicists and reawakened interest in particles capable of traveling freely in a sufficiently good vacuum. The progress made during that period in vacuum technology was certainly not unrelated to the growth of interest in particle optics: a good vacuum is essential if the electric fields needed to give the particles their initial acceleration are not to break down, and the same is true of any electrostatic focusing or deflecting elements.

The theory advanced by L. de Broglie in 1924 was verified experimentally for the first time in 1927 by Davisson and Germer, who observed diffraction of electrons by the regular grating formed by the atoms of a crystal. The immense possibilities for exploring solids by means of electrons immediately became apparent, if transmission electron microscopes capable of a resolution 10^3 or 10^4 times better than the diffraction limit of the best optical microscopes could be constructed.

Apart from this particular point—the calculation of the theoretical resolving power of the electron microscope—all the optical properties of lenses and deflectors for charged particles were studied from the beginning without involving the wave aspect of the particles. Once the electrical potential and magnetic field distributions are known, particle trajectories can be calculated from which the essential properties of the optical systems can be established; the relevant quantities are defined by analogy with those familiar from the geometrical optics of centered light optical systems and prisms, including, in particular, their geometrical aberrations.

Several large industrial firms and numerous university laboratories became interested in developing high-magnification electron microscopes. This activity was not halted by the war, for new needs became apparent with the result that fresh aspects of particle optics were investigated. Thus the design of high-frequency tubes using intense electron beams and of isotope separators capable of yielding appreciable quantities of uranium 235 became possible only after new problems concerning the mutual interaction of charged particles had been solved; these effects had hitherto been neglected in devices using beams of low-current density.

By the early 1950s, the geometrical optics of optical systems with rotational symmetry or with a plane of symmetry had few secrets from the specialists in this field. Since everyone knew that the two fundamental aberrations of lenses or prisms—aperture aberration and chromatic aberration—could not be eliminated, unlike the case of glass lenses, systems with minimum aberrations were sought. With the gradual improvement of construction techniques, affecting both the mechanical parts and the electrical supplies, high-quality electron microscopes with a resolution better than 10 Å appeared on the market. These instruments provided not only a highly magnified image of an extremely thin object but also the diffraction pattern of the zone through which the electron beam passed.

New fields of application were emerging, however: large high-energy particle accelerators, which required the development of RF or microwave generators capable of furnishing several tens of megawatts in pulsed operation, and a new family of instruments for the quantitative analysis of solid specimens, which would thus go beyond mere qualitative observation. The first of these applications provoked a spurt of intense activity, devoted to strong focusing optical systems, as a result of which it became possible to accelerate and focus electron or proton beams to energies in the giga-electron-volt range (1 GeV = 10^9 eV). During the same period, the 1950s, a new generation of instruments of more modest size was born, which were to revolutionize analytical techniques. The earliest of these was the electron microprobe, in which the characteristic X rays emitted by a solid bombarded with electrons were used to investigate the distribution of a particular chemical element at the surface of the solid; in the earliest models, the specimen was moved under a static probe, but the advantage of scanning the probe over a stationary specimen was soon recognized and the necessary scanning unit incorporated. The concentration of the element in question within a volume element of the order of 1 μm^3 could be estimated to a good approximation.

The effort that went into producing electron microprobes—electron beams converging to a very small spot—naturally led to the commercial development of scanning microscopes, which gave an image of the surface of a massive specimen on a cathode-ray tube; the secondary electrons emitted by the specimen were used to create the signal, and the resulting image had almost unlimited depth of field and a resolution of the order of a few hundred angstroms.

Over the years, these microprobe instruments were improved, in order to reduce the spot size while keeping the probe current as high as possible. The brightness of the electron source, already known to be an important parameter in transmission electron microscopes, now became the vital quantity to be increased, and field emission tips began to be incorporated into microprobe instruments not long after the appearance of the equipment needed to provide the very high vacuum (UHV) required. These developments also acted as a stimulus in the design of energy analyzers and filters.

The constant efforts to ameliorate both the optical system and the technological aspects of the transmission electron microscope (TEM), associated with a better understanding of the way in which the image is formed, gradually pushed the resolution limit down to 2–3 Å with electrons of 100–200 keV. The age-old dream of seeing individual atoms, or at least an "image" of atoms, however imperfect, seemed to be on the brink of becoming a reality. In order to improve the resolution still further, and also to enable thicker specimens to be examined (of the order of micrometers in thickness, rather than a few hundred angstroms), very high-voltage microscopes were built (first at 1 MeV and later at 3 MeV). Innumerable problems, connected with the optical system, parasitic radiation, and mechanical vibration, had to be overcome before these cumbersome instruments reached practical resolutions in the angstrom range.

It was against this background that the idea of constructing a scanning microscope with a probe only a few angstroms in diameter provided by a field emission gun was born, in the mid-1960s. Such a microscope would have much the same resolution as a traditional TEM, for thin specimens, and the image would be displayed using information conveyed by the transmitted electrons. It was some years before the partisans of the TEM came to recognize the advantages of the scanning transmission electron microscope (STEM), but commercial models are now finding their way into many laboratories and a number of high-voltage STEMs are now being constructed or planned. It was in fact with a STEM that individual atoms of a specimen were first observed directly, in 1970, and similar TEM micrographs appeared shortly after, in 1971.

All these instruments—electron microscopes, both TEM and STEM, X-ray microanalyzers, particle accelerators at medium and high energies,

mass spectrometers, and even their more humble relations such as television cameras and tubes—are indispensable tools, not only for physicists, chemists, and biologists in the field of pure research, but also for
applied scientists and engineers striving to develop new materials and
new devices for use in all the so-called "applied" sciences, electronics
in particular. Numerous international congresses, and the spectacular
results that have been obtained with such instruments, have made the
latter familiar throughout the scientific world and indeed to an even wider
public, thanks to popular texts and to television.

Although their merits are beyond discussion, these high-prestige instruments have somewhat obscured the existence of a wide variety of
other devices using low-current beams of particles. These are used to
obtain a better knowledge of the physical, electronic, or chemical properties of surfaces, for quantitative analysis of thin films or chemical com-
pounds, for microfabrication of electronic components smaller than a
micrometer in dimension, or in optoelectronics as image converters
for images obtained with radiation imperceptible to the unaided eye. Likewise, turning to beams of high-power density, we draw attention to electron tubes for microwave generation already mentioned, electron beam
welders, sources and injectors of electron and ion beams for accelerators,
and the electron beams in the gigawatt range with which controlled fusion
could be achieved.

All of these devices are the outcome of 50 years of research and effort toward what we might call the domestication of charged particles in
the service of mankind.

A vast literature has grown up around the better-known charged particle instruments. In these new volumes, which may be regarded as a con-
tinuation of "Focusing of Charged Particles," Vols. 1 and 2 (A. Septier,
ed., Academic Press, New York, 1967), we have tried to cover the many
devices that have proved so useful in surface studies, in the analysis of
solids and gases, and in the microfabrication of electronic components,
but without going beyond the bounds of geometrical optics.

The object of the first three articles in Supplement 13A is to bring up
to date the general methods, described in "Focusing of Charged Particles,"
for calculating the properties of optical systems or particle beams. In the
first article, newly developed numerical methods of solving the equations
of Laplace and Poisson are described, whereby potentials and magnetic
field distributions can be calculated very accurately. Techniques for
studying the trajectories and aberrations of optical systems are then considered, with particular attention given to the practical formulas from
which they can be evaluated in concrete situations and to procedures
for optimizing complex systems. In the second of this group of articles,

the fundamental characteristics of real beams with nonvanishing emittance are examined, together with a critical account of the various diagnostic methods by which these characteristics can be investigated.

The last two articles in Supplement 13A and the first in Supplement 13B provide descriptions of ion microprobes operating in very different energy ranges and for quite different purposes. First, scanning transmission ion microscopes (STIM) are considered, a prototype of which is already functioning with 50-keV protons; these microscopes use point and field emission ion sources, which will shortly be ready for incorporation into any high-resolution ion microprobe system for the inspection or fabrication of microcircuits. The next article is devoted to ion microprobes, intended essentially for the local chemical analysis of solids using the X rays emitted when the specimen is bombarded with 2–3-MeV ions; this recent technique is more sensitive than its electron counterpart. Finally in this group, low-energy scanning and fixed-beam ion microprobes are considered; by analyzing the secondary ions emitted, the surface distribution of a particular element can be established with a resolution of the order of micrometers. We felt that it would be useful to compare the methods of obtaining the image and the performances of the two types of microprobe systems.

Two pieces of equipment used in the electronics industry for the production of components and in particular for microminiaturization are then described. First, ion implanters are considered, with which semiconductors can be locally doped; numerous problems concerning ion production, purification, and transport of the beam and focusing have arisen and the solutions are described. The various instruments, derived from the SEM, that use electron microprobes to etch electron-sensitive resins directly are then described; these are employed when the size of the components required is so small that masks can no longer be made. The scanning pattern of the probe is then controlled by computer.

In the three final articles of Supplement 13B, devices for analyzing mass or energy are described. Mass analysis is required when the substance to be analyzed, which may be a solid or a gas, is converted into ions, whereas energy analysis is required when an electron beam is used as an active element to excite or detect atoms or molecules at a surface or in a gas cell. Thus in the first of these articles, it seemed appropriate to describe recent progress in the field of mass spectrometers and isotope separators, particularly for applications involving radioactive substances with very short lifetimes, created artificially by bombarding a solid target with particles from an accelerator. For surface analysis by secondary ion mass spectrometry (SIMS) and the analysis of residual gases in ultrahigh vacuum chambers, quadrupole mass filters are now used extensively; the next article therefore describes the improvements that are continually being made to these, to provide even better resolution and transmission. Finally, in the last article, we turn to low-energy electron studies. Energy analysis of beams of slow electrons and the need to render such beams monochromatic have created a profusion of devices, each with its own particular domain of application. We therefore felt that a critical comparison of the properties of these analyzers would be welcomed by users confronted with a bewilderingly wide choice. Among the most common applications, we may mention Auger analysis, ESCA, and low-energy electron spectroscopy.

Not all devices using particle beams are discussed in these volumes but even so, the amount of material is too great to be contained in a single volume and we have therefore made a somewhat arbitrary division between Supplements 13A and B.

It is a pleasure to thank all the authors who have contributed articles for these volumes, despite all the other calls of a busy professional life on their time, and thus to share with the reader their personal reflections and the fruit of their wide experience.

A. Septier

Contents of Part B

Applied Charged Particle Optics

PART A

ADVANCES IN ELECTRONICS AND ELECTRON PHYSICS. SUPPLEMENT 13A

Numerical Methods for Computing Electrostatic and Magnetic Fields

P. BONJOUR

Institut d'Electronique Fondamentale
Université Paris
Orsay, France

I. INTRODUCTION

This article is devoted to the numerical computation of fields in electron optical systems by means of a digital computer. We mainly consider the magnetic systems for which Poisson's equation must be solved. The problem of electrostatic lenses has been dealt with in the book "Focusing of Charged Particles" (Weber, 1967), and the methods presented here are perfectly suitable for a numerical solution of Laplace's equation. The calculations have been made in such a way that the equations obtained are

1

convenient for systems with an axial symmetry, and only minor changes are needed to establish equations valid for other systems, those with a symmetry of translation, for instance.

First, in Section II, we briefly review the equations of electrostatics and present a method of calculation specific to electrostatic lenses; by solving a system of integral equations, the charges carried by the conductors are computed, and the potential within the lens is deduced from them. In Section III, we review the fundamental equations of magnetostatics, then present the various functions suitable for the calculation, with the corresponding partial derivative equations. Section IV deals with the principle of the network method, the various meshes used, and the ways of generating them. In this method, the partial derivative equations are replaced by difference equations, which are established in several ways, as shown in Section V. It is possible either to use a local expansion of the unknown function, as in the finite difference method, or start from a global estimation of the energy to deduce the differential equation by means of the variational principle. These difference equations are solved either by iterative methods, which were used first and have been fully studied theoretically, or by direct methods, which have been introduced more recently.

In Section VI, we deal with the solution of the equations, which is made more complicated by the nonlinearity resulting from the permeability local variations. Finally, in Section VII, we give two examples of computed axial flux density in superconducting lenses to illustrate the calculation methods previously developed.

II. Electrostatic Lenses

The properties of electrostatic lenses can be deduced from the potential function V. The potential can be created in one of two ways: (1) by means of conductors held at constant and known potentials, in which case Laplace's equation has to be solved; or (2) by means of charges located on conductors, in which case the method of charge densities is used.

A. Equations of Electrostatics

Conductors held at constant potentials create an electric field $\mathbf{E}$, which is derived from a potential V. The conductors are separated by empty space or by materials. These media are characterized from an electrostatic viewpoint by their permittivity (ϵ_0 for the vacuum, ϵ_i for the ith material medium). Also, in the case of lenses handling high-intensity beams, the presence of the charge of the focused particles must be taken into account, and here the volume density of the beam will be called ρ.

Outside the conductors, the potential satisfies Poisson's equation

$$\nabla^2 V = -\rho/\epsilon \tag{1}$$

or, if the beam charge is negligible, Laplace's equation

$$\nabla^2 V = 0 \tag{2}$$

The solutions of Eqs. (1) and (2) must also satisfy the so-called boundary conditions, which are as follows.

1. On conductor i, held at potential V_i, we must have

$$V(x, y, z) = V_i$$

2. On the surface separating two media i and j

$$\mathbf{n} \times (\mathbf{E}_j - \mathbf{E}_i) = 0, \qquad \mathbf{n} \cdot (\epsilon_j \mathbf{E}_j - \epsilon_i \mathbf{E}_i) = \sigma \tag{3}$$

where σ is the surface density of charges possibly located there and $\mathbf{n}$ the normal unit vector directed from i to j.

3. If the surface charge density σ of certain conductors is known instead of their potential, the preceding equations give

$$\epsilon_i \mathbf{E}_i \cdot \mathbf{n} = \sigma, \qquad \mathbf{n} \times \mathbf{E}_i = 0$$

where $\mathbf{n}$ is directed toward the outside of the conductor.

Equations (1) and (2), when written in a system of cylindrical coordinates, and Eqs. (3) have the same mathematical form as Eqs. (14)–(16), which represent the magnetostatic properties of a system of currents and media by means of the magnetic scalar potential. They can be written in general form (19), and the methods for solving Eq. (19), described thereafter, can be applied without restriction to the case of the electrostatic potential.

B. The Charge Density Method

In this method pioneered by Read *et al.* (1971), the unknown quantities are the superficial charges appearing on the conductors, and the potential in each point is given by an integral equation taken over all the charges. In particular, the calculated potential must be constant on each conductor. Let us consider a simple case to illustrate the method.

Figure 1 shows a two-cylinder lens. Let us assume that the walls of the cylinders are of negligible thickness. From a mathematical viewpoint, the superficial charges located on the inside and the outside of the cylinder walls can be considered to be a unique charge with a value equal to the

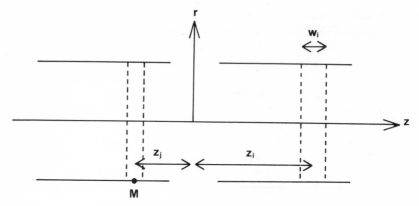

FIG. 1. A two-cylinder lens with the axis of coordinates for the use of Read's method. The tubes are divided into rings of a w_i width and the potential is computed in M.

sum of the inner and outer charges. Each cylinder is divided into $n/2$ circular rings, and the superficial charge density is assumed to be uniform over each ring. These rings are of variable width and are made narrower near the gap, where the charge density changes most rapidly. The potential produced by each ring is similar to that produced by a circle of radius R carrying the same charge. The potential V_i at a point with coordinates r, z, resulting from a charge q_i uniformly distributed over a circle of radius R, lying in the plane $z = z_i$ is given by (Durand, 1964)

$$V_i(r, z) = \frac{q_i k_i}{4\pi^2 \epsilon_0 \sqrt{Rr}} K(k_i) \tag{4}$$

where

$$k_i^2 = \frac{4Rr}{(R + r)^2 + (z - z_i)^2}$$

and $K(k)$ is the complete elliptic integral of the first kind. By applying to some point M located on the jth ring in the plane $z = z_j$ and introducing the inner and outer superficial density σ_i of the ith ring, with a surface s_i, we obtain

$$V_i(R, z_j) = (s_i \sigma_i k_i / 2\pi^2 \epsilon_0 R) K(k_i)$$

The potential at this point M resulting from the contribution of all the rings of the two cylinders is then

$$V(R, z_j) = (1/2\pi^2 \epsilon_0 R) \sum_1^n s_i \sigma_i k_i K(k_i) \tag{5}$$

In this expression, the term $i = j$ must be evaluated separately, for $K(1)$ becomes infinite. If the ring widths cannot be assumed to be 'infinitely small, that is, if w_i is not sufficiently small compared with $z_j - z_i$, Eq. (4) has to be replaced by a more complex one (Durand, 1964), which expresses $V_i(r, z)$ by means of an elliptic integral of the third kind. An equation such as Eq. (5) is written for each of the n rings that comprise the lens. A linear system of n equations is obtained, in which the second members are known since $V(R, z_j)$ is equal to the potential of the left-hand or right-hand cylinder, according to the value of z_j. At first, this system was solved by an iterative method, in which the errors between the calculated and the applied potentials were used to obtain improved estimates of the superficial charge densities. Then Harting and Read (1976) solved it by the classical Gauss triangularization method.

This charge density method has been used to compute aperture lenses (Read 1970), two-cylinder lenses (Read et al., 1971), and three-cylinder lenses (Adams and Read, 1972). In these papers, they give computed cardinal elements and spherical aberration coefficients. A data book by Harting and Read (1976) deals with these same types of lenses, and also unequal diameter two-cylinder lenses, double- and triple-rectangular tube lenses, double- and triple-slit lenses and thick-walled two-cylinder lenses.

III. MAGNETOSTATICS OF VACUUM AND MEDIA

A. Fundamental Equations

Let us consider volumes V_1, V_2, . . . of magnetizable materials placed in the magnetic field of a volume V_0 carrying currents with a volume density $\mathbf{J}_0$ and a superficial density $\mathbf{K}_0$. Each element of material with a volume dV becomes a dipole with a magnetic moment equal to $\mathbf{M}\,dV$ under the influence of the local magnetic induction $\mathbf{B}$, and

$$\mathbf{M} = (\mu_0^{-1} - \mu^{-1})\mathbf{B} \qquad (6)$$

where μ is the magnetic permeability of the material and the ratio μ/μ_0 is its relative permeability. In ferromagnetic materials, the relation between $\mathbf{B}$ and $\mathbf{M}$ is no longer linear at high field. The permeability will still be defined by Eq. (6), μ now being a function of $\mathbf{B}$.

The vector $\mathbf{B}$ satisfies the two relations (Durand, 1968)

$$\nabla \times (\mathbf{B}/\mu) = \mathbf{J}_0, \qquad \nabla \cdot \mathbf{B} = 0 \qquad (7)$$

At the surface between two media i and j, the boundary conditions are

$$\mathbf{n} \times (\mathbf{B}_j/\mu_j - \mathbf{B}_i/\mu_i) = \mathbf{K}_{ij}, \qquad \mathbf{n} \cdot (B_j - B_i) = 0$$

in which $\mathbf{K}_{ij}$ is a superficial current that may circulate on the interface between media i and j.

By developing $\nabla \times \mathbf{B}$ in Eq. (7), we have

$$\mu^{-1} \nabla \times \mathbf{B} + \nabla(\mu^{-1}) \times \mathbf{B} = \mathbf{J}_0$$

and by introducing the vector potential $\mathbf{A}$, we finally have

$$\nabla^2 \mathbf{A} + \mu^{-1}(\nabla\mu \times (\nabla \times \mathbf{B})) = -\mu \mathbf{J}_0 \qquad (8)$$

Equation (8) is reduced to

$$\nabla^2 \mathbf{A} = -\mu_0 \mathbf{J}$$

when the medium is homogeneous.

The boundary conditions for $\mathbf{A}$ are

$$\mathbf{n} \times [(\nabla \times \mathbf{A}_j)/\mu_j - (\nabla \times \mathbf{A}_i)/\mu_i] = \mathbf{K}_{ij}, \qquad \mathbf{n} \cdot (\mathbf{A}_j - \mathbf{A}_i) = 0 \qquad (9)$$

B. Systems Associated with the Currents

The solution of the vector equation (8) is simplified very much if we consider systems associated with the currents, as first suggested by Durand (1955).

1. Definitions

Let us consider fictitious point magnetic charges q as a helpful intermediate in the calculation. From these charges, superficial σ^* and volume ρ^* densities can be created. Let us also consider magnetic dipoles of moment $\mathbf{p}$ whose superficial and volume densities are, respectively, τ^* and $\mathbf{P}^*$. To simplify the language, we will speak of polarized surfaces and volumes.

These charges and dipoles create a magnetic field $\mathbf{E}^*$ derivating from a magnetic scalar potential V^* and generally, the equations of electrostatics can be written for all the starred quantities. For example,

$$\mathbf{E}^* = -\nabla V^*, \qquad \mu_0 \nabla^2 V = -\rho^*$$

Let us say that a system of magnetic charges and dipoles, defined by the quantities $\mathbf{E}^*$, V^*, $\mathbf{P}^*$, etc. is associated to a system of currents defined by the quantities $\mathbf{B}$, $\mathbf{A}$, $\mathbf{J}$, etc. if in every point in space, it is possible to write

$$\mathbf{B} = \mu_0 \mathbf{E}^* + \mathbf{P}^* \tag{10}$$

It can be noticed at once that even though $\mathbf{E}^*$ derives from a potential, $\mathbf{P}^*$ does not depend on this condition. Therefore, the sum (10) can become solenoidal in order to be equal to $\mathbf{B}$ in every point. Further, Ampère's law applied to Eq. (10) shows that we necessarily have

$$\int_c \mathbf{P}^* \cdot \mathbf{dl} = \mu_0 I$$

2. Elementary Associated Systems

An infinite half-plane covered with a superficial density

$$d\tau^* = \mu_0 K \, dx$$

of perpendicular magnetic dipoles can be associated with a strip of width dx carrying a superficial current $K \, dx$ (Fig. 2).

Another associated system is a half-parallelepiped with a dipole volume density P^*, $P^* = \mu_0 K$.

In a composite system, a polarized volume P^* is followed by a polarized half-plane $d\tau^*$.

A tube of current $J \, dx \, dy$ can be associated to an infinite parallelepiped with a dipole volume density $dP^* = \mu_0 J$ per unit of length (Fig. 3). Another system is composed of the polarized volume followed by a half-plane covered with $d\tau^* = \mu_0 J \, dx \, dy$.

The system associated to a loop of current (Fig. 4) is composed of dipoles perpendicular to a bordered surface S having the loop for boundary with a density $\tau^* = \mu_0 I$.

3. Systems Associated with a Solenoid

The above results enable us to describe systems associated with a thick solenoid.

A disk with a r radius and a volume density

$$dP^* = \mu_0 J \, dr$$

can be associated with the tube of current carrying an intensity $J \, dr \, dz$ in Fig. 5. By integrating between the inner radius a and the outer radius c, we separate the volume of the solenoid into two regions with the following polarizations:

$$P^* = \mu_0 J(c - a), \quad 0 \leqslant r < a, \quad P^* = \mu_0 J(c - r), \quad a \leqslant r < c$$

limited by the planes $z = \pm b$, the solenoid length being $2b$.

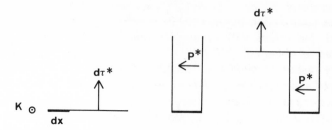

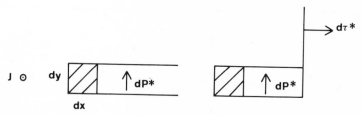

FIG. 2. Systems associated with a strip of width dx carrying a current $K\ dx$. **K** is directed forward with respect to the plane of the figure.

FIG. 3. Systems associated with a tube of current $J\ dx\ dy$. **J** is directed forward with respect to the plane of the figure.

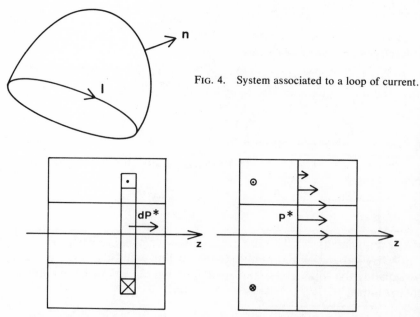

FIG. 4. System associated to a loop of current.

FIG. 5. (Left) System associated to an elementary tube of current of a solenoid. (Right) Global system for the solenoid.

Therefore, the associated system is composed of two cylinders with a volume polarization parallel to the z axis (Fig. 5). This is the simplest system, but others with composite superficial and volume polarization also can be obtained.

The system associated to the tube of current $J\ dr\ dz$ in Fig. 6 is composed of a circular torus BA with a volume density $dP^* = -\mu_0 J\ dr$.

Between B and C and between C and D, there is a superficial density $\tau^* = -\mu_0 J\ dr\ dz$. By integrating, we obtain

$$P^* = -\mu_0 J(r - a)$$

with the volume ABCD,

$$\tau^* = -\mu_0 J(c - a)(b - z)$$

At point B on the lateral surface of abscissa z,

$$\tau^* = 2\mu_0 Jb(c - a)$$

in the symmetry plane CD. The ampere-turns NI of the solenoid are related to J by

$$NI = 2Jb(c - a)$$

Finally, we obtain the system shown in Fig. 6. In the paper by Durand (1955), other systems associated to a thick or thin solenoid can be found.

4. Example of a Magnetic Lens

Let us take a last example for the symmetrical magnetic lens whose cross section is shown in Fig. 7, where AB is the symmetry axis, IJKL a

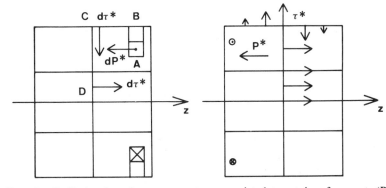

FIG. 6. (Left) Another elementary system associated to a tube of current. (Right) Global system for the solenoid.

10   P. BONJOUR

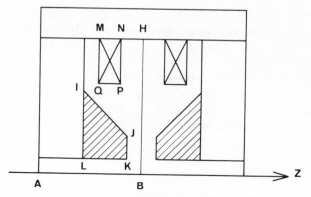

FIG. 7. Cross section of a symmetrical magnetic lens: IJKL is a pole piece and MNPQ an excitation coil.

pole piece, and MNPQ an excitation coil. The associated system is obtained by the method explained in the preceding paragraph. With NI the ampere-turns flowing in MNPQ, a density

$$P^* = - \mu_0 J(r - a)$$

is distributed in this volume.

Over BH and HN, there is a constant superficial polarization

$$\tau^* = \mu_0 NI$$

Over MN a polarization decreases linearly from $\mu_0 NI$ at N to zero at point M.

5. Use of the Associated Systems

By using an associated system, we replace the resolution of three partial derivative equations resulting from Eq. (8) by that of one equation only.

The system of currents J_0 and K_0 is replaced by an associated system with the densities τ^* and P^*. The volume polarization P^* can be replaced by the equivalent system of masses

$$\rho^* = - \nabla \cdot P^*, \qquad \sigma^* = n \cdot P^*$$

The system τ^*, ρ^*, and σ^* derives from a scalar potential V_0^*, which is related to the induction B_0 produced by the currents, and these quantities satisfy

$$\mathbf{B}_0 = - \mu \, \nabla V_0^* + \mathbf{P}^*$$

The magnetized media create a magnetic field derived from a scalar potential V'^*, and the whole magnetic field reacting upon them is

$$\mathbf{B}/\mu = -\nabla V'^* + \mathbf{B}_0/\mu = -\nabla V + \mathbf{P}^*/\mu$$

with $V = V_0^* + V'^*$. Remembering that $\mathbf{B}$ has a zero divergence, it gives

$$\mu \, \nabla^2 V + (\nabla V)(\nabla \mu) = -\rho^* \qquad (11)$$

This is the partial derivative equation of V, which becomes Poisson's equation within an homogeneous medium

$$\nabla^2 V = -\rho/\mu$$

Therefore, it is obviously interesting to choose $\mathbf{P}^*$ so that ρ^* should be zero everywhere, and Eq. (11) should become Laplace's equation. The systems associated with a solenoid, which we have described above, fulfill this condition.

C. Equations for the Axisymmetric Systems

Magnetic lenses are systems with axial symmetry so we will give the final equations by using cylindrical coordinates.

1. Equations for the Vector Potential A

In a system of cylindrical coordinates (r, θ, z), the currents and the vector potential have only one component along θ. Equation (8) becomes

$$\frac{\partial^2 A}{\partial r^2} + \frac{1}{r}\frac{\partial A}{\partial r} + \frac{\partial^2 A}{\partial z^2} - \frac{A}{r^2} + \frac{1}{\mu}\left[\frac{\partial \mu}{\partial r}\left(\frac{\partial A}{\partial r} + \frac{A}{r}\right) + \frac{\partial \mu}{\partial z}\frac{\partial A}{\partial z}\right] = -\mu J \qquad (12)$$

which becomes within an homogeneous medium

$$\frac{\partial^2 A}{\partial r^2} + \frac{1}{r}\frac{\partial A}{\partial r} + \frac{\partial^2 A}{\partial z^2} - \frac{A}{r^2} = -\mu J$$

The boundary conditions (9) give

$$A_1 = A_2$$

$$(1/\mu_2)(d/dn)(rA_2) - (1/\mu_1)(d/dn)(rA_1) = -rK \qquad (13)$$

The induction $\mathbf{B}$ is in a meridional plane; its components are

$$B_r = -\partial A/\partial z, \qquad B_z = (1/r)(\partial/\partial r)(rA)$$

2. Equations for the Scalar Potential V

The system associated with the currents being defined, V is the solution of

$$\frac{\partial^2 V}{\partial r^2} + \frac{1}{r}\frac{\partial V}{\partial r} + \frac{\partial^2 V}{\partial z^2} + \frac{1}{\mu}\left(\frac{\partial V}{\partial r}\frac{\partial \mu}{\partial r} + \frac{\partial V}{\partial z}\frac{\partial \mu}{\partial z}\right) = -\frac{\rho^*}{\mu} \tag{14}$$

with the boundary conditions

$$V_2 - V_1 = \tau^* \tag{15}$$

on every boundary covered with dipoles of density τ^* (eventually $\tau^* = 0$),

$$\mu_2\, dV_2/dn - \mu_1\, dV_1/dn = \sigma_2^* - \sigma_1^* \tag{16}$$

on every boundary covered on each side with densities σ_1^* and σ_2^* (eventually equal to zero).

When V has been obtained, it follows that

$$\mathbf{H} = -\boldsymbol{\nabla} V + \mathbf{P}^*/\mu, \qquad \mathbf{B} = \mu\mathbf{H}$$

3. Equations for the Flux Function

The flux of $\mathbf{B}$ through a circle of radius r centered on the z axis is equal to

$$\phi = \int A\, dl = 2\pi r A$$

The flux function F is then defined as

$$F = \phi/2\pi\mu_0 = rA/\mu_0$$

We may simplify Eqs. (12) and (13) by using F. Substituting A, we have

$$\frac{\partial^2 F}{\partial r^2} - \frac{1}{r}\frac{\partial F}{\partial r} + \frac{\partial^2 F}{\partial z^2} - \frac{1}{\mu}\left(\frac{\partial F}{\partial r}\frac{\partial \mu}{\partial r} + \frac{\partial F}{\partial z}\frac{\partial \mu}{\partial z}\right) = -\frac{r\mu J}{\mu_0} \tag{17}$$

with the boundary conditions

$$F_1 = F_2, \qquad \mu_2^{-1}\, dF_2/dn - \mu_1^{-1}\, dF_1/dn = rK/\mu_0 \tag{18}$$

Induction B is given by

$$B_r = -(\mu_0/r)\, \partial F/\partial r, \qquad B_z = (\mu_0/r)\, \partial F/\partial r$$

D. Conclusion

Using the functions F or V is the simplest way to calculate the induction within a magnetic lens by means of Eqs. (14) or (17), even in the regions where currents are flowing. To choose between the use of V or F, one must consider the following points:

1. The function F is zero on the symmetry axis. The axial induction must be calculated from the values of F in points located outside the z axis. This process is complicated and can result in a loss of precision.

2. On the external boundaries, either the values of V or F are given (Dirichlet-type condition), or their normal derivatives are specified (Neumann-type condition). When solving a Dirichlet problem, the convergence of the numerical methods is faster than that for a Neumann problem.

3. Equation (15) shows that the function V can be multivalued at some point, because there are layers of dipoles of density τ^* spread over some of the boundaries. When these boundaries are within the domain, it becomes difficult to take into account the existence of these layers, because the complexity of the programs increases and extra core memory is needed for the storage of these particular values of V.

Our conclusions are the following: to compute lenses whose topological shapes will not vary, and for which it is possible to reject the dipole layers on the external boundaries of the domain of calculation, a program using V will be simpler to write and will run faster. On the other hand, a program intended for the study of lenses in which the magnetic circuit and the coils may have very varied shapes will profit by using F, which makes the writing of the program more systematic and uses the core memory more efficiently.

In following sections, we will be able to study simultaneously Eqs. (14) and (17) by writing

$$\partial^2 y/\partial r^2 + (k/r)\,\partial y/\partial r + \partial^2 y/\partial z^2 + g(r, z, y) = f(r, z) \qquad (19)$$

in which $k = 1$ for the potential and $k = -1$ for the flux function. Moreover, it can be noticed that, when $k = 0$, Eq. (19) becomes the differential equation corresponding to two-dimension systems having a symmetry of translation in a plane perpendicular to the translation axis.

IV. DISCRETIZATION OF LAPLACE'S AND POISSON'S EQUATIONS AND GENERATION OF THE MESH

A magnetic lens is too complex a system for Eq. (19) to be solved by means of analytical functions of r and z, but solving Eq. (19) is now possible by using numerical methods.

A. Principle of the Network Method

In a meridional plane of the lens, we define a region closed by the axis and an arbitrary boundary Γ located far enough from the lens to assume that a slight shifting of this boundary will not modify the values of V or F within the lens. The values of V or F must be known along all the boundaries of this region in order to obtain a unique solution. On the symmetry axis, we have $F = 0$, and V has a zero normal derivative. We also admit that the magnetic field is tangent along Γ, that is, V has a zero normal derivative and F has a zero value. Inside the region bounded by the symmetry axis and by Γ, we draw a grid of lines that cross each other at points called nodes and divide the inside of the region into variously shaped meshes. The boundaries of these meshes will follow the boundaries of the various materials making up the magnetic regions or the excitation coils. Thus, the plane is divided into a number of subregions in which the nature of the magnetic material and the value of the current density are the same.

Instead of seeking a continuous function as a solution of Eq. (19), we seek a discrete function whose numerical values will have the following characteristics:

(a) They will be known only at the nodes of the mesh whose number is finite.

(b) They will have fixed values, or values permitting nullification of the normal derivative, at the nodes located on the region boundary.

(c) For each node within the region, a finite difference equation connects the value of the function for this point to the values at neighboring nodes. This difference equation is deduced from the partial derivative equation. The problem is said to have been discretized.

Condition (c) shows that the unknown values of the function are the solutions of a system of simultaneous linear equations. It is possible to demonstrate that the solution is unique and also that, when the distance between the nodes tends to zero, the solutions of the linear system have the values of the solution of the differential equation as a limit. The use of a fine mesh gives a more accurate solution than the use of a coarse mesh, but its use results in the solution of systems with several thousand unknowns. The network method is very widely used, whatever the shape of the lens under study. It always gives a result, which may be obtained more or less rapidly according to the distance between the nodes, the shape of the lens, and the nature of the boundary conditions.

B. Generation of the Mesh

The first step to use the network method is to draw the grid of lines that will define the nodes.

The simplest way is to use a regular grid of square or rectangular meshes whose sides are parallel or perpendicular to the revolution axis (Hesse, 1950); it may also be a grid of equilateral triangles (Southwell, 1946). However, the use of these simple networks has a serious drawback, which results from the uniform size of the mesh. The interesting function in the computation of the electrooptic characteristics of a magnetic lens is the axial induction, and it is known to vary very rapidly in the gap between the pole pieces. Having very numerous nodes in the region results in having equally numerous nodes outside the lens, where it is of little importance to know the field. Nevertheless, these points must be taken into account because of condition (c), and they increase considerably the size of the linear system.

To remedy this, grids with unequal meshes, obtained by distortion of a regular grid of rectangles or triangles, are now used.

By distorting a rectangle, a quadrilateral mesh can be obtained as it has been achieved by Munro (1972). Figure 8 shows an example of this type of network. A conical pole piece ABCD is in contact with the yoke along AD. EAB limits the pole bore, and the gap is located between the extremity BC and the boundary. For the sake of simplicity, some lines of the mesh must be made to coincide with the limits of the magnetic circuit and the coils. The figure shows that it is possible to draw fine meshes along the axis of symmetry in the gap between the pole pieces, then larger ones being between B and A, and still larger ones between A and E. In the same way, along IK, there are fine meshes opposite the pole face; they become larger and larger the farther away they are from the axis of revolution. In the pole piece ABCD, there are large quadrilateral meshes along AD and finer ones along BC.

It is easy to understand that in this partition of the plane into quadrangular meshes it is necessary that most of the limits of the magnetic circuit and the excitation coil be parallel or perpendicular to the axis of revolution and few limits cross the axis with an angle other than right.

To compute more complicated shapes, it is better to consider a mesh of irregular triangles whose use has been pioneered by Winslow (1967). The curved boundaries and interfaces of the cross section of the lens are approximated by straight segments that entirely coincide over the lines of the mesh. The inside of each subregion of the lens is triangulated, and this process can be applied to subregions of arbitrary shapes.

Figure 9 shows a mesh made with such triangles. The symmetry axis is AC and the lens possesses a symmetry plane AB. The whole of the magnetic circuit is C shaped, and is drawn in heavy lines. The excitation coil IJKL is rectangular and also drawn in heavy lines. The grid is composed

P. BONJOUR

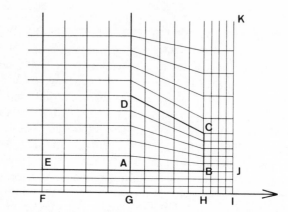

Fig. 8.   An example of a quadrilateral mesh superimposed over a pole piece ABCD and a yoke EAD.

mostly of irregular triangles, with a few right triangles where needed owing to the disposition of the boundaries or interfaces. It must be noticed that this network is obtained by distorting a network of equilateral triangles and that each internal node is surrounded by six triangles.

To write the difference equations according to condition (c), the position of each node must be known, and it would be extremely tedious to punch them as data cards in the computation of a large mesh with several thousand nodes. In the case of a regular grid, the size of the mesh is known, and it is enough to specify on which lines of the mesh the boundaries and interfaces of the lenses are situated.

A network, like that in Fig. 8, can be easily generated in an automatic way because the lines of the mesh are straight on every region. For instance, the position of the four points A, B, C, and D, and the number of

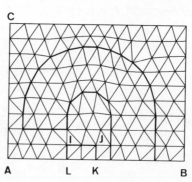

Fig. 9.   An example of a triangular mesh. AC is the symmetry axis. The magnetic circuit is C shaped; it is drawn in heavy lines as is the excitation coil IJKL.

nodes required between A and B, B and C, etc. are introduced as data cards. The intermediary nodes are supposed to be linearly distributed along AB, BC, etc. The computer then determines the position of each internal node by means of a linear interpolation. The pole bore is composed of the three separate rectangles BHIJ, AGHB, and EFGA in which the length of the mesh increases, and it is sufficient to give the position of the four vertices and the division of each side of the rectangle to complete the mesh inside it. Therefore, a comparatively small number of points has to be considered in the input data of the computation.

The network of irregular triangles can equally be created by the computer, by considering, like Winslow (1967), that it is a problem of potential in which the lines of the mesh play the role of equipotentials. Mathematically speaking, the coordinates r and z of each node satisfy Laplace's equations

$$\nabla^2 r = 0, \qquad \nabla^2 z = 0$$

These equations can be solved numerically by writing the following difference equations for each node:

$$r_0 = \frac{1}{6}\sum_{i=1}^{6} r_i, \qquad z_0 = \frac{1}{6}\sum_{i=1}^{6} z_i$$

in which the six nodes with indices i are the nearest neighbors to the node with index 0. These equations are solved by means of successive overrelaxation by using distinct overrelaxation parameters for the coordinates r and z and by automatically adjusting these parameters as will be explained in Section VI. This simple process generally leads to suitable grids, but it can be seen in Fig. 9 that the lines of the mesh tend to get nearer a convex boundary and further from a concave one. If the boundary is strongly convex, it may even happen that the mesh line closest to the convex side crosses it and passes into the concavity; then the network can no longer be used. To avoid such a drawback, a more elaborate computing process has been designed by Winslow (1967); a detailed description can be found in his paper. This method can also be applied to obtain an irregular quadrilateral network in Fig. 8 by considering the four first-neighboring nodes of each interior node (Winslow, 1963).

To complete the generation of the network, it is necessary to attribute a code to each node, specifying whether it is situated inside a subregion, or on an interface, or on an exterior boundary, etc., to designate the nature of the material and the value of the current density inside each of the four rectangles (or six triangles) that join at each node inside the network. For the nodes located on the exterior boundary of the mesh, the numbers four or six must be lowered according to the local position of the node.

V. Difference Equations

According to condition (c) in Section IV, a difference equation has to be written for each node in order to satisfy Eq. (19). Several methods can be used.

A. Method of the Taylor Series

This method is well adapted to a grid composed of rectangular or square meshes. It has been described by Weber (1967), and we give only a few particulars about it.

The function $y(r, z)$ in Eq. (19) is expanded into a Taylor series in the vicinity of a point P_0. The derivatives of y are related by Eq. (19) and by the equations obtained when differentiating Eq. (19) with respect to r and z. By truncating the Taylor series after terms of degree 2 or 4, an approximation of y of order 2 or 4 is obtained.

At a second-order approximation and for an ordinary node 0 of a rectangular mesh (Fig. 10) that is not located on an interface or a boundary, the following difference equation is obtained*:

$$2\mu_0(1 + \epsilon)y_0$$

$$= \epsilon[\mu_0 + k(\mu_1 - \mu_3)/4]y_1 + \epsilon[\mu_0 - k(\mu_1 - \mu_3)/4]y_3$$

$$+ [\mu_0(1 + k/2j) + k(\mu_2 - \mu_4)/4]y_2$$

$$+ \mu_0[(1 - k/2j) - k(\mu_2 - \mu_4)/4]y_4 - b^2\mu_0 f_0 \qquad (20)$$

The distance of node 0 to the symmetry axis is jb, and we have set $\epsilon = b^2/a^2$. At some point 0 located on the symmetry axis, and for the potential, Eq. (20) must be replaced by

$$2\mu_0(2 + \epsilon)V_0 = \epsilon[\mu_0 + (\mu_1 - \mu_3)/4]V_1 + \epsilon[\mu_0 - (\mu_1 - \mu_3)/4]V_3$$

$$+ 4\mu_2 V_2 - b^2\mu_0 f_0$$

The flux function F is zero on the symmetry axis.

Fourth-order approximation formulas are interesting for computing the nodes situated in the air or in a magnetic material whose permeability can be considered as a constant (iron far from saturation, for instance). They allow the use of larger meshes without greatly impairing the precision, and a smaller number of nodes; therefore, the calculation is shortened.

---

* In this section, μ_0 holds for the permeability at point 0, and ν_0 for the vacuum permeability. We apologize for this inconvenience.

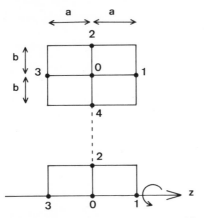

FIG. 10.   Disposition of the points used for the five-point difference equation in a field on and outside the axis of rotational symmetry.

Natali *et al.* (1972) have established numerous such expressions to calculate the electrostatic potential in double-cylinder lenses accurately. In their paper, difference equations suitable for those nodes located close to boundaries, symmetry planes, or the intersection of two boundaries can be found.

Durand (1957) has shown how an equation using the eight nodes surrounding the point 0 could be derived by means of the successive derivatives of Eq. (19) with respect to r and z.

When the point 0 is situated on the interface between two media, Eq. (19), must be replaced by the boundary conditions (15), (16), or (18). In these expressions, the first derivative is taken on each side of the boundary, and nonsymmetrical expressions computed at the suitable order of approximation are required. They can be found in Abramowitz and Stegun (1965). Therefore, each disposition of nodes requires a special expression, and simpler equations will be more systematically and easily obtained by other methods explained later.

B. Method of Integration of the Field Equations

The differential equations are obtained by discretizing a relation established by integrating Eq. (19) (Durand, 1968).

Equations (14) and (17) with their boundary conditions for the potential or the flux function can be written in the following general form:

$$\nabla \cdot (h \cdot \nabla y) = \phi(r, z) \tag{21}$$

$$h^+ (\partial y/\partial n)^+ - h^- (\partial y/\partial n)^- = C(l) \tag{22}$$

In the case of the potential, the values of h, ϕ, and C are

$$h = \mu r, \qquad \phi = -\rho^* r, \qquad C = -\sigma^* r \qquad (23)$$

while for the flux function

$$h = \nu_0/\mu r, \qquad \phi = -J, \qquad C = -K \qquad (24)$$

Let us consider a closed curve Γ in the plane r–z and the right cylinder of basis Γ, of unity height and let us integrate Eq. (21) in this volume. The application of Ostrogradsky's theorem reduces the first side to an integral taken along Γ, which gives

$$\int_\Gamma h \, \partial y / \partial n \, dl = \iint_S \phi \, ds \qquad (25)$$

S being the surface enclosed by Γ. In Eq. (25) the normal derivative of y appears, which is thus automatically taken into account when a portion of Γ coincides with a boundary; there lies the interest of this formulation. We are going to use the fundamental formula (25), eventually with the support of Eq. (22), to establish the differential equations for V and F within a rectangular mesh.

1. Second-Order Approximation

a. *Ordinary Point.* Let us consider the point 0 in Fig. 11 and the mesh ABCD. We apply Eq. (25) to the shaded rectangle whose sides are twice as small as those of ABCD. On the side MN, we have

$$\int_{MN} [h_b + z(\partial h/\partial z)_b + \cdots][(\partial y/\partial r)_b + z(\partial^2 y/\partial r \, \partial z)_b + \cdots] \, dz$$
$$= a h_b(\partial y/\partial r)_b + \cdots$$

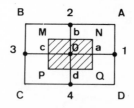

FIG. 11.   The meshes used for the field equation method. The path of integration of Eq. (25) is MNPQ.

This gives a second-order approximation

$$\int_{MN} = ah_b(y_2 - y_0)/b$$

To simplify the notation, we will admit until further notice that the symbol h_i stands for the quantity taken in the middle of the segment $0i$. Equation (25) finally gives

$$bh_1\frac{y_1 - y_0}{a} + ah_2\frac{y_2 - y_0}{b} + bh_3\frac{y_3 - y_0}{a} + ah_4\frac{y_4 - y_0}{b} = \phi_0ab$$

because the second member of Eq. (25) equals ϕ_0ab with a second-order approximation. Rearranging, it gives

$$[\epsilon(h_1 + h_3) + h_2 + h_4]y_0 = \epsilon h_1y_1 + h_2y_2 + \epsilon h_3y_3 + h_4y_4 - \phi_0b^2$$

We have for the potential (Fig. 11)

$$h_1 = jb\mu_a, \qquad h_2 = (j + \tfrac{1}{2})b\mu_b, \qquad h_3 = jb\mu_c, \qquad h_4 = (j - \tfrac{1}{2})b\mu_d$$

$$y = V, \qquad \phi_0 = -jb\,\rho_0$$

By substitution, this gives

$$[\epsilon(\mu_a + \mu_c) + \mu_b(1 + 1/2j) + \mu_d(1 - 1/2j)]V_0$$
$$= \epsilon\mu_aV_1 + \epsilon\mu_cV_3 + (1 + 1/2j)\mu_bV_2 + (1 - 1/2j)\mu_dV_4 + b^2\rho_0 \quad (26)$$

The similar expressions for the flux function are

$$h_1 = v_0/jb\mu_a, \qquad h_2 = v_0/(j + \tfrac{1}{2})b\mu_b$$
$$h_3 = v_0/jb\mu_c, \qquad h_4 = v_0/(j - \tfrac{1}{2})b\mu_d$$
$$y = F, \qquad \phi_0 = -J_0$$

and

$$[\epsilon(1/\mu_a + 1/\mu_c) + 1/\mu_b + 1/\mu_d]F_0$$
$$= \epsilon F_1/\mu_a + F_2/\mu_b(1 + \tfrac{1}{2}j) + \epsilon F_3/\mu_c$$
$$+ F_4/\mu_d(1 - \tfrac{1}{2}j) - J_0b^3a/v_0 \quad (27)$$

To use Eqs. (26) and (27), we must still calculate μ_a, μ_b, etc. For instance,

$$\mu_a = (\mu_0 + \mu_1)/2$$

For some point on the axis, Eq. (25) is applied to the shaded rectangle in Fig. 12, and we obtain for the potential

$$[\epsilon(\mu_a + \mu_c) + 4\mu_b]V_0 = \epsilon\mu_aV_1 + 4\mu_bV_2 + \epsilon\mu_cV_3$$

b. *Expression of the Boundary Conditions.*   In order to deal easily with all possible cases, we will divide Fig. 11 into four quadrants and establish an equation for each of them. Every disposition of boundaries will be treated by a suitable assembling of quadrants.

Let us consider the first quadrant in Fig. 13. Points 0, 5, 1 and 2 are nodes, and it is assumed that $\partial y/\partial r$ on 01 and $\partial y/\partial z$ on 02 are known. Let us apply Eq. (25) to the shaded rectangle of half dimensions; this gives

$$(\epsilon h_1 + h_2)y_0 = \epsilon h_1 y_1 + h_2 y_2 - bh_1(\partial y/\partial r)_1^5$$

$$- b^2 h_2(\partial y/\partial z)_2^5/a - (b^2/2)\phi_5 \qquad (28)$$

Each partial derivative has an index i and an exponent j. The partial derivative must be taken in the middle of the segment $0i$ toward the node j; ϕ_5 is taken in the middle of 05. The three other quadrants of Fig. 13 give, respectively,

$$(\epsilon h_3 + h_2)y_0 = \epsilon h_3 y_3 + h_2 y_2 - bh_3(\partial y/\partial r)_3^6$$

$$+ (b^2/a)h_2(\partial y/\partial z)_2^6 - (b^2/2)\phi_6 \qquad (29)$$

$$(\epsilon h_3 + h_4)y_0 = \epsilon h_3 y_3 + h_4 y_4 + bh_3(\partial y/\partial r)_3^7$$

$$+ (b^2/a)h_4(\partial y/\partial z)_4^7 - (b^2/2)\phi_7 \qquad (30)$$

$$(\epsilon h_1 + h_4)y_4 = \epsilon h_1 y_1 + h_4 y_4 + bh_1(\partial y/\partial r)_1^8$$

$$- (b^2/a)h_4(\partial y/\partial z)_4^8 - (b^2/2)\phi_8 \qquad (31)$$

Let us apply these relations to various dispositions of the boundaries.

(1) *Boundary parallel to z axis* (Fig. 14).   Figure 14a is obtained by assembling the two first quadrants in Fig. 13. Along the segment 02, we have

$$(\partial y/\partial z)_2^5 = -(\partial y/\partial z)_2^6$$

and by adding Eqs. (28) and (29)

$$[\epsilon(h_1^+ + h_3^+) + 2h_2]y_0 = \epsilon h_1^+ y_1 + \epsilon h_3^+ y_3 - bh_1^+(\partial y/\partial r)_1^5$$

$$- bh_3^+(\partial y/\partial r)_3^6 - (b^2/2)(\phi_5 + \phi_6)$$

In the same way, by adding Eqs. (30) and (31), Figure 14b leads to

$$[\epsilon(h_1^- + h_3^-) + 2h_4]y_0 = \epsilon h_1^- y_1 + \epsilon h_3 y_3 + bh_1^-(\partial y/\partial r)_1^8$$

$$+ bh_3^-(\partial y/\partial r)_3^7 - (b^2/2)(\phi_7 + \phi_8)$$

These two relations can be used to satisfy boundary conditions of the Neumann type. Figure 14c shows two different media meeting with

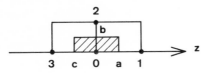

FIG. 12.   On the axis of rotational symmetry, Eq. (25) is applied to the shaded rectangle.

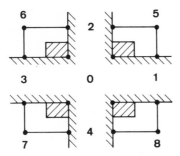

FIG. 13.   The division of Fig. 11 into four parts for the use of Eq. (25).

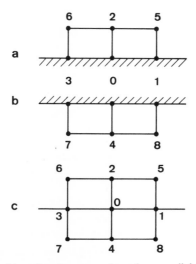

FIG. 14.   The disposition of nodes near a boundary parallel to the axis of rotational symmetry. (a) The domain is above the boundary; (b) the domain is under the boundary; (c) two media are in contact.

boundary conditions of the kind

$$y^+ = y^-, \qquad (h\ \partial y/\partial r)^+ - (h\ \partial y/\partial r)^- = C(z)$$

which is obtained by joining Figs. 14a and b together. Adding the corresponding equations, we have

$$[\epsilon(h_1^+ + h_1^- + h_3^+ + h_3^-) + 2(h_2 + h_4)]y_0$$

$$= \epsilon(h_1^+ + h_1^-)y_1 + \epsilon(h_3^+ + h_3^-)y_3 + 2h_2 y_2 + 2h_4 y_4$$

$$- b(C_1 + C_3) - b^2(\phi_5 + \phi_6 + \phi_7 + \phi_8)/2$$

In this expression, C_1 and C_3 are taken in the middle of 01 and 03.

(2) *Radial boundary.* To write a Neumann-type boundary condition, we add Eqs. (28) and (31) on one hand, (29) and (30) on the other, which gives

$$[2\epsilon h_1 + h_2^+ + h_4^+]y_0 = 2\epsilon h_1 y_1 + h_2^+ y_2 + h_4^+ y_4$$

$$- \left(\frac{b^2}{a}\right) h_4^+ \left(\frac{\partial y}{\partial z}\right)_4^8 - h_2^+ \left(\frac{b^2}{a}\right)\left(\frac{\partial y}{\partial z}\right)_2^5 - \left(\frac{b^2}{2}\right)(\phi_0 + \phi_8)$$

and

$$[2\epsilon h_3 + h_2^- + h_4^-]y_0 = 2\epsilon h_3 y_3 + h_2^- y_2 + h_4^- y_4$$

$$+ \left(\frac{b^2}{a}\right) h_4^- \left(\frac{\partial y}{\partial z}\right)_4^7 - \left(\frac{b^2}{a}\right) h_2^- \left(\frac{\partial y}{\partial z}\right)_2^6 - \left(\frac{b^2}{2}\right)(\phi_6 + \phi_7)$$

If we have two media in contact with the boundary conditions

$$y^+ = y^-, \qquad (h\ \partial y/\partial z)^+ - (h\ \partial y/\partial z)^- = C(r)$$

by adding we obtain

$$[2\epsilon(h_1 + h_3) + h_2^+ + h_2^- + h_4^+ + h_4^-]y_0$$

$$= 2\epsilon h_1 y_1 + 2\epsilon h_3 y_3 + (h_2^+ + h_2^-)y_2 + (h_4^+ + h_4^-)y_4$$

$$- b^2 \frac{\phi_5 + \phi_6 + \phi_7 + \phi_8}{2} - \left(\frac{b^2}{a}\right)(C_2 + C_4)$$

The formulas we have just demonstrated are suitable for establishing the boundary conditions between two media in very varied cases: (1) for two magnetized media in which no currents are flowing, σ, ρ, J and K are zero; (2) for a magnetized medium adjoining a conducting medium, J and K are zero within the magnetized medium, and $\mu = \nu_0$ within the conducting medium, which can be replaced by its associated system from which come the σ and ρ values to be used; (3) finally, for a superconducting medium that is replaced by a perfect diamagnetic substance, $\mu = 0$.

c. *Oblique Boundaries Passing through the Nodes.*   We will study other layouts, but to simplify the writing we will suppose that ϕ and C are zero ($h \, dy/dn$ is continuous).

To begin with, we must establish equations similar to Eq. (28) for each of the eight parts of the angle of vertex 0. For instance, we apply Eq. (25) to the shaded triangle in Fig. 15:

$$ah_7 \left(\frac{\partial y}{\partial r}\right)_3^7 + bh_3 \left(\frac{y_3 - y_0}{a}\right) - ah_7 \left(\frac{\partial y}{\partial r}\right)_7 - bh_7 \left(\frac{\partial y}{\partial z}\right)_7 = \frac{ab\phi_7}{4}$$

or

$$\epsilon h_3 y_0 = \epsilon h_3 y_3 + bh_3 \left(\frac{\partial y}{\partial r}\right)_3^7 + \left(\frac{b^2}{a}\right) h_7 \left(\frac{\partial y}{\partial z}\right)_7 - bh_7 \left(\frac{\partial y}{\partial r}\right)_7 - \left(\frac{b^2}{4}\right) \phi_7 \quad (32)$$

For the other triangle

$$h_4 y_0 = h_4 y_4 + \left(\frac{b^2}{a}\right) h_4 \left(\frac{\partial y}{\partial z}\right)_4^7 - \left(\frac{b^2}{a}\right) h_7 \left(\frac{\partial y}{\partial z}\right)_7 + bh_7 \left(\frac{\partial y}{\partial r}\right)_7 - \left(\frac{b^2}{4}\right) \phi_7$$
$$(33)$$

If we add Eqs. (32) and (33) supposing $h \, \partial y / \partial n$ to be continuous along 07, we obtain

$$(\epsilon h_3 + h_4) y_0 = \epsilon h_3 y_3 + h_4 y_4 + bh_3 \left(\frac{\partial y}{\partial r}\right)_3^7 + \left(\frac{b^2}{a}\right) h_4 \left(\frac{\partial y}{\partial z}\right)_4^7 - \left(\frac{b^2}{2}\right) \phi_7$$

that is, Eq. (30).

The formulas corresponding to the six other triangles are established in the same way. Let us give a few examples of applications.

(1) *Oblique boundary* (Fig. 16).   Above the boundary, we obtain by adding

$$2(\epsilon h_1 + h_2) y_0 = 2\epsilon h_1 y_1 + 2h_2 y_2 - \left(\frac{b^2}{a}\right) h_6 \left(\frac{\partial y}{\partial z}\right)_6$$

$$- bh_6 \left(\frac{\partial y}{\partial r}\right)_6 - \left(\frac{b^2}{a}\right) h_8 \left(\frac{\partial y}{\partial z}\right)_8 - bh_8 \left(\frac{\partial y}{\partial r}\right)_8$$

Below the boundary

$$2(\epsilon h_3 + h_4) y_0 = 2\epsilon h_3 y_3 + 2h_4 y_4 + \left(\frac{b^2}{a}\right) h_8 \left(\frac{\partial y}{\partial z}\right)_8$$

$$+ bh_8 \left(\frac{\partial y}{\partial r}\right)_8 + \left(\frac{b^2}{a}\right) h_6 \left(\frac{\partial y}{\partial z}\right)_6 + bh_6 \left(\frac{\partial y}{\partial r}\right)_6$$

P. BONJOUR

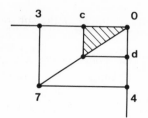

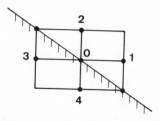

FIG. 15. The use of Eq. (25) when
the mesh is divided into eight parts.

FIG. 16. Disposition of the nodes
near an oblique boundary.

These two equations are used to write the Neumann boundary conditions.
By adding, we obtain the condition at the limit between two media, which
is

$$[\epsilon(h_1 + h_3) + h_2 + h_4]y_0 = \epsilon h_1 y_1 + h_2 y_2 + \epsilon h_3 y_3 + h_4 y_4$$

(2) *Obtuse or reentrant angle* (Fig. 17). The two Neumann-type
conditions are

$$[2\epsilon h_1 + 2h_2 + h_4^+]y_0 = 2\epsilon h_1 y_1 + 2h_2 y_2 + h_4^+ y_4$$

$$- \left(\frac{b^2}{a}\right) h_4^+ \left(\frac{\partial y}{\partial z}\right)_4^8 + \left(\frac{b^2}{a}\right) h_6 \left(\frac{\partial y}{\partial z}\right)_6 + bh_6 \left(\frac{\partial y}{\partial r}\right)_6$$

on the right-hand side of the boundary,

$$[2\epsilon h_3 + h_4^-]y_0 = 2\epsilon h_3 y_3 + h_4^- y_4$$

$$+ \left(\frac{b^2}{a}\right) h_4^- \left(\frac{\partial y}{\partial z}\right)_4^7 - \left(\frac{b^2}{a}\right) h_6 \left(\frac{\partial y}{\partial z}\right)_6 - bh_6 \left(\frac{\partial y}{\partial r}\right)_6$$

on the left-hand side.

At the vertex of an obtuse angle, between two media, by adding we
obtain

$$[2\epsilon(h_1 + h_3) + 2h_2 + h_4^+ + h_4^-]y_0$$

$$= 2\epsilon h_1 y_1 + 2h_2 y_2 + 2\epsilon h_3 y_3 + (h_4^+ + h_4^-)y_4$$

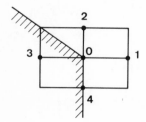

FIG. 17. Disposition of the nodes near an obtuse angle.

d. *Other Uses of* Eq. (25).   The contour of integration Γ of Eq. (25) can have an arbitrary shape, and we have not used the rectangular characteristics of the mesh in the preceding paragraphs. Winslow (1967) has used Eq. (25) to establish the difference equations of the flux function for a mesh of irregular triangles with the following hypotheses: (1) the values of F are known at the vertices of the triangles and F varies linearly over each triangle; (2) h and ϕ are constant within each triangle. This gives an approximation of the second order at least. Each node is surrounded by six triangles, and the integration contour Γ is, as suggested in Winslow's (1967) paper, an irregular dodecagon whose vertices are alternatively the centroids of the triangles and the middle points of the adjacent sides. Figure 18 shows one of the six triangles 012 associated to node 0. A and B are the middle points of the sides and C is the triangle centroid; therefore, ABC is the portion of the integration contour Γ associated with the triangle 012. The inside part of this contour is shaded. Because of the hypothesis of linear variation, F must be written within the triangle as

$$F = a + br + cz$$

By applying to the three points 0, 1, and 2, we obtain a linear system whose solution gives

$$\frac{\partial F}{\partial r} = b = \frac{(F_1 - F_0)(z_2 - z_0) - (F_2 - F_0)(z_1 - z_0)}{(r_1 - r_0)(z_2 - z_0) - (r_2 - r_0)(z_1 - z_0)}$$

$$\frac{\partial F}{\partial z} = c = \frac{(F_2 - F_0)(r_1 - r_0) - (F_1 - F_0)(r_2 - r_0)}{(r_1 - r_0)(z_2 - z_0) - (r_2 - r_0)(z_1 - z_0)} \tag{34}$$

in which r_i and z_i are the coordinates of the point i.

It is easy to see that the integral appearing in the first member

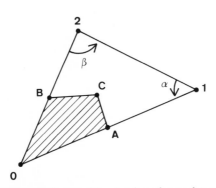

FIG. 18.   The use of Eq. (25) in one of the six triangular meshes surrounding the node 0. The path of integration of Eq. (25) is ABC.

$\int_{AC} h \, dF/dn \, dl$ is the modulus of the vector product $\nabla F \times \mathbf{AC}$, that is, the triple scalar product $\mathbf{K} \cdot (\nabla F \times \mathbf{AC}) = \nabla F \cdot (\mathbf{AC} \times \mathbf{K}) = \nabla F \cdot \mathbf{AC}^-$ in which $\mathbf{K}$ is the unit vector that orients the plane in the trigonometric sense, and $\mathbf{AC}^-$ is vector $\mathbf{AC}$ rotated by $-\pi/2$. Therefore, the first member of Eq. (25) is written as

$$\nabla F \cdot \mathbf{AC} + \nabla F \cdot \mathbf{CB} = \nabla F \cdot \mathbf{AB} = \frac{z_2 - z_1}{2} b + \frac{r_1 - r_2}{2} c$$

Substituting b and c gives

$$\int_{ACB} = h[(z_1 - z_2)(z_0 - z_2) + (r_1 - r_2)(r_0 - r_2)](F_1 - F_0)/2\Delta$$

$$+ h[(z_2 - z_1)(z_0 - z_1) + (r_2 - r_1)(r_0 - r_1)](F_2 - F_0)/2\Delta \quad (35)$$

in which Δ represents the denominator of b and c.

The coefficient of $(F_1 - F_0)$ in Eq. (35) equals the scalar product $\mathbf{12} \cdot \mathbf{10}$. With the orientations of the angles shown in Fig. 18, we have

$$\mathbf{21} \cdot \mathbf{20} = \overline{21} \cdot \overline{20} \cos \beta, \qquad \mathbf{12} \cdot \mathbf{10} = \overline{12} \cdot \overline{10} \cos \alpha$$

Here Δ is the double of the area A of the triangle 012, that is,

$$A = \overline{21} \cdot \overline{20} \sin \beta = \overline{12} \cdot \overline{10} \sin \alpha$$

Finally Eq. (35) is expressed as

$$(h/2)[(F_1 - F_0) \cot \beta + (F_2 - F_0) \cot \alpha]$$

The second member of Eq. (25) is written as

$$\iint_s = -JA/3$$

since the shaded area is equal to one-third of that of the triangle 012.

By summing for the six triangles surrounding the point 0, we notice that each vertex is associated to two adjacent triangles and to an α angle and a β angle, which are the angles of these two triangles opposite to the common side.

Let us consider the triangle i defined by its three vertices 0, i, and $i + 1$, put an index i for all the values associated to it, number the six triangles from 1 to 6, and add the six equations similar to Eq. (35). Equation (25) is finally written as

$$\sum_{i=1}^{i=6} [(h_i \cot \alpha_i + h_{i+1} \cot \beta_{i+1})/2](F_{i+1} - F_0) + A_i J_i/3 = 0 \quad (36)$$

with

$$h_i = \frac{\nu_0}{\mu_i(r_0 + r_i + r_{i+1})/3}$$

When these expressions are used, $i = 7$ must be replaced by $i = 1$. Equation (36) is the difference equation for some node 0 located within the network and surrounded by six triangles. For a node located on the exterior boundary of the domain, the number of triangles associated to the node is less than six. An equation of a form similar to Eq. (36) can be derived, in which the summation is taken over the triangles associated with the node. It simplifies the writing of the program if we consider that a node on the boundary is also associated with six triangles by giving a zero value to the h_i coefficients of the triangles located outside the domain.

Therefore, Eq. (36) is absolutely general, and it reinforces the interest of using an irregular triangular mesh. Whatever the shape of the magnetic circuits to be computed, the finite difference equation (36) applies to any node, provided that we introduce the values of the permeability and of the current associated to each triangle, which depend on its position in relation to the magnetized media and the excitation coils.

2. Fourth-Order Approximation

Formulas valid at the fourth-order approximation can be derived from Eq. (25), provided that the quantities h, $\partial y/\partial n$, and ϕ are developed at a suitable order of approximation. Bonjour (1972) has given such formulas for a rectangular mesh, but they require the consideration of nodes that are not first-neighbor nodes of node 0, nor are they suitable for nodes neighboring the interfaces or the exterior boundaries of the domain. Then Eq. (25) must be written for each particular node, using the dissymmetrical expressions of the derivatives when necessary. In the end, this makes their use rather difficult.

C. Method of the Finite Elements

In the method of finite elements, the solution of a problem continuous in the mathematical sense is replaced by that of an equivalent discrete problem in which some property of the whole can be considered as the sum of the properties of the various parts; therefore, it will be additive. Such an approach will be rewarding if the property of each part (or element) can be calculated independently from the other elements. This method has been proposed by Courant (1943), but it remained ignored until the early 1960s when Zienkiewicz and Cheung (1965) applied it to the calculation of mechanical structures. Since then, it has made rapid progress in various fields: fluid mechanics, heat conduction, stress and strain analysis, repartition of potential and field, etc. One can refer to the books by Zienkiewicz (1967, 1971) on these subjects.

The additive property is a quantity of the same nature as energy. We know that the kinetic, potential, electric, etc., energy of a system is equal to the sum of the kinetic, potential, and electric energies of the elements that comprise the system. The differential equations of the system can be obtained by means of the variational principle: In mechanics, the fundamental laws of dynamics are equivalent to the principle of least action or of Hamilton, in optics, Descartes' laws are equivalent to Fermat's principle, etc. In the same way, the finite difference equations are obtained by applying the variational principle to a discretized expression of the energy.

In magnetostatics,* the magnetic energy stored in an element of volume dv has a value $B^2 \, dv/\mu$, and it has been shown (Durand, 1968) that the magnetic energy of a system is

$$W = \iiint [\mathbf{J} \cdot \mathbf{A} - (2\mu)^{-1}(\nabla \times \mathbf{A})^2] \, dv \qquad (37)$$

The variational principle states that the energy W is extremum, that is, slight variations dA of A produce variations of W that are of the order of $(dA)^2$.

Introducing the expression of the flux function in Eq. (37) and using a little algebra, the energy becomes

$$W = \iiint [2\nu_0 J \cdot F - (\nu_0^2/\mu r)(\nabla F)^2] \, dr \, d\theta \, dz \qquad (38)$$

We will calculate the magnetic energy in a system discretized by means of triangular meshes as in Fig. 18 and with a second-order approximation.

In this approximation, F varies linearly over the triangle 012, and we take two local axes of coordinates passing at point C and parallel to the z and r axes. In the local system, F can also be written as

$$F = a' + b'r' + c'z'$$

---

* In electrostatics, the finite-element method applies to the expression (Durand, 1964)

$$W = \iiint [(\epsilon/2)(\nabla V)^2 - \rho V] \, dv$$

with

$$a' = (F_1 + F_2 + F_0)/3, \qquad b' = b, \qquad c' = c$$

given by Eq. (34) because the expression of ∇F does not change in the local axes. Integrating the first term of Eq. (38) gives

$$4\pi\nu_0 JA(F_1 + F_2 + F_0)/3$$

in which A is the area of the triangle 012. To calculate the second term of Eq. (38) we admit that r varies little from its value at the centroid

$$\bar{r} = (r_1 + r_2 + r_0)/3$$

Finally, the energy W_{012} associated with the triangle 012 is written as

$$W_{012} = 4\pi\gamma_0 A[J(F_1 + F_2 + F_0)/3 - (\nu_0/2\mu\bar{r})(b^2 + c^2) \qquad (39)$$

The energy stored in the system is the sum of the quantities such as Eq. (39) for all the triangular elements. This expression can be used in two different ways:

a. Let us consider some particular node 0 surrounded by six nodes numbered from 1 to 6. In the expression of the total energy, F_0 appears in six expressions of the form Eq. (39) $W_{0,i,i+1}$ (i between 1 and 6). The variational principle states that if F_0 is given a slight variation dF_0 while all the other values of F are fixed, the total energy is stationary, that is,

$$\partial W/\partial F_0 = 0 = (\partial/\partial F_0)(W_{012} + W_{023} + \cdots + W_{061})$$

Differentiating Eq. (39) gives

$$\frac{\partial W_{012}}{\partial F_0} = 4\pi\nu_0 A \left[\frac{J}{3} - \frac{\nu_0}{\mu\bar{r}_{012}} \left(b\frac{db}{dF_0} + c\frac{dc}{dF_0} \right) \right]$$

$$= 4\pi\nu_0 \left\{ \frac{JA}{3} + \frac{\nu_0}{\mu\bar{r}} \frac{F_1 - F_0}{2\Delta}[(z_1 - z_2)(z_0 - z_2) + (r_1 - r_0)(r_0 - r_2)] \right.$$

$$\left. + \frac{\nu_0}{\mu\bar{r}} \frac{F_2 - F_0}{2\Delta}[(z_2 - z_1)(z_0 - z_1) + (r_2 - r_1)(r_0 - r_1)] \right\}$$

In this expression, the coefficients of $F_1 - F_0$ and $F_2 - F_0$ are similar to those in Eq. (35). Introducing the angles α and β, the derivative of the energy is written

$$\frac{\partial W_{012}}{\partial F_0} = 4\pi\nu_0 A \left[\frac{J}{3} - \frac{\nu_0}{\mu\bar{r}} \frac{(F_1 - F_0)\cot\beta + (F_2 - F_0)\cot\alpha}{2} \right]$$

By summing the six partial derivatives and equating to zero, we come back to Eq. (36).

We may call this derivation "classical," because, as in the other two methods, we have regarded only the nodes and we have obtained a difference equation expressing the differential properties of the field in the vicinity of the node.

b.   The actual point in the finite element method is to consider each triangle as a basic element. The total energy is the sum of the energies stored within each triangle and a slight variation of F_0, F_1, and F_2 must result in a zero variation of the total energy. For instance,

$$\frac{\partial W_{012}}{\partial F_0} = + \frac{\nu_0}{\mu \bar{r}} \left\{ F_0 \left[\frac{(z_2 - z_1)^2 + (r_1 - r_2)^2}{4A} \right] \right.$$

$$+ F_1 \left[\frac{(z_2 - z_1)(z_0 - z_2) + (r_1 - r_2)(r_2 - r_0)}{4A} \right]$$

$$\left. + F_2 \left[\frac{(z_2 - z_1)(z_1 - z_0) + (r_1 - r_2)(r_0 - r_1)}{4A} \right] \right\} - \frac{JA}{3} \quad (40)$$

in which the term $- 4\pi\nu_0$ has been omitted and we have two similar expressions for the other derivatives in relation to F_1 and F_2. Equation (40) can be written

$$\partial W_{012}/\partial F_0 = (\nu_0/4\mu\bar{r}A)[(b_0^2 + c_0^2)F_0$$

$$+ (b_0 b_1 + c_0 c_1)F_1 + (b_0 b_2 + c_0 c_2)F_2] - (JA/3)$$

setting

$$a_i = r_k z_j - r_j z_k, \qquad b_i = z_k - z_j, \qquad c_i = r_j - r_k$$

and the other coefficients by cyclic permutation on i, j, and k.

The other two derivatives are written in a similar way. The application of the variational principle to the element can be summarized in the form of a matrix

$$[\partial W/\partial F_i] = [A_{ij}][F_j] - [B_i] \quad (41)$$

in which $[\partial W/\partial F_i]$, $[F_i]$, and $[B_i]$ are three component vectors and $[A_{ij}]$ is a 3×3 square matrix whose general element is

$$A_{ij} = (\nu_0/4\mu\bar{r}A)(b_i b_j + c_i c_j) \quad (42)$$

Zienkiewicz and Cheung (1965) have shown that the coefficients a_i, b_i, and c_i occur in the linear expression of function F in the triangular element, which can be transformed into

$$F = \frac{a_0 + b_0 r + c_0 z}{2A} F_0 + \frac{a_1 + b_1 r + c_1 z}{2A} F_1 + \frac{a_2 + b_2 r + c_2 z}{2A} F_2$$

Let us number the elements with an index m ($1 \leq m \leq M$) and the nodes with i ($1 \leq i \leq N$). Equation (41) expresses the derivative of the energy of the element m in relation to F_i; B_i, which is constant within the element, only depends on m and must be written B_m. Considering all the nodes and writing Eq. (41) again in the form of a matrix, we have

$$[\partial W_m / \partial F_i] = [A_{ij}][F_j] + [B_m]$$

where $[\partial W_m / \partial F_i]$, $[F_j]$, and $[B_m]$ are vectors with N components among which three only are zero. $[A_{ij}]$ is a square matrix $N \times N$ in which all the elements but nine are zero. For those nine elements the indices i and j are such that the nodes of indices i and j belong to the element m; they are given by

$$A_{ij} = (\nu_0 / 4\mu \bar{r} A)(b_i b_j + c_i c_j)$$

The variational principle means that the derivatives of the total energy W in relation to the F_i are zero. By adding the contributions of each element and having the result equal zero, we have

$$\partial W / \partial F_i = \sum_1^M \partial W_m / \partial F_i = \sum_1^M \sum_1^N A_{ij} F_j - \sum_1^M B_m$$

or by permutating the order of the summations

$$\partial W / \partial F_i = \sum_1^N F_j C_{ij} - \sum_1^M B_m \tag{43}$$

with $C_{ij} = \Sigma_1^M A_{ij}$.

The summation is taken over all the elements, but it is only when the nodes i and j belong to the element m that the coefficient A_{ij} brings a nonzero contribution to C_{ij}. It is obvious that in the derivation of Eq. (43), a special treatment of the boundaries is not needed. The energy of an element adjacent to the exterior limit of the domain is still expressed by Eq. (39), and it is added to the total energy W in the same way. Only a node on the boundary belongs to fewer elements, and there will be fewer non zero A_{ij} coefficients in the expression of the C_{ij}.

The preceding derivations have been made by assuming that the network was composed of triangular meshes, but Munro (1972, 1975) has used the finite element method with a grid of quadrilateral meshes in the following way. Each mesh is divided into two triangular elements, which is done in two different ways (Fig. 19). The total energy is the same in the two types of triangularization and the sum of the energies of the two networks still satisfies the variational principle. Some node 0 is associated to six shaded elements in the left-hand mesh shown in Fig. 19, and by

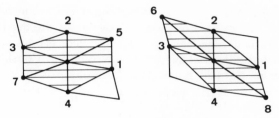

FIG. 19.   The two ways of subdividing quadrilateral meshes into triangular elements.

deriving the energy, we obtain a difference equation between seven points in which the nodes 1, 2, 3, 4, 5, and 7 intervene.

In the right-hand mesh we also obtain an equation between seven points relating the nodes 1, 2, 3, 4, 6, and 8. By adding, 12 elements are made to contribute, and we obtain a nine-point equation of the form

$$\sum_1^N F_j C_{0j} - \sum_1^M B_m = 0$$

with nine nonzero C_{0j}. Each C_{0j} is the sum of the 12 A_{0j} nonzero coefficients such as the nodes 0 and j belong to one of the 12 elements shaded in Fig. 19. The derivation of the difference equations is achieved by means of two types of triangularization, and the author says that it gives a greater precision than if only one of the two meshes was used.

Besides, it is possible to work directly with rectangular elements. Figure 20 shows a rectangular element whose sides are parallel to the z and r axes; it is associated with four nodes. With two points 1 and 2 to determine the variation of F along the side 12, this variation is necessarily linear in x, and this ensures the continuity of F along 12. In the same way, F is a linear function in y along the side 23. Finally, we can write the following expression of F in the element

$$F = a + br + cz + drz \tag{44}$$

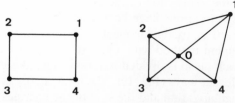

FIG. 20.   (Left) The nodes used in a rectangular element. (Right) The subdivision of a quadrilateral element into four triangular elements with elimination of the node 0 in the final expression.

It is easy to verify that the tangential component of ∇F is continuous along the four sides of the element.

Such an expression cannot be written for a quadrilateral element, but it can be introduced in the following way. The quadrilateral 1234 in Fig. 20 is divided into four triangular elements that meet at point 0, by tracing the two diagonals. The energy of the quadrilateral is the sum of the energies of the four triangular elements. Let us suppose that a linear variation of F exists over each of the triangles. When we write the system (43), the partial derivative of the energy with respect to F_0 is

$$\partial W/\partial F_0 = C_0 F_0 + \sum_1^4 C_{0i} F_i - \sum_1^4 B_m = 0$$

Solving for F_0 and carrying it into $\partial W/\partial F_1$, $\partial W/\partial F_4$, we eliminate the variable F_0, which only appears in these four partial derivatives. Through this expedient, we achieve a quadrilateral element. The shape of the surface $F(r, z)$ in this derivation is that of a four-sided pyramid, even when the quadrilateral becomes a rectangle, while Eq. (44) gives an hyperboloid of one sheet.

Thus far, we have assumed F to be a linear function within the element (so-called linear element), but we may imagine elements of higher order in which F will be given by a polynomial of degree 2, 3, etc. Then, extra nodes must be added on the sides or within the element. But it is essential to notice that, because of the position of these nodes, these high-order elements can still be used when they have a side adjacent to the interfaces or the exterior boundaries, and the way to obtain (41) is not modified. This is a major difference from the methods of Taylor series and of field integrals for which the approximations of an order higher than 2 require numerous particular cases to be considered in the vicinity of the boundaries.

Figure 21a shows a triangular element in which F is represented by a complete polynomial of the third degree; there are ten coefficients in this development and ten nodes to determine them.

The expression of the energy of the element is still obtained by Eq. (38). The matrix $[A_{ij}]$ of Eq. (41) is obtained from matrices with numerical coefficients valid whatever the shape of the triangle, from some trigonometric functions of the vertex angles, and the area of the triangle. All the details concerning the expression of $[A_{ij}]$ will be found in a paper by Sylvester (1969).

It is also possible to obtain rectangular elements of high order; they are classified into two families. In the elements of the "Serendipity" family, the extra nodes are located on the element boundary, while in the Lagrange family, there are also some within the element. Figure 21 shows a third-order element from each family: on each side the function F is repre-

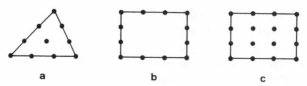

FIG. 21.   Three examples of third-order elements. (a) In a triangular element, the nodes are the vertices, the centroid, and points equally spaced on the sides. (b) Rectangular element of the "Serendipity" family: the 12 nodes are equally spaced on the sides. (c) Lagrangian rectangular element: The nodes are equally spaced on the sides and within the element.

sented by a cubic function. In the Lagrange element (Fig. 21c), the function F is the product of two cubic functions

$$F = (a + br + cr^2 + dr^3)(e + fz + gz^2 + hz^3)$$

Developing this, we must determine 16 coefficients by means of the 16 nodes. In the "Serendipity" family (Fig. 21b), the expression of F is of the fourth degree and has a particular form

$$F = (a + br)(c + dz)[e + f(r^2 + z^2)]$$

If r or z are constant, we do have a cubic function, but the development of F contains only 12 coefficients to be determined by means of the 12 nodes.

Helpful information concerning the use of these high-order rectangular elements will be found in the book by Zienkiewicz (1971). In a problem, it may also be interesting to use elements of different orders; a boundary with a complicated shape may require the use of numerous small linear elements to follow its contour accurately, while in another region a small number of large high-order elements is sufficient for an accurate computation.

Finally, since the total energy is the sum of the elementary energies, whatever the shape of the element, it is possible to mix elements of various shapes to cover the domain in which the solution is to be found as accurately as possible. This possibility of assembling elements of various shapes and orders gives to the finite element method a matchless versatility to discretize Poisson's equation, while numerous constraints concerning the shape and disposition of the meshes in relation to the boundaries prevent the other two methods from using high-order approximations.

VI. Solution of the Set of Difference Equations

The set of difference equations makes up a system of simultaneous equations whose solution will give the values of the y function at each node. When the permeability does not depend on the induction, the set is one of linear equations; otherwise, a nonlinear set is obtained. The system of simultaneous equations is characterized by its high rank, equal to the number of nodes and by the sparsity of the coefficient matrix, and it can be solved either by iterative or direct methods.

A. Iterative Methods

1. Linear Problem

They are successive approximation methods, easy to program, which work in the following way. The first equation of the system

$$\sum_j a_{ij} y_i = b_i, \qquad 1 \leqslant i \quad \text{and} \quad j \leqslant n \tag{45}$$

is solved to obtain the first unknown y_1, the ith equation to obtain the ith unknown y_i, and so on. By this method (Gauss–Seidel method; Durand, 1960), the unknowns are corrected in turn, each in terms of the others, and the latest corrected values are used to correct the next unknown. The rate of convergence of this process is very low.

Calling iteration the complete sweep of the whole array of the unknowns, and $y_i(k)$ the value of the ith unknown in the course of the kth iteration, the difference $y_i(k + 1) - y_i(k)$ is a correction that is added to $y_i(k)$. To speed up the convergence, this correction is multiplied by a factor ω. The $y_i(k + 1)$ value becomes

$$a_{ii} y_i(k + 1) = a_{ii} y_i(k) + \omega \left[b_i - \sum_1^{i-1} a_{ij} y_j(k + 1) - \sum_{i+1}^{n} a_{ij} y_j(k) - a_{ii} y_i(k) \right]$$

$$\tag{46}$$

in which the first sum is taken over all the unknowns already corrected, and the second one over those not yet corrected. Here ω is the accelerating factor and this is known as the Frankel–Young or successive overrelaxation method. Frankel (1950) and Young (1954) have shown that there is a value ω_0 giving the highest possible rate of convergence. Using Eq. (46) with an arbitrary value ω, they deduce ω_0 by

$$\omega_0 = \frac{2}{1 + 1 - (x_M + \omega - 1)^2 / \omega^2 x_M} \tag{47}$$

in which x_M is the largest eigenvalue of one matrix characteristic of the problem. Several methods have been suggested to determine ω_0 while carrying out the calculation, and Carré's (1961) method seems to give the most satisfactory results. x_M can be calculated from one of the three following quantities:

(a) the absolute value of the largest component of the vector displacement $[Y(k + 1)] - [Y(k)]$;
(b) the sum of the absolute values of the components of the vector;
(c) the length of this vector.

Each of these quantities is approximately multiplied by x_M from one iteration to the next, and Carré uses the quantity (b). Carré's method has been discussed by Birtles and Dirmikis (1973). They have concluded that it is better to use quantity (b) rather than (a) or (c), and suggested several ways of speeding up the convergence, drawn from their own experiences.

With a clever method due to Pearson (1969), the ω_0 associated with a fine mesh can be deduced from the ω_0 associated with a coarse one, which is s times larger. The coarse-mesh ω_0 is computed s^2 times more quickly than the fine-mesh ω_0.

2. Nonlinear Problem

When the variations of the permeability with the field in ferromagnetic regions are considered, the a_{ij} coefficients of Eq. (45) are no longer constants. The system of differential equations remains linear with respect to the unknowns y_i, but with variable coefficients. The use of iterative methods to solve this type of problem has not been justified mathematically, but it is experimentally found there may be convergence, provided that the network has no extreme mesh distortions. There are two possible methods.

a. *Linearized Overrelaxation Method.* In this method (Trutt, 1963), the function y or the permeability are alternatively calculated at each node. Starting from initial y values, a first set of permeabilities is calculated, then a first iteration is made for y. The new permeabilities and a_{ij} are then calculated, and this is repeated until a satisfactory convergence of y and the permeabilities is obtained. The nonlinear system is replaced by a sequence of linear problems whose coefficients are modified in the course of the calculation. This is easily worked out, but oscillations of y may appear when the permeabilities vary too quickly during the iterations. The stability can be maintained by underrelaxing the a_{ij} coefficients at each iteration:

(a) At the end of the kth iteration, new coefficients a'_{ij} are calculated.
(b) For the $(k + 1)$st iteration, underrelaxed values are taken:

$$a_{ij}(k + 1) = a_{ij}(k) + t[a'_{ij} - a_{ij}(k)]$$

We have then a sequence of linear problems that converges, provided t is sufficiently small.

The value of t depends on the nonlinearity of the problem, but it remains small. Some t values between 0.12 and 0.2 have been found suitable in very varied fields such as highly saturated rotating machines, magnets for nuclear physics and electron lenses. In nonlinear regions, the Gauss–Seidel method must be used for the sake of stability, and the Frankel–Young one in linear regions to increase the rate of convergence. Winslow (1967) has modified Carré's method to obtain ω_0. He calculated x_M by means of quantity (c), and Eq. (47) when modified gives

$$\omega' = \frac{2}{\{1 + [1 - (x_M + \omega - 1)^2/\omega^2 x_M]^{1/2}\}} - \omega''$$

The constant $\omega'' = 0.01$ prevents ω' from continuous increase. The ω_0 factor used in the next iterations then becomes

$$\omega_0(k + 1) = \omega_0(k) + b[\omega' - \omega_0(k)]$$

The constant $b = 0.05$ damps the variations of ω_0, so that there are no instabilities in the ω_0 values. In nonlinear problems, the ω_0 values are smaller than those in the corresponding linear problems, and values of 1.3–1.6 are quite common.

b. *Nonlinear Overrelaxation Method.* Let us consider the difference equation

$$y_0 \sum a_i = \sum a_i y_i + b \tag{48}$$

assuming that the y_i are held fixed and the a_i vary with y_0, and solve Eq. (48) by Newton's method. Differentiating Eq. (48) gives

$$(y_0 + dy_0) \cdot \sum (a_i + (\partial a_i/\partial y_0) \, dy_0) = \sum a_i y_i + \sum (\partial a_i/\partial y_0) \, y_i \, dy_0$$

or

$$dy_0 = \frac{(\Sigma a_i y_i/\Sigma a_i) - y_0}{1 + \dfrac{\Sigma(\partial a_i/\partial y_0)(y_0 - y_i)}{\Sigma a_i}} \tag{49}$$

The numerator represents the variation of y_0 in the linear case and the denominator corrects this value taking the nonlinearity into account. The calculation is made as follows: y_0 is calculated by Eq. (48), then dy_0 by Eq. (49), then $y' = y_0 + dy_0$. Then we overrelax

$$y_0(k + 1) = y_0(k) + \omega_0[y' - y_0(k)]$$

Again, the ω_0 values are in the 1.3–1.6 range.

B. Direct Methods

Historically, the iterative methods have been developed first, because they need a small amount of core memory: a rectangular network of $I \times J$ nodes for which Eq. (48) contains K nonzero a_i coefficients needs only $I \times J \times (K + 1)$ words. The large computers with virtual memory capability have promoted the use of direct methods to solve Eq. (45). The solution is directly obtained; there is no need to determine an overrelaxation parameter and no problems of convergence to deal with. But, on the other hand, we now need $I \times J \times (J + 3)$ words, assuming that J is less than I and using the fact that the matrix A is a symmetrical band matrix, as can be seen from the expressions of the a_{ij} coefficients. Munro (1972, 1975) has used the Gauss triangularization method adapted to the case of a band matrix. The square-root method (Cholewski's method) can also be used, which is advantageous besides because it decreases the roundoff errors.

Whatever the method, the solution of the nonlinear system is still obtained by means of an iterative process using Newton's method (Sylvester and Chari, 1970). However, instead of applying it successively to each node as in the iterative methods, it is applied at once to the whole set of nodes. Assuming that we have approximate solutions y_j of the system (45), a set of residuals r_i can be calculated:

$$r_i = \sum a_{ij} y_j - b_i$$

with y_1 varying with dy_1, and y_2 with dy_2, . . . in the ith equation, we have

$$(y_1 + dy_1)[a_{i1} + (\partial a_{i1}/\partial y_1) \, dy_1]$$

$$+ (y_2 + dy_2)[a_{i2} + (\partial a_{i2}/\partial y_i) \, dy_2] + \cdot \cdot \cdot = b_i$$

Developing and rearranging, we have

$$(\partial/\partial y_1)(a_{i1} y_1) \, dy_1 + (\partial/\partial y_2)(a_{i2} y_2) \, dy_2 + \cdot \cdot \cdot = -r_i$$

or in a matrix form

$$[(\partial/\partial y_j)(a_{ij} y_j)][dy] = -[r]$$

The variations dy_j of y_j are calculated by solving this system. The coefficient matrix is still a symmetrical band matrix and one of the methods mentioned above can be used. Then, the new approximation of y is

$$[y] = [y] + [dy]$$

and it can be used as the starting vector of a new approximation. These iterations are repeated until the largest component or the length of the residual vector is less than a specified value.

VII. Results

As a conclusion to this article, we present some curves of computed axial induction for two types of lenses. These two lenses are intended to handle electron beams in the megavolt range, and they are fitted with superconducting excitation coils.

The first lens has the general aspect shown in Fig. 7. Its external diameter is 110 mm and its thickness 68 mm. The pole bore has a diameter of 4 mm and the gap is 6 mm wide. The magnetic circuit is made of Permendur (cobalt steel), except for the pole pieces, which are machined in holmium (Bonjour, 1974). This lens has been computed by means of the method of field integrals, using a rectangular mesh. Various cone semi-angles of the pole pieces can be computed when b/a varies. The function chosen for the calculation is the magnetic scalar potential V, and the excitation coil is replaced by its associated system as shown in Section III. In Fig. 22, the lens and two curves of the axial induction have been drawn, with the same length scale. The maximum axial induction is 3.6 T for an excitation of 47 kAt, and of 6 T for 118 kAt. The central part of these curves is bell shaped, and there is a considerable leakage field in the pole bore spreading farther and farther as the excitation increases. The shape of these curves, as well as the values of the flux density within the magnetic circuit, show that this is highly saturated. In a classical lens, the magnetic emf NI must be localized within the gap between the polefaces. For 118 kAt, $NI/4$ is found between the polefaces, $NI/4$ within each of

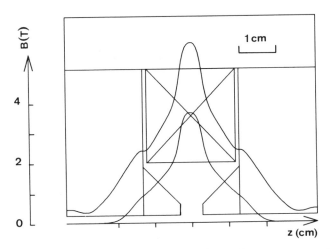

FIG. 22. Two computed axial field curves superimposed over a cross section of the lens and drawn at the same scale.

the pole pieces, and the remainder in the yoke. All these phenomena are due to the inadequate size of the magnetic circuit.

The design shown in Fig. 23 is much more satisfactory from this viewpoint. This lens has a 220-mm diameter and a 180-mm thickness. The pole bore has a diameter of 12 mm and the gap is 12 mm wide. The pole pieces are holmium disks embedded in a bulky magnetic circuit made of cobalt steel. They have a diameter of 70 mm, and their thickness is chosen so that they extend to the points where the flux density is weak enough for the cobalt steel permeability to be higher than that of holmium ($B <$ 2.75 T). This lens has been computed by means of a network of irregular triangles, which allows one to follow accurately the curved shape of the external part of the magnetic circuit. The flux function is calculated by Eqs. (36). The two curves correspond to 50 and 80 kAt excitations, for which the maximum axial flux densities are 3.17 and 4.5 T, respectively. As a benefit from the improved shape of the field curve, the subsequent computation of the electrooptical characteristics show that smaller focal lengths and spherical and chromatic aberration coefficients are obtained for the same accelerating voltage.

The computation also gives the induction and the permeability at each

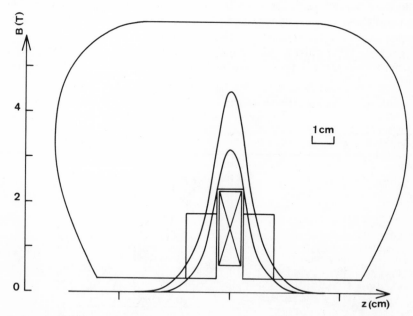

FIG. 23. Two computed axial field curves superimposed over a cross section of the lens and drawn at the same scale.

node within the magnetic circuit. Then, the highly saturated regions can easily be sorted out by inspecting the results, and the design improved by modifying the shape of the saturated region or using another better adapted material (Bonjour, 1975). Thus, through a succession of local modifications and by checking at each step to see if the electrooptical constants are getting better, the design is improved until a final satisfactory project is achieved.

REFERENCES

Abramowitz, M., and Stegun, I. (1965). "Handbook of Mathematical Functions," Ch. 25. Nat. Bur. Std., U.S. Dept. Commerce.
Adams, A., and Read, F. H. (1972). *J. Phys. E: Sci. Instr.* **5**, 150.
Birtles, A. B., and Dirmikis, D. (1973). *Arch. Elektron Ubertrag* **27**, 37.
Bonjour, P. (1972). *C. R. Acad. Sci. Paris* **275B**, 773.
Bonjour, P. (1974). *J. Microsc. (Paris)* **20**, 219.
Bonjour, P. (1975). *J. Phys. E: Sci. Instr.* **8**, 761.
Carré, B. A. (1961). *Comput. J.* **4**, 73.
Courant, R. (1943). *Bul. Am. Math. Soc.* **49**, 1.
Durand, E. (1955). *Ann. Phys. Paris* **10**, 883.
Durand, E. (1957). *C. R. Acad. Sci. Paris.* **244**, 2355.
Durand, E. (1960). "Solutions Numériques des Equations Algébriques." Masson, Paris.
Durand, E. (1964). "Electrostatique." Masson, Paris.
Durand, E. (1968). "Magnétostatique." Masson, Paris.
Frankel, S. P. (1950). *Math. Tab. Aid. Comput.* **4**, 65.
Harting, E., and Read, F. H. (1976). "Electrostatic Lenses." Elsevier, Amsterdam.
Hesse, M. B. (1950). *Proc. Phys. Soc. B* **63**, 386.
Munro, E. (1972). Computer aided design methods in electron optics, PhD thesis, Cambridge.
Munro, E. (1975). A set of Computer Programms for calculating the properties of Electron Lenses, Cambridge Univ. Eng. Dep., Rep. CUED/B—ELECT/TR 45.
Natali, S., Di Chio, D., and Kuyatt, C. E. (1972). *J. Res. Nat. Bur. Std. A, Phys. Ch.* **76A**, 27.
Pearson, J. S. (1969). *Electron. Lett.* **5**, 558.
Read, F. H. (1970). *J. Phys. E: Sci. Instr.* **3**, 127.
Read, F. H., Adams, A., and Soto-Montiel, J. R. (1971). *J. Phys. E: Sci. Instr.* **4**, 625.
Southwell, R. W. (1946). "Relaxation Methods in Theoretical Physics." Oxford Univ. Press, London and New York.
Sylvester, P. (1969). *Int. J. Eng. Sci.* **7**, 849.
Sylvester, P., and Chari, V. K. (1970). *IEEE Trans. Power Appar. Syst.* **PAS-89**, 1642.
Trutt, F. C. (1963). *IEEE Trans. Aerosp.* **12**, 430.
Weber, C. (1967). *In* "Focusing of Charged Particles" (A. Septier, ed.) Vol. 1, p. 45. Academic Press, New York.
Winslow, A. M. (1963). UCRL—7312, Lawrence Radiation Lab., Livermore, Calif.
Winslow, A. M. (1967), *J. Comput. Phys.* **2**, 149.
Young, D. M. (1954). *Trans. Am. Math. Soc.* **76**, 92.

Zienkiewicz, O. C. (1967). "The Finite Element Method in Structural and Continuum Mechanics". McGraw-Hill, London.
Zienkiewicz, O. C. (1971). "The Finite Element Method in Engineering Science." McGraw-Hill, London.
Zienkiewicz, O. C., and Cheung, Y. K. (1965). *Engineer* **220,** 507.

Numerous results concerning the computation of magnetic fields can be found in the *Proceedings of the International Conferences on Magnet Technology:* 1st Conf., Stanford, 8–10/9/1965. 2nd Conf., Oxford, 11–13/7/1967. 3rd. Conf., Hamburg, 19–22/5/1970. 4th Conf., Brookhaven, 19–22/9/1972. 5th Conf., Rome, 21–25/4/1975. 6th Conf., Bratislava, 29/8–2/9/1977.

Such results also can be found in the *Proceedings of the Conferences on the Computation of Magnetic Fields* (COMPUMAG): 1st Conf., Oxford, 31/3–2/4/1976. 2nd Conf. Grenoble, 4–6/9/1978.

ADVANCES IN ELECTRONICS AND ELECTRON PHYSICS, SUPPLEMENT 13A

Methods of Computing Optical Properties and Combating Aberrations for Low-Intensity Beams

P. W. HAWKES

Laboratoire d'Optique Electronique
Centre National de la Recherche Scientifique
Toulouse, France

I. INTRODUCTION

The past decade has seen a vast increase in the use of numerical methods in particle optics, which may be classified for the most part as computer-aided design. Simultaneously, and in some cases spurred on by the numerical work, progress has been made on the theoretical front. In the present article, we give some account of developments in aberration studies and of attempts to design corrected systems, for particle beams of low current density: beams in which space charge forces are negligible, except perhaps at a crossover near to the gun where the Boersch effect may increase the energy spread of the particles (Lejeune and Aubert, this volume). The results, or the approaches at least, are therefore applicable to instruments of many types, from such commercially available de-

45

vices as electron microscopes and their numerous relatives to experimental columns involving high-frequency components, for example. Deflection systems and prisms will only be mentioned in passing, however, since they were very thoroughly studied in *Focusing of Charged Particles* (Septier, 1967), and modern developments are discussed in Part B of this supplement.

A knowledge of the dominant behavior of any device is of course necessary before we can contemplate discussion of its aberrations. Indeed, not all devices can be conveniently described in terms of paraxial properties and aberrations. In Section II, therefore, we examine the form of the equations of motion appropriate in some illustrative cases and indicate which numerical methods have been found most suitable for their solution. We also draw attention to sources of recent information on numerical methods, since this is too vast a subject to be examined more than superficially here.

The third section of the article is devoted to aberration coefficients: to their structure, their representation in matrix form, and to the calculation of the aberrations of combinations of components. Although we use the example of rotationally symmetric electron lenses to illustrate the principles in question, the results are very general and can easily be extended to many other situations. This section ends with a brief account of the use of a computer algebra language to lighten the task of obtaining formulas for aberration coefficients in new types of systems.

Section IV is concerned with optimization and the partial correction of aberrations. We first describe the constrained minimization procedure, developed by Moses for quadrupole studies but found very useful for round lenses too, and the introduction of dynamic programming into electron optics by Szilágyi. We briefly mention progress in aberration correction by foils and other unconventional means and describe the limited progress that has been made in the use of microwave lenses.

Finally, we draw attention to the very ambitious experimental program of aberration correction in the Technische Hochschule at Darmstadt.

The final section reflects a change in attitude toward aberrations that became noticeable in the late 1960s. Scherzer's (1947) various proposals had been pursued both theoretically and experimentally, for some twenty years, and it had become clear that spherical and chromatic aberration in electron microscopes, the main optical obstacles to higher resolution, could be reduced but only at the cost of a considerable and highly undesirable increase in instrumental complexity. Meanwhile, the 1960s had witnessed the introduction of transfer theory into electron optics (Hanszen, 1971); the idea of tolerating a certain measure of aberration and rendering the degraded image more faithful in a subsequent step, with the aid of the computer, began to seem more attractive than aberration correction in the microscope. Indeed, too little spherical aberration could be positively disadvantageous, owing to the fact that phase contrast plays a dominant role at high resolution, and the phase shifts due to spherical aberration and defocus are used to transform phase variations into amplitude variations in the conventional electron microscope. Nevertheless, some reduction of the spherical aberration coefficient is still very much to be desired. For a defocus of $(C_s\lambda)^{1/2}$, the phase contrast transfer function first passes through zero at a spacing of $0.7(C_s\lambda^3)^{1/4}$, which for the values of C_s currently available is of the order of a few angstroms. If we keep λ constant (that is, operate at the same accelerating voltage), an improvement in the "resolution," as measured by the cutoff value, by a given factor, can only be obtained by decreasing C_s by the same factor, raised to the fourth power; a fivefold improvement thus requires a reduction in C_s to $C_s/625$.

We make no attempt to describe the numerical methods in use in digital image processing; many excellent general texts are available, and a few have now been devoted specifically to electron images. These are listed in Section V. Rather, we draw attention to the effect that these ideas have had, and are having, on the design of microscopes and their accessories; in particular, we mention microscope–computer interfaces and the privileged position of the scanning instruments in this respect.

II. Numerical Methods of Solving Equations of Motion

The equations of motion that are encountered in the study of particle beam behavior are of course all derived from the relativistic form of Newton's equations but vary according to the nature of the device: Is the optic axis straight or curved? Is there a plane or axis of symmetry? Is a division into paraxial properties and aberrations permissible? Even in the simplest case, that of rotationally symmetric systems, there is no single recipe that can be given; the equations need quite different treatment in electron guns, where the electrons set out virtually from rest, in magnetic lenses, where their speed is constant, and in electrostatic lenses, where they may be reflected if the potential is such that the lens becomes a mirror. Similarly, the form in which the results are expressed varies considerably with the device in question: for guns, it is the brightness and position of the crossover that are of interest; for lenses, mirrors, prisms, and any component that has a dominant linear behavior perturbed by aberrations, we compute cardinal elements and aberration coefficients as a function of geometry and excitation; for secondary electron detectors, some suitably defined efficiency will perhaps be adequate. As a final general remark, we recall that either time or position (and conceivably both) may be the more suitable independent variable. In very many situations, the point of arrival of the particles beyond the device is of importance but the time of arrival is not—in these cases, we eliminate time from the equations of motion and study the dependence of (at worst) two of the spatial coordinates on the third. Symmetry may further simplify this stage. If, however, time is an important consideration, as it is in the study of microwave cavities used as electron lenses, we must retain it, but, as the microwave example demonstrates, it may still be advantageous to adopt a space coordinate as independent variable.

A. Forms of the Equations of Motion

The equations describing the motion of charged particles in any device that creates a magnetic flux distribution $\mathbf{B}$ and/or an electric field $\mathbf{E}$ have the general form

$$\frac{d}{dt}\left\{\frac{m_0\mathbf{v}}{(1 - v^2/c^2)^{1/2}}\right\} = -e(\mathbf{E} + \mathbf{v} \times \mathbf{B}) \tag{1}$$

where $\mathbf{v}$ denotes the particle velocity, and c the speed of light. The charge is denoted by $-e$ so that for electrons e is positive and equal to 0.16 aC. In static fields, it is not difficult to show that

$$v = \frac{2\eta\{\phi(1 + \epsilon\phi)\}^{1/2}}{1 + 2\epsilon\phi} \tag{2}$$

where

$$\mathbf{E} = -\text{grad } \phi, \quad \eta = (e/2m_0)^{1/2} \approx 3 \times 10^5 \ \text{C}^{1/2} \ \text{kg}^{-1/2}$$
$$\epsilon = e/2m_0c^2 \approx 1 \ \text{MV}^{-1}$$

the origin of ϕ is chosen so that $\phi = 0$ where the particles are stationary.

In the numerous practical situations in which the position of the particles is of interest but not the dependence of position on time, it is usually convenient to eliminate time with the aid of Eq. (2). If we adopt arc length s as independent variable, Eq. (1) becomes

$$\frac{d}{ds}\left[\{\phi(1 + \epsilon\phi)\}^{1/2}\frac{d\mathbf{r}}{ds}\right] = -\frac{1}{2}\frac{1 + 2\epsilon\phi}{\{\phi(1 + \epsilon\phi)\}^{1/2}}\mathbf{E} + \eta\left(\mathbf{B} \times \frac{d\mathbf{r}}{ds}\right) \tag{3}$$

If the axial coordinate (z) is the most convenient independent variable, as is very often the case, we write

$$ds = \{1 + (dx/dz)^2 + (dy/dz)^2\}^{1/2} dz \tag{4}$$

so that Eq. (3) now becomes

$$\frac{d}{dz}\left[\left\{\frac{\phi(1 + \epsilon\phi)}{1 + (dx/dz)^2 + (dy/dz)^2}\right\}^{1/2}\frac{d\mathbf{r}}{dz}\right]$$

$$= -\tfrac{1}{2}(1 + 2\epsilon\phi)\left\{\frac{1 + (dx/dz)^2 + (dy/dz)^2}{\phi(1 + \epsilon\phi)}\right\}^{1/2}\mathbf{E} + \eta(\mathbf{B} \times d\mathbf{r}/dz) \quad (5)$$

At this point, a decision must be taken on the strategy best suited to the problem under investigation. If the device has high symmetry and there is every reason to believe that it can be analyzed in terms of paraxial properties and aberrations, then it is best to expand ϕ and the components of $\mathbf{B}$ (or $\mathbf{A}$, $\mathbf{B}$ = curl $\mathbf{A}$) in a power series, substitute these into Eq. (5) and extract paraxial equations and higher-order equations. If, on the other hand, there is little or no simplifying symmetry or if the trajectories are liable to depart so far from the paraxial region (or occupy so wide a region) that exact solutions of Eq. (5) are preferable, then we may need to work with a form of Eq. (5) directly. Indeed, if aberrations of higher order than the primary (third-order, if the axis is straight) aberrations are to be computed, it may well be easier to solve Eq. (5) directly and extract the aberration coefficients of different orders by differentiation than to embark on the herculean task of deriving analytic expressions for the aberration coefficients. The third- and fifth-order spherical aberration coefficients of an air-cored coil for use in a focal-separation β-ray spectrometer were obtained in this way by Foster (1968), and we shall meet another example below. Nevertheless, each new case needs to be assessed carefully, to establish which procedure is more suitable—in Foster's case, the task of writing sufficiently accurate predictor–corrector routines to permit repeated numerical differentiation was also very considerable. It is, however, generally true that any simplification permitted by the symmetry of the system will be worthwhile. Thus, Underwood (1978) has performed further calculations on air-cored coils, using cylindrical polar coordinates with arc length as an independent variable, and obtained an immense saving in computer time compared with those of Foster, who used cartesian coordinates with axial coordinate (z) as independent variable. Such examples could be multiplied but we draw attention to these studies because of the extremely high accuracy attained.

If a formalism yielding paraxial properties and aberrations is appropriate, as is the case for round lenses, mirrors, quadrupoles, and prisms, the equations of motion are well known (see Septier, 1967; Glaser, 1952, 1956; Grivet, 1972; or indeed most texts on particle optics). We shall not list all these here; we merely draw attention to the fact that special precautions are necessary when dealing with mirrors, owing to the fact that the inclinations of rays with respect to the axis are not small in the vicinity of the point of reflection. The independent variable has therefore to be chosen with some caution. This point is discussed in the early work of Recknagel (1936, 1937) and in a study of the aberrations of mirrors by Schiske (1957); a full account is to be found in Glaser (1952, 1956) and the question is examined in, for example, Grivet (1972). More recently, Kel'man et al. (1971a, b, 1972a, c, 1973b) have reconsidered the formalism usually adopted for studying electron mirrors. The paper by Kel'man et al. (1972c) complements earlier studies of rotationally symmetric systems; a new independent variable is introduced, instead of time, and a list of third-order aberration coefficients is given for the electrostatic case. This new variable, which Kel'man et al. denote by ζ, is identical with the axial coordinate z on the axis but elsewhere satisfies the equation

$$d\zeta/dt = \pm 2\eta\{\Phi(\zeta)\}^{1/2} \tag{6}$$

where the plus sign is to be used for particles incident on the mirror (traveling from $z \rightarrow -\infty$ toward $z \rightarrow +\infty$) and the minus sign for those reflected from it. Writing $z = \zeta + \eta(\zeta)$, so that

$$\Phi(z) = \Phi(\zeta) + \Phi'(\zeta)\eta(\zeta) + \cdots \tag{7}$$

the equations of motion including terms up to third order in radial distance take the following form, where $u = r \exp(i\theta)$ and (r, θ, z) is a cylindrical polar coordinate system:

$$u''(\zeta) + \frac{\Phi'(\zeta)}{2\Phi(\zeta)} u'(\zeta) + \frac{\Phi''(\zeta)}{4\Phi(\zeta)} u(\zeta) = \frac{\Phi''''(\zeta)}{32\Phi(\zeta)} u^2(\zeta)u^*(\zeta) - \frac{\Phi'''(\zeta)}{4\Phi(\zeta)} u(\zeta)\eta(\zeta) \tag{8a}$$

$$\eta'(\zeta) - \frac{\Phi'(\zeta)}{2\Phi(\zeta)} = -\frac{1}{2} u'(\zeta)u^{*'}(\zeta) - \frac{\Phi''(\zeta)}{8\Phi(\zeta)} u(\zeta)u^*(\zeta) \tag{8b}$$

Further analysis of these equations leads to a self-consistent treatment of the paraxial properties and aberrations of electrostatic mirrors, which avoids the problems associated with the region in which the particles are reflected.

In two later papers, Kel'man et al. (1973b) extend this work to cover the case of mirrors in which a magnetic field may be present as well as the electrostatic field. A very full account of such systems is given here, including integrals for all the aberration coefficients. Curves and tables for a particular (electrostatic) case are to be found in a later paper by Sekunova (1977); a practical application of this work in mirror electron microscopy is outlined by Sekunova and Yakushev (1975).

Another device that does not lend itself to the usual electron optical treatment of electrostatic lenses is the cathode lens, in which the electrons are accelerated from rest in an electrostatic field. This situation arises in image converters, for example, in electron emission microscopes and of course in electron guns. Since the transformation of axial coordinates used by Kel'man et al. to study electron mirrors was introduced to circumvent the problems arising from large values of ray gradient, it is not surprising that the same transformation can be used to analyze cathode lenses. The analytically simple case of electrostatic fields with cylindrical (not rotational) symmetry is studied in Kel'man et al. (1972b) and extended to the rotationally symmetric case (cf. Septier, 1954; Soa, 1959) in Kel'man et al. (1973a).

In two final papers, Kel'man et al. (1974b) consider the still more general case of "composite" cathode lenses, that is, lenses consisting of superimposed electrostatic and magnetic fields. Formulas are given for the geometrical and chromatic aberration coefficients, including those associated with the presence of a magnetic field at the cathode surface. The reader may recall that the refractive index cannot be made isotropic over this surface if the component of the magnetic field normal to it does not vanish—that is, rays and their ray or momentum vectors cannot all be simultaneously normal to the cathode surface (e.g., Sturrock, 1955). The general theory of systems with straight axes, based on the transformation of Kel'man et al., is given in Daumenov et al. (1978).

Before leaving the transformation of the optic axis coordinate introduced by Kel'man et al., we draw attention to two papers by Kel'man et al. (1973c) on rotationally symmetric electrostatic devices used as *transaxial* mirrors. The term "transaxial" was introduced by Strashkevich (1962) in connection with quadrupoles, to describe systems in which the optic axis lies in a plane normal to the axis of symmetry of the system. The transaxial mirrors considered by Kel'man et al. are rotationally symmetric but the electrons must now be pictured arriving between the electrodes (Fig. 1). Such mirrors are of interest since the spherical aberration is less than that of comparable rotationally symmetric mirrors, in one direction at least. In the papers of Kel'man et al. (1973c) the paraxial equations are given and expressions for the aberration coefficients are derived. (For a study of the potential distribution in electrostatic transaxial immersion and einzel lenses, see Mel'nikov and Kossovskaya, 1975. See too Manabaev, 1976, and Kel'man et al., 1974a.)

In this context, we draw attention to a very interesting series of papers by Hahn, who has introduced a different transformation of the axial coordinate that again permits a unified treatment of ordinary lenses, electrostatic and magnetic, electron mirrors, and cathode lenses.

The appropriate transformation is discussed very fully in Hahn (1965),

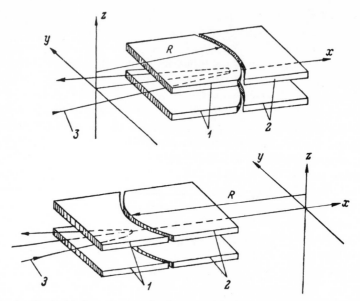

FIG. 1. Typical trajectories in a simple transaxial mirror. Notice that the particles remain close to a plane parallel to the electrodes—not, as in the more familiar configuration,
perpendicular to them. (After Kel'man *et al.*, 1973c.)

and its applicability to lenses, mirrors and cathode lenses is briefly explained in Hahn (1971). Without going into detail, we mention that the z
coordinate is now replaced by an angle, $\omega(z)$ [which in the special case of
Glaser's bell-shaped field, reduces to arc tan (z/d)]; this angle or "phase
function" $\omega(z)$ is a function of an "amplitude function" $\mathbf{p}(z)$. The general
solutions of the equations of motion can be expressed quite simply in
terms of these two functions, $\mathbf{p}$ and ω. The latter satisfy differential equations, the form and properties of which are examined at great length by
Hahn; they are not reproduced here as they convey little when taken out
of context, but we wish to stress that by mapping the entire optic axis into
a finite domain, Hahn is able to avoid a number of problems that otherwise arise. Furthermore, he has carried the calculations through to the
point where aberration coefficients can be explicity evaluated. The axial
transformation introduced by Hahn can be used to analyze a variety of related electron-optical devices: electrostatic velocity filters of the retarding
field type (Hahn, 1961, 1964), quadrupole systems (Hahn, 1969–1970) and
round electrostatic and magnetic lenses with imperfect rotational symmetry (Hahn, 1966).

Before leaving this topic, we make the general comment that mapping
the infinite domain, $-\infty \leq z \leq \infty$, into a finite domain has many ancillary
advantages, particularly for numerical work where continuous functions

are replaced by sets of sample values and analysis is abandoned in favor of algebra. For an example of this, see a brief note by Hahn (1975), describing a matrix formalism for calculating the properties of a "macrolens" from those of the elementary "microlenses" of which it is composed, the latter associated with the individual sample values of the field or potential on the axis.

In the case of time-dependent fields, it is again often possible to construct paraxial equations and aberration formulas, but time is now of paramount importance. We briefly consider the problem of microwave cavities as electron lenses, to which a certain amount of attention has recently been paid (see Section IV,B,2). The approaches adopted in the two main recent studies differ slightly in the way in which the electromagnetic field components are treated. Here we follow Oldfield (1973a,b), whose analysis follows closely that familiar in other branches of electron optics. Unlike Matsuda and Ura (1974a,b), however, he does not calculate aberration coefficients.

We set out from the Lagrangian L,

$$L = m_0 c^2 \{1 - (1 - v^2/c^2)^{1/2}\} + e\phi - e\mathbf{A} \cdot \mathbf{v} \tag{9}$$

where the electric and magnetic fields are now given by

$$\mathbf{E} = -\text{grad } \phi - \partial \mathbf{A}/\partial t, \qquad \mathbf{B} = \text{curl } \mathbf{A} \tag{10}$$

It is convenient to use the position coordinate on the optic axis as independent variable, and we therefore introduce a new time variable, τ, which measures the difference between the time taken by a particle traveling along the optic axis to reach some plane $z = $ constant and the time taken by a particle following an off-axis path. We therefore write

$$t = T(z) + \tau \tag{11}$$

where $T(z)$ is the reciprocal of the particle velocity as a function of z. In order to derive variational equations with respect to z from the Lagrangian, we write

$$M = L \, dt/dz \tag{12}$$

and so

$$\delta \int_A^B M \, dz = 0 \tag{13}$$

After some manipulation, we find that

$$M = M_1 + M_2 \tag{14}$$

$$M_1 = m_0 c^2 [T' + \tau' - \{(T' + \tau)^2 - (r'^2 + r^2\theta'^2 + 1)/c^2\}^{1/2}]$$

$$M_2 = e\phi(T + \tau') - e(A_r r' + A_\theta r\theta' + A_z) \tag{15}$$

in cylindrical polar coordinates; primes denote differentiation with respect to z. The equations of motion are the Euler equations of Eq. (13), namely,

$$\frac{d}{dz}\left(\frac{\partial M}{\partial q'}\right) - \frac{\partial M}{\partial q} = 0 \tag{16}$$

for $q = \tau, r,$ and θ. Expanding M as a power series in $r, r', \theta, \theta', \tau,$ and τ' enables us to derive first the axial equation, which describes the motion of electrons along the axis, $T(z)$, then the paraxial equations, describing the variation of the position and time coordinates and yielding corresponding cardinal elements, and, last, the aberrations. This expansion is performed in detail by Oldfield; the results are as follows:

$$M_1 = M_1^{(1)} + M_1^{(2)} + M_1^{(3)} + \cdots \tag{17}$$

where

$$M_1^{(1)} = \tau' m_0 c^2 (1 - acT')$$

$$M_1^{(2)} = (m_0 ca/2)(r'^2 + r^2\theta'^2 + \tau'^2 c^2 a^2) \tag{18}$$

$$M_1^{(3)} = -(m_0 c^3 a^3 T'/2)\{\tau'(r'^2 + r^2\theta'^2) + \tau'^3 c^2 a^2\}$$

For M_2, we select the gauge such that $\phi = 0$ and so

$$M_2 = -e(A_r r' + A_\theta r\theta' + A_z)$$
$$\mathbf{B} = \text{curl } \mathbf{A}, \quad \text{div } \mathbf{A} = 0, \quad \mathbf{E} = -\partial\mathbf{A}/dt \tag{19}$$

The form of M_2 is different for cavities excited in transverse magnetic (TM) and transverse electric (TE) modes. We therefore consider these separately.

1. TM-Mode Equations

M_2 may consist of two contributions, one from the cavity itself, the other from any static axially symmetric magnetic field that may be present. Characterizing the latter by $A_{\theta s}$, the only nonzero component of $\mathbf{A}$, we obtain

$$M_2 = -(e/\omega) \cos \omega t (E_r r' + E_z) - eA_{\theta s} r\theta' \tag{20}$$

in which the cavity frequency is ω. Writing

$$E_r = -\tfrac{1}{2} r E_0' + \tfrac{1}{16} r^3 (E_0''' + \beta^2 E_0') - \cdots$$

$$E_z = E_0 - \tfrac{1}{4} r^2 (E_0'' + \beta^2 E_0) + \tfrac{1}{64} r^4 (E_0'''' + 2\beta^2 E_0'' + \beta^4 E_0) + \cdots \tag{21}$$

$$A_{\theta s} = (r/2) B_{0s} - (r^3/16) B_{0s}'' + \cdots$$

where

$$E_0 = E_z(0, z), \qquad B_{0s} = B_z(0, z), \qquad \beta = \omega/c = 2\pi/\lambda \qquad (22)$$

we find

$$M^{(1)} = \tau' m_0 c^2(1 - acT') + \tau e E_0 \sin \omega T$$

$$M^{(2)} = \tfrac{1}{2} m_0 ca(r'^2 + r^2\theta'^2 + \tau'^2 c^2 a^2) \qquad (23)$$

$$+ \frac{e}{\omega} \cos \omega T \left\{ \frac{rr'E_0'}{2} + \frac{r^2}{4} (E_0'' + \beta^2 E_0) + \frac{\tau^2 E_0 \omega^2}{2} \right\} - \frac{r^2\theta' e B_{0s}}{2}$$

$M^{(1)}$ yields the *axial equation* giving $T(z)$:

$$eE_0 \sin \omega T - m_0 c^3 a^3 T'' = 0 \qquad (24)$$

$M^{(2)}$ gives us the *paraxial time equation* (for τ)

$$\tau'' - 3\tau' c^2 a^2 T'T'' - (2\tau e \omega E_0/ca^3) \cos \omega T = 0 \qquad (25)$$

and, after introduction of a rotating coordinate system,

$$u = w \exp(-i\chi), \qquad w = r \exp(i\theta), \qquad \chi' = \epsilon c B_{0s}/a \qquad (26)$$

the *paraxial space equation* (for u):

$$u'' - u'c^2a^2T'T'' - (\epsilon cu/a)\{(\beta^2/\omega)E_0 \cos \omega T \\ + T_0'E_0' \sin \omega T - (\epsilon c/a)B_{0s}^2\} = 0 \qquad (27)$$

2. TE-Mode Equation

Oldfield now finds

$$M^{(1)} = \tau' m_0 c^2(1 - acT') \\ M^{(2)} = (m_0 ca/2)(r'^2 + r^2\theta'^2 + \tau'^2 c^2 a^2) - \tfrac{1}{2}r^2 e\theta'(B_{0s} + B_0 \sin \omega T) \qquad (28)$$

The *axial time equation* now reduces to the simple form

$$T' = \text{constant} \qquad (29)$$

as it must, since there is no acceleration in the z direction.

The *paraxial time equation* is also very simple:

$$\tau' = \text{constant} \qquad (30)$$

while the paraxial space equation is now

$$u'' + u\{(\epsilon c/a)(B_{0s} + B_0 \sin \omega T)\}^2 = 0 \qquad (31)$$

We reproduce these equations here to show how ubiquitous in particle optics is the basic structure of paraxial properties and aberrations: in electron guns, lenses, quadrupoles, prisms, mirrors, and even microwave cavities, there is an interesting range of properties that can be described in terms of cardinal elements and aberration coefficients. In the case of microwave cavities used as electron lenses, we associate the notions of foci, focal lengths, and principal planes with time as well as with space, at least in the case of TM modes. Further details can be found in the papers listed above.

Another important case in which time is of transitory importance is that of electron guns of the thermal or thermal-field (TF) emission type. The reason here is not that the time of emergence of individual electrons from the gun is of any intrinsic importance but that the effect of the space charge field due to the emitted beam itself must be included, in the neighborhood of the cathode. This is an awkward problem, and has recently been solved by means of an iterative procedure by Hauke (1977). In this work, a large number of trajectories are first calculated, using the potential distribution created by the gun electrodes alone, the initial conditions (time and place of emission from the cathode surface) being chosen according to a probability distribution that takes into account such factors as the Maxwellian distribution of energy, Lambert's law for the angle of emission, and the Richardson equation for the total current. The resulting space charge potential is then computed and added to that of the electrodes, after which the process is repeated until there is no further charge in the potential. From this point on, information about the time at which the electrons reach points along their trajectories is no longer needed and the brightness or emittance can be obtained in the usual way.

Even apart from considerations of space charge, electron guns are always among the more difficult devices to study numerically, largely because the potential distribution must be known with such high accuracy in the cathode region where the electrons are still traveling relatively slowly (1 eV corresponds to 600 km sec^{-1}). This aspect of the problem is of course common to both thermal and field emission guns. Recent information on this question, which is outside the scope of the present chapter, may be found in the papers by Wiesner and Everhart (1969), Worster (1969a,b, 1970), Crewe (1970), Kamminga and Francken (1971), Rauh (1971), Kuroda and Suzuki (1972), Munro (1972), Veneklasen (1972), Veneklasen and Siegel (1972), Crewe (1973), Munro (1973), Kamminga (1973), Wiesner (1973), Wiesner and Everhart (1973, 1974), Engel et al. (1974), Kuroda (1974), Kuroda and Suzuki (1974a,b,c), Kuroda et al. (1974a,b), Kuroda and Suzuki (1975), Cleaver (1975), Speidel and Vorster (1975), Hainfeld (1977), Rauh and Kern (1978), Riddle (1978), Kern et al. (1978), Hoch et al. (1978), Kern (1978), Cleaver (1978–1979), Bell and Swanson (1979), Broers (1979), Orloff and Swanson (1979), Kurz (1979),

Speidel *et al.* (1979), Tamura (1979), Cleaver (1980), and Lauer (1980); see Lejeune and Aubert, this volume, and Knauer (1979).

B. *Numerical Methods of Trajectory Tracing*

This subject has a long history and a very extensive literature; it has been studied both at low energies (up to 1 MeV or a few megavolts) and at high energies in the domain of particle accelerators. In this present section, we draw attention to various types of procedure that are available and give a few examples of their application. We shall say little about the problems of trajectory tracing in accelerators since specialized computer programs have been developed for this task. Particularly clear accounts of the numerical analysis involved are to be found in Miller (1966) and Lambert (1977); the latter in particular is an invaluable starting point for deeper investigation when the standard procedures fail for some reason.

The differential equations that arise in trajectory tracing are ordinary differential equations; the boundary conditions that determine the choice of a particular solution from the infinite set of general solutions are most commonly initial values although boundary value problems do also occur (see Walsh, 1977, for a very thorough and readable survey of numerical methods applicable to the latter category, which is notoriously more intractable than that of initial value problems).

The methods of solving initial value problems arising with ordinary differential equations may be grouped into two broad classes*: the linear multistep methods and the single-step Runge–Kutta methods. In both cases, we first reduce the pth order differential equation to be solved to a set of first-order equations of the form

$$\mathbf{y}' = \mathbf{f}(x, \mathbf{y}) \tag{32}$$

and seek approximate values of $\mathbf{y}(x)$ on the discrete point set $\{x_n | x_n = a + nh, n = 0, 1, 2, \ldots, N, Nh = b - a\}$. The step length h is normally constant, although the full domain in which the solution is sought may well be divided into subdomains, each of which has its own step length. In the linear multistep methods, we attempt to generate the solution $\{\mathbf{y}_n\}$ by setting $\mathbf{y}_q = \mathbf{s}_q(h)$, $q = 0, 1, \ldots, k - 1$, where the values of $\mathbf{s}$ denote starting values and

$$\sum_{j=0}^{k} a_j \mathbf{y}_{n+j} = h \sum_{j=0}^{k} b_j \mathbf{f}_{n+j} \tag{33}$$

---

* The terminology adopted in the following paragraphs has been chosen in conformity with that of Lambert (1977), whose definitions we follow closely.

where f_n denotes $f(x_n, y_n)$; the coefficients a_j and b_j are constants such that neither a_k nor $|a_0| + |b_0|$ vanishes and k (≥ 1) is the step number. If b_k vanishes, the method is said to be explicit and no iteration is required; otherwise, the method is implicit and nonlinear equations must be solved at each step. The predictor–corrector methods that have been widely used in particle trajectory calculations (see Kasper, 1980, Hawkes, 1973, or texts on particle optics for references) are obtained by combining implicit and explicit procedures.

The other class, generically known as Runge–Kutta methods, are one-step methods. The solution $\{y_n\}$ is given explicitly by

$$y_0 = s, \qquad y_{n+1} - y_n = h\phi(x_n, y_n, h) \tag{34}$$

in which

$$\phi(x, y, h) = \sum_{r=1}^{R} c_r k_r \tag{35}$$

and

$$k_r = f\left(x + ha_r, y + \sum_{s=1}^{R} b_{rs}k_{rs}\right), \qquad r = 1, 2, \ldots, R \tag{36}$$

The b_{rs} are constants and $a_r = \Sigma_{s=1}^{R} b_{rs}$. Traditionally b_{rs} vanishes for $s \geq r$, and the sequence $\{y_n\}$ is obtained directly. Lambert (1977) draws attention to the natural generalization in which $b_{rs} \neq 0$ for $s \geq r$, which produces implicit (or semi-implicit, in the intermediate case $b_{rs} = 0$ for $s > r$) methods.

Experience shows that one of the widely available Runge–Kutta packages is adequate for very many problems of particle optics unless very high accuracy is essential for some special reason. For electron lens calculations, the Numerov method (e.g., Miller, 1966) is particularly convenient since it is designed for second-order differential equations containing no first-order derivative. This method is strictly speaking a multistep procedure, though it is often regarded as a close relative of the Runge–Kutta group. The order of a Runge–Kutta procedure may be high: in a recent study, Hairer (1978), for example, has examined a tenth-order Runge–Kutta routine.

Initial value problems for ordinary differential equations formed one of the principal themes of a congress held in 1976. Much interesting discussion is to be found in the proceedings (Bulirsch et al., 1978).

C. Some Typical Applications

Trajectory tracing is the second major stage in calculating the properties of any component, the first being devoted to calculating the potential or field distribution. The methods used in these two steps are very different, but, in practice, the programs are organized into a suite that permits the user to pass through both stages, iteratively if required, without any reorganization of the results of the first stage. The very flexible multipurpose program package written by Munro (1973) is a good example of such a suite. With it, Munro has calculated the properties of such diverse devices as triode field-emission guns, superconducting and snorkel lenses and different types of secondary electron detectors. A standard Runge–Kutta routine was used for ray tracing.

The use of methods of both classes—Runge–Kutta and predictor–corrector—is illustrated by the work of Lenz (1973). The former were successfully used in cases in which paraxial properties and aberration coefficients were required: pinhole lenses (Martin, 1972; Guckenberger and Heil, 1972), electron accelerators and a low-aberration demagnifying electron optical microrecorder (Koops, 1972a, b, 1973a, b), for example; the latter were invoked in studying electrostatic filter lenses, in which some electrons are transmitted while others are reflected, and conical edge focusing systems, where the electrons travel far from the axis (Noven, 1963, 1965; Kunath, 1972; Typke and Hoppe, 1972; Kunath, 1976; Typke et al., 1976). In the work of Natali et al. (1972a,b), various electrostatic lenses are studied. In order to achieve the desired accuracy, a predictor–corrector method (that of Hamming) is adopted; since the procedure is not self-starting, a Runge–Kutta routine is used to compute the first few trajectory values, after which the predictor–corrector sequence takes over. The appropriate formulas are reproduced in Natali et al. (1972a). An extensive collection of tables and graphs of electrostatic lens properties (with electron spectrometers in mind), with details of the numerical methods employed, is given in Harting and Read (1976).

A very different application is examined in a paper by Galejs and Kuyatt (1978), who study the focusing properties and distortion in energy analyzers with crossed electrostatic and magnetic fields. We refer to their paper for an account of earlier studies of such analyzers, which are known generically as Wien filters, and for the advantages of the configuration studied by these authors, namely a uniform electrostatic field and a toroidal magnetic field (Andersen, 1967; Andersen and Le Poole, 1970; Collins, 1973). This work is interesting in the present context in that the authors derive the aberration coefficients by solving the exact equations of motion with sufficient accuracy to be able to deduce the aberration coefficients by matching the points of arrival of rays having different initial gradients to a polynomial. This recalls the procedure used by Foster (1968), referred to earlier.

At the major particle accelerator laboratories, highly perfected program suites for trajectory tracing in systems consisting of multipoles and deflection magnets have been developed (see Herrmannsfeldt, 1973, for example). An extremely flexible interactive system for analyzing and designing ion beam systems is described by Hicks *et al.* (1976); this permits on-line investigation of trajectories in dipoles and quadrupoles (using the program TRANSPORT written at Stanford Linear Accelerator Center), in more complicated magnetic geometries and in electrostatic systems where space charge cannot be neglected. Of the many possible applications of such a system, Hicks *et al.* (1976) draw attention to the configurations of interest for isotope separation and ion implantation.

Examples could of course be multiplied, since almost every numerical study of some electron optical device uses trajectory tracing and many contain much useful advice permitting the newcomer to avoid pitfalls and blind alleys, thus saving time and perhaps reducing frustration. In the last resort, though, trajectory tracing can only be learned by writing programs for oneself, not by reading the accounts, however instructive, of others.

III. ABERRATION COEFFICIENT STRUCTURE

A. Aberration Polynomials

Formulas have been available for many years for the primary aberration coefficients of round electrostatic and magnetic lenses, quadrupole lenses, and for the deflection systems that are often used in conjunction with these. Recently, formulas have been derived for some systems not previously examined and, with the increasing availability of computer algebra (see Section III,D below), the task of obtaining such formulas has become much less daunting. The earlier formulas for the aberration coefficients of lenses (round lenses or quadrupoles) all have the form of integrals from object plane to image, the integrands containing potential functions and paraxial solutions, for the case in which object and image are real. When either or both of the latter are virtual, the "asymptotic" coefficients must be used, in which the integrals are semi-infinite or extend over the whole length of the optic axis.

These situations need to be distinguished only when the real object or image is immersed in one of the lens fields, a situation that occurs relatively infrequently. Nevertheless, the object is usually immersed in the objective of an electron microscope and may be inside the field region in the probe-forming lens of a scanning instrument. Most lenses and related components simply transfer an intermediate image, real or virtual, from one plane to another; this is the case for all the lenses of electron microscopes and related probe devices, apart from the objective, for the individual quadrupoles of corrector units, and of course for the components of beam transfer systems. Real (objective) aberration coefficients vary in a complicated way with object position and for this reason, they are commonly tabulated for electron lenses only for the object position corresponding to very high magnification. Asymptotic aberration coefficients, on the other hand, exhibit a much simpler dependence on object position and we now describe this in some detail, for round lenses and quadrupoles. It is perhaps worth pointing out that this dependence would probably have been noticed a great deal sooner had it not been for the fact that almost none of the major textbooks of electron optics devoted space to asymptotic aberrations, which were considered briefly by Sturrock (1955), in detail by Seman (1958), and by Lenz (1956b, 1957), whose *Optik* paper is essentially the "standard reference." There were thus no lists of aberration coefficients, comparable with those for the real coefficients, in which the underlying structure could readily be recognized. Such lists were not published until much later: for round lenses in Hawkes (1970a) and for quadrupoles in Hawkes (1970b). Nevertheless, the polynomial dependence of the aberration coefficients on object position was established for a restricted class of lens aberrations much earlier by Verster* (1963) but this too passed largely unnoticed, no doubt owing to the fact that the result was buried in a long study, primarily devoted to a very different subject of comparatively limited interest, namely gauze lenses. The polynomial structure is found for real (objective) aberrations only in the case of Newtonian model field distributions, that is, fields for which a fixed set of cardinal elements can be used irrespective of object position (Hawkes, 1968a, b). Nevertheless, it is still a useful approximation for non-Newtonian fields such as the Grivet–Lenz model (see Fig. 2), $B(z) = B_0 \operatorname{sech}(z/d)$ as shown numerically in Hawkes (1970e); in practice, however, it is rare that objectives or probe-forming lenses are used in conditions that require a knowledge of any but the high-magnification values of the various parameters.

* Verster credits the idea of seeking aberration coefficients independent of object position to van Heel (1953) and Brouwer (1957), although Brouwer does not himself include van Heel's book in his bibliography and a later edition of this book (1964), which I have consulted, refers to Brouwer (in fact, the reference is to Brouwer's later book, 1964, which is of course more accessible than his thesis). Nevertheless, the electron optical case is significantly different from the optical situation, for in the latter, it is natural to consider the transfer from a *pair* of planes to the *pair* of planes conjugate to them; this does not suit the electron optical formalism at all well, though it makes for sparser matrices.

Brouwer's approach (also set out in Brouwer and Walther, 1967) recalls the work of Smith (1921–1922, 1923–1924; see also Pegis, 1961), which likewise does not readily lend itself to translation into electron optical terms. In view of this, it is reasonable to regard Verster's work as a new contribution to aberration studies and not a mere extension of the light optical theory.

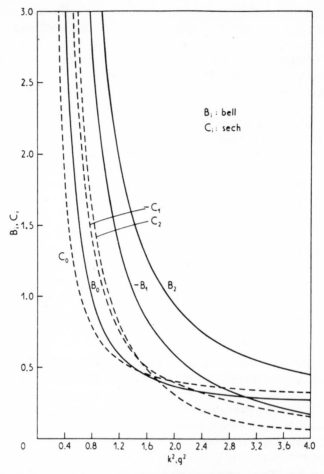

Fig. 2. Representation of C_s as a fourth-order polynomial in reciprocal magnification, m, for a non-Newtonian field, the Grivet–Lenz distribution, and a Newtonian field, Glaser's bell-shaped distribution. For the Grivet–Lenz field, $C_s/a = \Sigma_0^4\, C_i m^i$, $C_4 = C_0$, $C_3 = C_1$; for the bell, $C_s/a = \Sigma_0^4\, B_i m^i$, $B_4 = B_0$, $B_3 = B_1$. In view of the smoothness of the curves, it is not surprising that the polynomial is so good an approximation.

The reason for the polynomial structure of the asymptotic coefficients is easily understood if we recall that each coefficient has the general form $\int f G^m H^n\, dz$, where f is a function containing terms of the appropriate field or potential expansion for the component in question and $G(z)$, $H(z)$ are a pair of linearly independent solutions of the paraxial ray equations. (For systems such as quadrupoles, G and H each have two components, but there is no fundamental change in the reasoning.) The rays $G(z)$ and $H(z)$

may occur differentiated, but this does not affect the result. For round lenses, the rays $G(z)$ and $H(z)$ are normally defined by the boundary conditions

$$\lim_{z \to -\infty} G(z) = 1, \qquad \lim_{z \to -\infty} H(z) = z - z_0 \qquad (37)$$

where z_0 denotes object position. If we introduce the ray $\overline{G}(z)$ such that

$$\lim_{z \to \infty} \overline{G}(z) = 1 \qquad (38)$$

we know that H can be expressed as a linear combination of G and $\overline{G}$ since the paraxial equation can have only two linearly independent solutions, thus:

$$H(z) = \alpha G(z) + \beta \overline{G}(z) \qquad (39)$$

From the boundary conditions characterizing G, $\overline{G}$, and H, it is easy to show that if we write

$$\lim_{z \to -\infty} \overline{G}(z) = (z - z_{F0})\overline{G}'_0 \qquad (40)$$

then $\beta \overline{G}'_0 = 1$, and since $\overline{G}'_0 = 1/f_0$, $\beta = f_0$.
Likewise, $(z_0 - z_{F0})/f_0 = m$, and so

$$H(z) = (-mG + \overline{G})f_0 \qquad (41)$$

where f_0 is the asymptotic object focal length and $m = 1/M$. The parameter ρ is defined by

$$\rho = f_0/f_i \qquad (42)$$

and is thus equal to unity when any electrostatic lenses present have no overall accelerating or retarding action. The plane $z = z_{F0}$ is the asymptotic object focus; corresponding quantities in image space have the subscript i.

In the case of the primary (third-order) geometrical aberrations of round lenses, the degree $m + n$ of $G^m H^n$ in the aberration integrands is four so that each can clearly be written as a polynomial of at most fourth degree in the reciprocal magnification, m. A very similar structure emerges for quadrupoles, except that two magnifications, M and N, must now be introduced, and the polynomials now contain terms of the form $m^p n^q$, where $m = 1/M$, $n = 1/N$, and, again for the primary geometrical aberrations, $p + q \leq 4$. Furthermore, the coefficients that occur in these polynomials are affected by any symmetries the system may possess. This lightens the task of calculating them analytically and provides a useful check if they are obtained empirically. For systems for which analytical expressions for the polynomial coefficients are not available and difficult to derive, the latter can be obtained by calculating the aberration coefficient(s) in question for a number of object positions by direct ray tracing and using matrix inversion or a least-squares fitting procedure.

1. *Round Lenses*

For electrostatic or magnetic lenses with rotational symmetry, we write

$$x_i/M - x_0 = (x_0/f_i)(Ks_0 + 2Au_0 + Dr_0 + av_0)$$

$$+ \alpha_0(Cs_0 + 2Ku_0 + Fr_0 + 2kv_0) - (y_0/f_i)(ks_0 + au_0 + dr_0)$$

$$y_i/M - y_0 = (y_0/f_i)(Ks_0 + 2Au_0 + Dr_0 + av_0) \tag{43}$$

$$+ \gamma_0(Cs_0 + 2Ku_0 + Fr_0 + 2kv_0) + (x_0/f_i)(ks_0 + au_0 + dr_0)$$

in which

$$r_0 = (x_0^2 + y_0^2)/f_i^2, \qquad s_0 = \alpha_0^2 + \gamma_0^2$$

$$u_0 = (x_0\alpha_0 + y_0\gamma_0)/f_i, \qquad v_0 = (x_0\gamma_0 - y_0\alpha_0)/f_i \tag{44}$$

and α_0 and γ_0 denote x_0' and y_0' respectively. The various aberration coefficients have the following structure.

a. *Spherical Aberration*

$$C = C_4m^4 + C_3m^3 + C_2m^2 + C_1m + C_0 \tag{45}$$

where

$$C_4 = \kappa\rho^3, \qquad C_3 = (4\mu - f_0/2)\rho^2, \qquad C_2 = (2\lambda + \nu)\rho$$

$$C_1 = 4\zeta - f_0/2, \qquad C_0 = \nu/\rho \tag{46}$$

b. *Coma*

$$K = K_3m^3 + K_2m^2 + K_1m + K_0 \tag{47}$$

where

$$K_3 = -\kappa\rho^2, \quad K_2 = -(3\mu - f_0/2)\rho, \quad K_1 = -(\lambda + \pi), \quad K_0 = -\zeta/\rho \tag{48}$$

c. *Astigmatism and Field Curvature*

$$A = A_2m^2 + A_1m + A_0, \qquad F = F_2m^2 + F_1m + F_0 \tag{49}$$

where

$$A_2 = F_2 = \kappa\rho, \qquad A_1 = F_1 = 2\mu - f_0/2$$

$$A_0 = \pi/2\rho, \qquad F_0 = \lambda/\rho \tag{50}$$

d. Distortion

$$D = D_1 m + D_0 \tag{51}$$

where

$$D_1 = -\kappa, \qquad D_0 = -(\mu - f_0/2)/\rho \tag{52}$$

e. Anisotropic Coma (k), Astigmatism (a), and Distortion (d)

$$k = -(\psi\rho^2 m^2 + \tau\rho m + \sigma), \qquad a = 2\psi\rho m + \tau, \qquad d = \tau \tag{53}$$

The coefficients of the various powers of m represent magnification-independent integrals, one form of which is given below; many alternative versions can be constructed by partial integration. The terms "lim" in κ and ν prevent the integrals from diverging; partial integration of the term in N in the integrands cancels them.

$$\kappa = -4f_i^4 \int_{-\infty}^{\infty} (M_1 G^4 + M_2 G^2 G'^2 + N G'^4)\, dz - \tfrac{1}{2} \lim_{z \to \infty} (z - z_{Fi})$$

$$\nu = -4 \int_{-\infty}^{\infty} (M_1 H^4 + M_2 H^2 H'^2 + N H'^4)\, dz + \tfrac{1}{2} \lim_{z \to -\infty} (z - z_{Fo})$$

$$\pi = -8f_i^2 \int_{-\infty}^{\infty} (M_1 G^2 H^2 + M_2 GG'HH' + NG'^2 H'^2)\, dz + 2f_0^2 \int_{-\infty}^{\infty} M_5\, dz$$

$$\lambda = -4f_i^2 \cdot \int_{-\infty}^{\infty} \{M_1 G^2 H^2 + \tfrac{1}{2} M_2 (G^2 H'^2 + G'^2 H^2)$$

$$+ NG'^2 H'^2\}\, dz - 2f_0^2 \int_{-\infty}^{\infty} M_5\, dz \tag{54}$$

$$\mu = 4f_i^3 \int_{-\infty}^{\infty} \{M_1 G^3 H + \tfrac{1}{4} M_2 (G^2)'(GH)' + NG'^3 H'\}\, dz$$

$$\zeta = 4f_i \int_{-\infty}^{\infty} \{M_1 GH^3 + \tfrac{1}{4} M_2 (GH)'(H^2)' + NG'H'^3\}\, dz$$

$$\psi = f_i^3 \int_{-\infty}^{\infty} (M_3 G^2 + M_4 G'^2)\, dz, \qquad \sigma = f_i \int_{-\infty}^{\infty} (M_3 H^2 + M_4 H'^2)\, dz$$

$$\tau = 2f_i^2 \int_{-\infty}^{\infty} (M_3 GH + M_4 G'H')\, dz$$

where

$$M_1 = \frac{1}{128} \left(\frac{V}{V_i}\right)^{1/2} \left(\frac{\sigma \Phi''''}{V} - \frac{\Phi''^2}{V^2} - \frac{2\sigma\Phi''}{V} \cdot \frac{\eta^2 B^2}{V} - \frac{\eta^4 B^4}{V^2} + \frac{4\eta^2 BB''}{V}\right)$$

$$M_2 = -\frac{1}{16} \left(\frac{V}{V_i}\right)^{1/2} \left(\frac{\sigma\Phi''}{V} + \frac{\eta^2 B^2}{V}\right)$$

$$M_3 = \frac{1}{16} \left(-\frac{\sigma\Phi''}{V} \cdot \frac{\eta B}{V^{1/2}} + \frac{\eta B''}{V^{1/2}} - \frac{\eta^3 B^3}{V^{3/2}}\right) \tag{55}$$

$$M_4 = -\frac{\eta B}{4 V^{1/2}}, \qquad M_5 = -\frac{1}{8}\left(\frac{V_i}{V}\right)^{1/2} \frac{\eta^2 B^2}{V}, \qquad N = -\frac{1}{8}\left(\frac{V}{V_i}\right)^{1/2}$$

The rays $G(z)$ and $H(z)$ satisfy the boundary conditions (37) with $z_0 = z_{Fo}$, and we note that now

$$\lim_{z\to\infty} G(z) = -(z - z_{Fi})/f_i, \qquad \lim_{z\to\infty} H(z) = f_0 \tag{56}$$

so that $H(z) = f_0 \overline{G}(z)$.

A particularly simple form for the special case of purely magnetic lenses is to be found in the general survey of magnetic lens theory that forms the opening chapter of Hawkes (1980a).

The fact that a knowledge of only six quantities, in the electrostatic case, or nine in the magnetic case, provides complete information about the asymptotic aberration coefficients for all object positions is beginning to affect the presentation of lens properties. Heritage (1972, 1973), for example, has calculated the appropriate quantities for a symmetric magnetic lens. These quantities have been much more extensively used by Kuyatt *et al.* (1973, 1974), who has studied them in depth and tabulated them for two-tube electrostatic lenses operating over a wide range of voltage ratios. See also the book by Harting and Read (1976).

2. Quadrupole Lenses

The corresponding structures for quadrupoles and octopoles are listed in full in a paper by Hawkes (1970b), where some special cases of interest are also considered. Here we simply list the results, referring to that paper for supplementary information concerning notation and definitions, and in particular, the notion of astigmatic objects and images.

We now have

$$\frac{x_i}{M} - x_0 = (3000)\left(\frac{x_0}{f_i}\right)^3 + (1200)\frac{x_0 y_0^2}{f_i g_i^2} + (0030)\alpha^3 + (0012)\alpha\gamma^2$$

$$+ (2010)\frac{x_0^2}{f_i^2}\alpha + (0210)\frac{y_0^2}{g_i^2}\alpha + (1101)\frac{x_0 y_0}{f_i g_i}\gamma$$

$$+ (1020)\frac{x_0}{f_i}\alpha^2 + (1002)\frac{x_0}{f_i}\gamma^2 + (0111)\frac{y_0}{g_i}\alpha\gamma \tag{57}$$

$$\frac{y_i}{N} - y_0 = (0300)\left(\frac{y_0}{g_i}\right)^3 + (2100)\frac{x_0^2 y_0}{f_i^2 g_i} + (0003)\gamma^3 + (0021)\alpha^2\gamma$$

$$+ (2001)\frac{x_0^2}{f_i^2}\gamma + (0201)\frac{y_0^2}{g_i^2}\gamma + (1110)\frac{x_0 y_0}{f_i g_i}\alpha$$

$$+ (0120)\frac{y_0}{g_i}\alpha^2 + (0102)\frac{y_0}{g_i}\gamma^2 + (1011)\frac{x_0}{f_i}\alpha\gamma$$

The aberration coefficients have the following structure.

a. *Aperture Aberrations*

$$(0030) = \sum_{i=0}^{4} (0030)_i m^i, \qquad (0012) = \sum_{i,j=0}^{2} (0012)_{ij} m^i n^j$$

$$(0003) = \sum_{i=0}^{4} (0003)_i n^i, \qquad (0021) = \sum_{i,j=0}^{2} (0021)_{ij} m^i n^j$$

b. *Comas*

$$(1020) = \sum_{i=0}^{3} (1020)_i m^i, \qquad (0102) = \sum_{i=0}^{2} (0102)_i n^i$$

$$(1002) = \sum_{i=0}^{1}\sum_{j=0}^{2} (1002)_{ij} m^i n^j, \qquad (0120) = \sum_{i=0}^{2}\sum_{j=0}^{1} (0120)_{ij} m^i n^j$$

$$(0111) = \sum_{i=0}^{2}\sum_{j=0}^{1} (0111)_{ij} m^i n^j, \qquad (1011) = \sum_{i=0}^{1}\sum_{j=0}^{2} (1011)_{ij} m^i n^j$$

c. *Astigmatisms* (58)

$$(2010) = \sum_{i=0}^{2} (2010)_i m^i, \qquad (0201) = \sum_{i=0}^{2} (0201)_i n^i$$

$$(0210) = \sum_{i=0}^{2} (0210)_i m^i, \qquad (2001) = \sum_{i=0}^{2} (2001)_i n^i$$

$$(1101) = \sum_{i,j=0}^{1} (1101)_{ij} m^i n^j, \qquad (1110) = \sum_{i,j=0}^{1} (1110)_{ij} m^i n^j$$

d. *Distortions*

$$(3000) = \sum_{i=0}^{1} (3000)_i m^i, \qquad (1200) = \sum_{i=0}^{1} (1200)_i m^i$$

$$(0300) = \sum_{i=0}^{1} (0300)_i n^i, \qquad (2100) = \sum_{i=0}^{1} (2100)_i n^i$$

The coefficients $(pqrs)_i$ and $(pqrs)_{ij}$ are themselves simply related to a set of integrals. We write

$$\rho = f_0/f_i = g_0/g_i = (V_0/V_i)^{1/2}$$

e. Aperture Aberrations

$(0030)_4 = -4(4000)\rho^3,$

$(0030)_3 = \{4(3010) - f_0/2\}\rho^2,$

$(0030)_2 = -4(2020)\rho,$

$(0030)_1 = 4(1030) - f_0/2,$

$(0030)_0 = -4(0040)\rho^{-1},$

$(0003)_4 = -4(0400)\rho^3$

$(0003)_3 = \{4(0301) - g_0/2\}\rho^2$

$(0003)_2 = -4(0202)\rho$

$(0003)_1 = 4(0103) - g_0/2$

$(0003)_0 = -4(0004)\rho^{-1}$

$(0012)_{22} = -2(2200)_F \, \rho^3,$

$(0012)_{21} = 2(2101)\rho^2,$

$(0012)_{12} = \{2(1210) - f_0/2\}\rho^2,$

$(0012)_{20} = -2(2002)\rho,$

$(0012)_{11} = -2(1111)\rho,$

$(0012)_{02} = -2(0220)\rho,$

$(0012)_{10} = 2(1012) - f_0/2,$

$(0012)_{01} = 2(0121),$

$(0012)_{00} = -2(0022)_F \, \rho^{-1},$

$(0021)_{22} = -2(2200)_G \, \rho^3$

$(0021)_{21} = \{2(2101) - g_0/2\}\rho^2$

$(0021)_{12} = 2(1210)\rho^2 \qquad (59)$

$(0021)_{20} = -2(2002)\rho$

$(0021)_{11} = -2(1111)\rho$

$(0021)_{02} = -2(0220)\rho$

$(0021)_{10} = 2(1012)$

$(0021)_{01} = 2(0121) - g_0/2$

$(0021)_{00} = -2(0022)_G \, \rho^{-1}$

f. Comas

$(1020)_3 = 12(4000)\rho^2,$

$(1020)_2 = \{-9(3010) + 3f_0/2\}\rho,$

$(1020)_1 = 6(2020),$

$(1020)_0 = -3(1030)\rho^{-1},$

$(0102)_3 = 12(0400)\rho^2$

$(0102)_2 = \{-9(0301) + 3g_0/2\}\rho$

$(0102)_1 = 6(0202)$

$(0102)_0 = -3(0103)\rho^{-1}$

$(1002)_{12} = 2(2200)_F \, \rho^2,$

$(1002)_{11} = -2(2101)\rho,$

$(1002)_{02} = \{-(1210) + f_0/2\}\rho,$

$(1002)_{10} = 2(2002),$

$(1002)_{01} = (1111),$

$(1002)_{00} = -(1012)\rho^{-1},$

$(0120)_{21} = 2(2200)_G \, \rho^2$

$(0120)_{11} = -2(1210)\rho$

$(0120)_{20} = \{-(2101) + g_0/2\}\rho$

$(0120)_{10} = (1111)$

$(0120)_{01} = 2(0220) \qquad (60)$

$(0120)_{00} = -(0121)\rho^{-1}$

$(0111)_{21} = 4(2200)_F \, \rho^2,$

$(0111)_{20} = -2(2101)\rho,$

$(0111)_{11} = \{-4(1210) + f_0\}\rho,$

$(0111)_{10} = 2(1111),$

$(0111)_{01} = 4(0220),$

$(0111)_{00} = -2(0121)\rho^{-1},$

$(1011)_{12} = 4(2200)_G \, \rho^2$

$(1011)_{02} = -2(1210)\rho$

$(1011)_{11} = \{-4(2101) + g_0\}\rho$

$(1011)_{10} = 4(2002)$

$(1011)_{01} = 2(1111)$

$(1011)_{00} = -2(1012)\rho^{-1}$

g. *Astigmatisms*

$(2010)_2 = -12(4000)\rho,$

$(2010)_1 = 6(3010) - 3f_0/2,$

$(2010)_0 = -2(2020)\rho^{-1},$

$(0201)_2 = -12(0400)\rho$

$(0201)_1 = 6(0301) - 3g_0/2$

$(0201)_0 = -2(0202)\rho^{-1}$

$(1101)_{11} = -4(2200)_F\,\rho,$

$(1101)_{10} = 2(2101),$

$(1101)_{01} = 2(1210) - f_0,$

$(1101)_{00} = -(1111)\rho^{-1},$

$(1110)_{11} = -4(2200)_G\,\rho$

$(1110)_{10} = 2(2101) - g_0$

$(1110)_{01} = 2(1210)$

$(1110)_{00} = -(1111)\rho^{-1}$

$(0210)_2 = -2(2200)_F\,\rho,$

$(0210)_1 = 2(1210) - f_0/2,$

$(0210)_0 = -2(0220)\rho^{-1},$

$(2001)_2 = -2(2200)_G\,\rho$

$(2001)_1 = 2(2101) - g_0/2$

$(2001)_0 = -2(2002)\rho^{-1}$

$$(61)$$

h. *Distortions*

$(3000)_1 = 4(4000),$

$(3000)_0 = \{-(3010) + f_0/2\}\rho^{-1},$

$(0300)_1 = 4(0400)$

$(0300)_0 = \{-(0301) + g_0/2\}\rho^{-1}$

$(1200)_1 = 2(2200)_F,$

$(1200)_0 = \{-(1210) + f_0/2\}\rho^{-1},$

$(2100)_1 = 2(2200)_G$

$(2100)_0 = \{-(2101) + g_0/2\}\rho^{-1}$

$$(62)$$

The quantities $(pqrs)$, $p + q + r + s = 4$, denote the following integrals:

$$(4000) = f_i^4 \int_{-\infty}^{\infty} (A_x G_x^4 + B_x G_x^2 G_x'^2 + N G_x'^4)\,dz + \tfrac{1}{8} \lim_{z\to\infty} (z - z_{Fi})$$

$$(0400) = g_i^4 \int_{-\infty}^{\infty} (A_y G_y^4 + B_y G_y^2 G_y'^2 + N G_y'^4)\,dz + \tfrac{1}{8} \lim_{z\to\infty} (z - z_{Gi})$$

$$(0040) = \int_{-\infty}^{\infty} (A_x H_x^4 + B_x H_x^2 H_x'^2 + N H_x'^4)\,dz - \tfrac{1}{8}\rho \lim_{z\to-\infty} (z - z_{Fo})$$

$$(0004) = \int_{-\infty}^{\infty} (A_y H_y^4 + B_y H_y^2 H_y'^2 + N H_y'^4)\,dz - \tfrac{1}{8}\rho \lim_{z\to-\infty} (z - z_{Go})$$

$$(3010) = 4f_i^3 \int_{-\infty}^{\infty} \{A_x G_x^3 H_x + \tfrac{1}{4}B_x(G_x^2)'(G_x H_x)' + N G_x'^3 H_x'\}\,dz$$

$$(0301) = 4g_i^3 \int_{-\infty}^{\infty} \{A_y G_y^3 H_y + \tfrac{1}{4}B_y(G_y^2)'(G_y H_y)' + N G_y'^3 H_y'\}\,dz$$

$$(1030) = 4f_i \int_{-\infty}^{\infty} \{A_x G_x H_x^3 + \tfrac{1}{4}B_x(G_x H_x)'(H_x^2)' + N G_x' H_x'^3\}\,dz$$

$$(0103) = 4g_i \int_{-\infty}^{\infty} \{A_y G_y H_y^3 + \tfrac{1}{4}B_y(G_y H_y)'(H_y^2)' + N G_y' H_y'^3\}\,dz$$

$$(2020) = 6f_1^2 \int_{-\infty}^{\infty} \{A_x G_x^2 H_x^2 + \tfrac{1}{6} B_x (G_x^2 H_x'^2 + G_x'^2 H_x^2$$
$$+ (G_x^2)'(H_x^2)') + NG_x'^2 H_x'^2\} \, dz$$

$$(0202) = 6g_1^2 \int_{-\infty}^{\infty} \{A_y G_y^2 H_y^2 + \tfrac{1}{6} B_y (G_y^2 H_y'^2 + G_y'^2 H_y^2 + (G_y^2)'(H_y^2)')$$
$$+ NG_y'^2 H_y'^2\} \, dz$$

$$(2002) = f_1^2 \int_{-\infty}^{\infty} \{CG_y^2 H_y^2 + B_x G_x^2 H_y'^2 + B_y G_x'^2 H_y^2 + 2NG_x'^2 H_y'^2$$
$$+ RG_x H_y (G_x H_y' - G_x' H_y)\} \, dz$$

$$(0220) = g_1^2 \int_{-\infty}^{\infty} \{CH_x^2 G_y^2 + B_x H_x^2 G_y'^2 + B_y H_x'^2 G_y^2 + 2NH_x'^2 G_y'^2$$
$$+ RH_x G_y (H_x G_y' - H_x' G_y)\} \, dz$$

$$(2200) = f_1^2 g_1^2 \int_{-\infty}^{\infty} \{CG_x^2 G_y^2 + B_x G_x^2 G_y'^2 + B_y G_x'^2 G_y^2 + 2NG_x'^2 G_y'^2$$
$$+ RG_x G_y (G_x G_y' - G_x' G_y)\} \, dz$$

$$(2200)_\mathrm{F} = (2200) + \tfrac{1}{4} \lim_{z \to \infty} (z - z_{\mathrm{Fi}}), \qquad (2200)_\mathrm{G} = (2200) + \tfrac{1}{4} \lim_{z \to \infty} (z - z_{\mathrm{Gi}})$$

$$(0022) = \int_{-\infty}^{\infty} \{CH_x^2 H_y^2 + B_x H_x^2 H_y'^2 + B_y H_x'^2 H_y^2 + 2NH_x'^2 H_y'^2$$
$$+ RH_x H_y (H_x H_y' - H_x' H_y)\} \, dz$$

$$(0022)_\mathrm{F} = (0022) - \tfrac{1}{4}\rho \lim_{z \to -\infty} (z - z_{\mathrm{Fo}}), \qquad (0022)_\mathrm{G} = (0022) - \tfrac{1}{4}\rho \lim_{z \to -\infty} (z - z_{\mathrm{Go}})$$

$$(2101) = 2f_1^2 g_1 \int_{-\infty}^{\infty} [CG_x^2 G_y H_y + B_x G_x^2 G_y' H_y' + B_y G_x'^2 G_y H_y + 2NG_x'^2 G_y' H_y'$$
$$+ \tfrac{1}{2} R\{G_x^2 (G_y H_y)' - (G_x^2)' G_y H_y\}] \, dz$$

$$(1210) = 2f_i g_1^2 \int_{-\infty}^{\infty} [CG_x H_x G_y^2 + B_x G_x H_x G_y'^2 + B_y G_x' H_x' G_y^2 + 2NG_x' H_x' G_y'^2$$
$$+ \tfrac{1}{2} R\{G_x H_x (G_y^2)' - (G_x H_x)' G_y^2\}] \, dz$$

$$(1012) = 2f_i \int_{-\infty}^{\infty} [CG_x H_x H_y^2 + B_x G_x H_x H_y'^2 + B_y G_x' H_x' H_y^2 + 2NG_x' H_x' H_y'^2$$
$$+ \tfrac{1}{2} R\{G_x H_x (H_y^2)' - (G_x H_x)' H_y^2\}] \, dz$$

$$(0121) = 2g_1 \int_{-\infty}^{\infty} [CH_x^2 G_y H_y + B_x H_x^2 G_y' H_y' + B_y H_x'^2 G_y H_y + 2NH_x'^2 G_y' H_y'$$
$$+ \tfrac{1}{2} R\{H_x^2 (G_y H_y)' - (H_x^2)' G_y H_y\}] \, dz$$

$$(1111) = 4f_i g_i \int_{-\infty}^{\infty} [CG_x H_x G_y H_y + B_x G_x H_x G'_y H'_y + B_y G'_x H'_x G_y H_y$$

$$+ 2NG'_x H'_x G'_y H'_y + \tfrac{1}{2}R\{G_x H_x(G_y H_y)' - (G_x H_x)' G_y H_y\}] \, dz \tag{63a}$$

in which

$$A_x = \frac{1}{128} \left(\frac{V}{V_i}\right)^{1/2} \left(\frac{\sigma\Phi''''}{V} - \frac{\Phi''^2 + D^2}{V^2} - \frac{4}{3}\frac{\sigma D''}{V} + 2\frac{D\Phi''}{V^2} + \frac{8}{3}\frac{\eta Q''}{V^{1/2}}\right) + \frac{1}{2}\,\Xi$$

$$A_y = \frac{1}{128} \left(\frac{V}{V_i}\right)^{1/2} \left(\frac{\sigma\Phi''''}{V} - \frac{\Phi''^2 + D^2}{V^2} + \frac{4}{3}\frac{\sigma D''}{V} - 2\frac{D\Phi''}{V^2} - \frac{8}{3}\frac{\eta Q''}{V^{1/2}}\right) + \frac{1}{2}\,\Xi$$

$$B_x = -\frac{\sigma}{16} \left(\frac{V}{V_i}\right)^{1/2} \frac{\Phi'' - D}{V}, \qquad B_y = -\frac{\sigma}{16} \left(\frac{V}{V_i}\right)^{1/2} \frac{\Phi'' + D}{V} \tag{63b}$$

$$C = \frac{1}{64} \left(\frac{V}{V_i}\right)^{1/2} \left(\frac{\sigma\Phi''''}{V} - \frac{\Phi''^2 - D^2}{V^2}\right) - 3\Xi$$

$$N = -\frac{1}{8} \left(\frac{V}{V_i}\right)^{1/2}, \qquad R = \frac{1}{4}\frac{\eta Q}{V_i^{1/2}}$$

The function $\Xi(z)$ characterizes any octopole potentials:

$$\Xi(z) = \left(\frac{V}{V_i}\right)^{1/2} \left(\frac{\sigma D_1(z)}{V} - 2\frac{\eta Q_1(z)}{V^{1/2}}\right)$$

B. Aberration Matrices

There has been a considerable revival of interest, as we shall see in Section IV,A,4, in designing lens combinations such that some optically desirable condition is satisfied: electron microscope projector systems with minimal distortion, for example. Although we can use direct minimization, as described is Section IV,A,1, considerable physical insight into the way in which the conditions are satisfied can be gained by studying the structure of the aberration coefficients of combinations. Since matrix techniques are so convenient for studying paraxial problems (see Steffen, 1965, or Banford, 1966, for example), it is natural to enquire whether they can simplify the task of calculating the aberration coefficients of combinations. We find that not only do they provide a very convenient way of manipulating the cumbersome expressions involved but that, with their aid, the coefficients that occur in the aberration polynomials of the combination can be expressed in terms of those of the individual members. This has only as yet been examined in any detail for round lenses and quadrupoles but it can be extended without difficulty to include any beam components. In particular, the technique is well suited to the matching of different types of component: the incorporation of an energy analyser of the Castaing–Henry or magnetic type into a focusing system is a good example of this. For reasons of space, however, the following discussion is restricted to systems of round lenses and quadrupoles.

1. Round Lenses

The paraxial equations of motion governing the position (x, y, z) of an electron in a rotationally symmetric electrostatic field characterized by its axial potential $\Phi(z)$ and a magnetic field characterized by axial values $B(z)$ take the form

$$x'' + \frac{\sigma\Phi'}{2V} x' + \frac{\sigma\Phi'' + \eta^2 B^2}{4V} x = 0 \tag{64}$$

with an identical expression for y, where σ denotes $1 + 2\epsilon\Phi$ and $V = \Phi(1 + \epsilon\Phi)$. The cartesian coordinate frame rotates so that the angle between asymptotic object and image is $\frac{1}{2}\eta \int_{-\infty}^{\infty} (B/V^{1/2})\ dz$.

Denoting the asymptotic foci by z_{Fo} and z_{Fi} in object and image space and the corresponding focal lengths by f_o and f_i (both positive for a converging lens), we find that position and slope coordinates are related thus:

$$\begin{pmatrix} x_i \\ \alpha_i \end{pmatrix} = \mathbf{M_1} \begin{pmatrix} x_o \\ \alpha_o \end{pmatrix}, \qquad \begin{pmatrix} y_i \\ \gamma_i \end{pmatrix} = \mathbf{M_1} \begin{pmatrix} y_o \\ \gamma_o \end{pmatrix} \tag{65}$$

where

$$x = \alpha_o(z - z_o) + x_o, \qquad y = \gamma_o(z - z_o) + y_o \tag{66}$$

represent an incident asymptote, and

$$x = \alpha_i(z - z_i) + x_i, \qquad y = \gamma_i(z - z_i) + y_i \tag{67}$$

the emergent asymptote to the same ray; z_o and z_i are a pair of conjugate planes, and

$$\mathbf{M_1} = \begin{pmatrix} -(z_i - z_{Fi})/f_i & 0 \\ -1/f_i & (z_o - z_{Fo})/f_i \end{pmatrix} = \begin{pmatrix} M & 0 \\ -1/f_i & \rho m \end{pmatrix} \tag{68}$$

in which, we recall, M denotes the magnification, $m = 1/M$, and (Eq. 42)

$$\rho = f_o/f_i = (V_o/V_i)^{1/2} \tag{69}$$

We shall often use the "convergence," c, rather than the focal length; this is defined by

$$c = -1/f_i \tag{70}$$

Including third-order aberrations, the coordinates x_i and y_i are given as functions of the object coordinates (x_o, y_o) and gradients (α_o, γ_o) by Eqs.

(43), in which the invariants r_0, s_0, u_0, and v_0 are defined by Eqs. (44). It is convenient to write $w_i = x_i + iy_i$ whereupon Eqs. (43) can be united into one large matrix equation, thus:

$$\mathbf{w}_m = \mathbf{M}\mathbf{w}_0 \tag{71}$$

in which we write $\mathbf{w}_m$ rather than $\mathbf{w}_i$, to indicate that the magnification of the image is M. This is convenient when we consider lens combinations. The matrix $\mathbf{M}$ has a natural block structure (Hawkes, 1970c)

$$\mathbf{M} = \begin{pmatrix} \mathbf{M}_1 & \mathbf{M}_2 \\ \mathbf{M}_3 & \mathbf{M}_4 \end{pmatrix} \tag{72}$$

in which $\mathbf{M}_1$ is defined by Eq. (68), $\mathbf{M}_3$ is null, $\mathbf{M}_2$ contains the aberration coefficients, and $\mathbf{M}_4$, which is generated by $\mathbf{M}_1$, effectively codes the rules for combining aberrations. We write $\mathbf{M}_2$ in the form

$$\mathbf{M}_2 = \begin{pmatrix} Mm_{11} & Mm_{12} & Mm_{13} & Mm_{14} & Mm_{15} & Mm_{16} & Mm_{17} & Mm_{18} \\ m_{21} & m_{22} & m_{23} & m_{24} & m_{25} & m_{26} & m_{27} & m_{28} \end{pmatrix} \tag{73}$$

where

$$
\begin{array}{ll}
m_{11} = -c^3(D + id), & m_{15} = -c(K + ik) \\
m_{12} = c^2 F, & m_{16} = C \\
m_{13} = c^2(2A + ia), & m_{17} = c^2 a \\
m_{14} = -2cK, & m_{18} = -2ck
\end{array} \tag{74}
$$

The matrix $\mathbf{M}_4$ has the form

$$\mathbf{M}_4 = \begin{pmatrix}
M^3 & 0 & 0 & 0 & 0 & 0 & 0 & 0 \\
cM^2 & \rho M & 0 & 0 & 0 & 0 & 0 & 0 \\
cM^2 & 0 & \rho M & 0 & 0 & 0 & 0 & 0 \\
c^2 M & \rho c & \rho c & \rho^2 m & 0 & 0 & 0 & 0 \\
c^2 M & 0 & 2\rho c & 0 & \rho^2 m & 0 & 0 & 0 \\
c^3 & \rho c^2 m & 2\rho c^2 m & 2\rho^2 cm^2 & \rho^2 cm^2 & \rho^3 m^3 & 0 & 0 \\
0 & 0 & 0 & 0 & 0 & 0 & \rho M & 0 \\
0 & 0 & 0 & 0 & 0 & 0 & \rho c & \rho^2 m
\end{pmatrix} \tag{75}$$

The polynomial structure of the aberration coefficients permits us to write

$$m_{11} = c^3(\kappa m + \mu/\rho + 1/2c + i\psi)$$

$$m_{12} = c^2\{\rho\kappa m^2 + (2\mu + \rho/2c)m + \lambda/\rho\}$$

$$m_{13} = c^2\{2\rho\kappa m^2 + 2(2\mu + \rho/2c)m + \pi/\rho + i(2\rho\psi m + \tau)\}$$

$$m_{14} = 2c\{\rho^2\kappa m^3 + \rho(3\mu + \rho/2c)m^2 + (\lambda + \pi)m + \zeta/\rho\}$$

$$m_{15} = c\{\rho^2\kappa m^3 + \rho(3\mu + \rho/2c)m^2 + (\lambda + \pi)m$$
$$\qquad + \zeta/\rho + i(\rho^2\psi m^2 + \rho\tau m + \sigma)\} \tag{76}$$

$$m_{16} = \rho^3\kappa m^4 + \rho^2(4\mu + \rho/2c)m^3 + 2\rho(\lambda + \pi)m^2$$
$$\qquad + (4\zeta + \rho/2c)m + \nu/\rho$$

$$m_{17} = c^2(2\rho\psi m + \tau)$$

$$m_{18} = 2c(\rho^2\psi m^2 + \rho\tau m + \sigma)$$

2. Quadrupole Lenses

A very similar structure can be constructed for quadrupole lenses, as explained in detail in Hawkes (1970d); for reasons of space, we give only brief indications here of the matrix forms that are encountered.

By analogy with Eq. (71), we now have

$$\mathbf{x}_m = \mathbf{M}\mathbf{x}_0, \qquad \mathbf{y}_n = \mathbf{N}\mathbf{y}_0 \tag{77}$$

in which $\mathbf{x}$ and $\mathbf{y}$ are 12-element column matrices (two paraxial components and ten aberration elements). The matrices $\mathbf{M}$ and $\mathbf{N}$ again have a natural block structure:

$$\mathbf{M} = \begin{pmatrix} \mathbf{M}_1 & \mathbf{M}_2 \\ \mathbf{M}_3 & \mathbf{M}_4 \end{pmatrix}, \qquad \mathbf{N} = \begin{pmatrix} \mathbf{N}_1 & \mathbf{N}_2 \\ \mathbf{N}_3 & \mathbf{N}_4 \end{pmatrix} \tag{78}$$

$\mathbf{M}_1$ and $\mathbf{N}_1$ are the familiar paraxial transfer matrices:

$$\mathbf{M}_1 = \begin{pmatrix} M & 0 \\ c_m & \rho m \end{pmatrix}, \qquad \mathbf{N}_1 = \begin{pmatrix} N & 0 \\ c_n & \rho n \end{pmatrix} \tag{79}$$

$\mathbf{M}_2$ and $\mathbf{N}_2$ contain the aberration coefficients

$$\mathbf{M}_2 = \begin{pmatrix} Mm_{11} & Mm_{12} \cdots Mm_{19} & Mm_{1,10} \\ m_{21} & m_{22} \cdots m_{29} & m_{2,10} \end{pmatrix} \tag{80}$$

$$\mathbf{N}_2 = \begin{pmatrix} Nn_{11} & Nn_{12} & \cdots & Nn_{19} & Nn_{1,10} \\ n_{21} & n_{22} & \cdots & n_{29} & n_{2,10} \end{pmatrix} \tag{81}$$

while $\mathbf{M}_3$ and $\mathbf{N}_3$ are null; $\mathbf{M}_4$ and $\mathbf{N}_4$ encapsulate the rules for combining aberrations. They have the following form:

$$\mathbf{M}_4 = \begin{pmatrix}
M^3 & 0 & 0 & 0 & 0 & 0 & 0 & 0 & 0 & 0 \\
0 & MN^2 & 0 & 0 & 0 & 0 & 0 & 0 & 0 & 0 \\
c_m M^2 & 0 & \rho M & 0 & 0 & 0 & 0 & 0 & 0 & 0 \\
0 & c_m N^2 & 0 & \rho m N^2 & 0 & 0 & 0 & 0 & 0 & 0 \\
0 & c_n MN & 0 & 0 & \rho M & 0 & 0 & 0 & 0 & 0 \\
c_m^2 M & 0 & 2\rho c_m & 0 & 0 & \rho^2 m & 0 & 0 & 0 & 0 \\
0 & c_n^2 M & 0 & 0 & 2\rho c_n Mn & 0 & \rho^2 Mn^2 & 0 & 0 & 0 \\
0 & c_m c_n N & 0 & \rho c_n mN & \rho c_m & 0 & 0\cdot & \rho^2 m & 0 & 0 \\
c_m^3 & 0 & 3\rho c_m^2 m & 0 & 0 & 3\rho^2 c_m m^2 & 0 & 0 & \rho^3 m^2 & 0 \\
0 & c_m c_n^2 & 0 & \rho c_n^2 m & 2\rho c_m c_n n & 0 & \rho^2 c_m n^2 & 2\rho^2 c_n mn & 0 & \rho^3 mn^2
\end{pmatrix}$$

$$\mathbf{N}_4 = \begin{pmatrix}
N^3 & 0 & 0 & 0 & 0 & 0 & 0 & 0 & 0 & 0 \\
0 & M^2 N & 0 & 0 & 0 & 0 & 0 & 0 & 0 & 0 \\
c_n N^2 & 0 & \rho N & 0 & 0 & 0 & 0 & 0 & 0 & 0 \\
0 & c_n M^2 & 0 & \rho M^2 n & 0 & 0 & 0 & 0 & 0 & 0 \\
0 & c_m MN & 0 & 0 & \rho N & 0 & 0 & 0 & 0 & 0 \\
c_n^2 N & 0 & 2\rho c_n & 0 & 0 & \rho^2 n & 0 & 0 & 0 & 0 \\
0 & c_m^2 N & 0 & 0 & 2\rho c_m mN & 0 & \rho^2 m^2 N & 0 & 0 & 0 \\
0 & c_m c_n M & 0 & \rho c_m Mn & \rho c_n & 0 & 0 & \rho^2 n & 0 & 0 \\
c_n^3 & 0 & 3\rho c_n^2 n & 0 & 0 & 3\rho^2 c_n n^2 & 0 & 0 & \rho^3 n^2 & 0 \\
0 & c_m^2 c_n & 0 & \rho c_m^2 n & 2\rho c_m c_n m & 0 & \rho^2 c_n m^2 & 2\rho^2 c_m mn & 0 & \rho^3 m^2 n
\end{pmatrix} \tag{82}$$

The polynomial expressions for m_{1j} and n_{1j} ($j = 1, 2, \ldots, 10$) may be extracted from Eqs. (58–62) and are listed explicitly in Hawkes (1970d).

The foregoing theory was developed with low-energy applications in mind, where a treatment in terms of a rectangular model terminated by fringing fields is often unsuitable. A matrix theory of the paraxial properties and aberrations of quadrupoles (and prisms) has been in use for studying beam transport systems for some years. A very full account has been published by Brown (1968), in which the earlier work of Brown *et al.* (1964) on sector magnets is generalized and extended to include quadrupoles. Here the emphasis is on the rectangular model and on the transfer relations between planes of particular geometrical (rather than optical)

significance (the two ends of the quadrupole, for example) and not necessarily between conjugate planes. The effects of fringing fields have been
analyzed by Lee-Whiting (1969, 1970) and Smith (1970); the latter should
not however be used without consulting Lee-Whiting (1972), in which
mistakes in Smith's paper are pointed out. The fringing fields have been
reexamined for both magnetic and electrostatic quadrupoles by Matsuda
and Wollnik (1972), who express their results in matrix terminology.

3. Sector Fields

The properties of sector fields were described in considerable detail in
(Septier, 1967) by Enge (1967) and Wollnik (1967b) and prisms are further
discussed in Part B of this supplement. Here we wish merely to draw attention to the fact that the aberrations of electrostatic and magnetic sector
fields have now been very thoroughly investigated by Wollnik and
Matsuda. The explicit formulas are extremely cumbersome and are therefore not reproduced here.

Consider a beam consisting of charged particles with a (narrow) range
of masses and energies, $m = \bar{m}(1 + \gamma)$ and $U = \bar{U}(1 + \delta)$, $\gamma \ll 1$, $\delta \ll 1$;
we follow Wollnik's notation except that his m_0 and U_0 are replaced by $\bar{m}$
and $\bar{U}$ since these quantities represent mean (or central) values of mass
and energy, respectively. The motion of a particle is characterized by two
position coordinates (u and v), two gradients (α and β), and the parame-
ters γ and δ. These are grouped into two vectors,* (u, α, γ, δ) and (v, β)
after which matrices characterizing first the paraxial transfer properties
and then the aberrations are defined (Wollnik, 1967a). The elements of
these matrices can be calculated for each of the regions into which the
sector field is conventionally divided; these component matrices are then
multiplied to give the total transfer matrix from entrance slit to ideal field
entrance boundary, through the incident fringing field, through the prism
itself, through the emergent fringing field, and, finally, from the ideal field
exit boundary to the exit slit.

In the paraxial approximation, the radial and axial transfer matrices
are 4×4 and 2×2 matrices, respectively. If, just as in the cases of
round lenses or quadrupoles, we retain the next higher order terms in the
vectors, the latter contain the following elements:

Radial
$$(u, \alpha, \gamma, \delta, u^2, u\alpha, u\gamma, u\delta, \alpha^2, \alpha\gamma, \alpha\delta, \gamma^2, \gamma\delta, \delta^2, v^2, v\beta, \beta^2) \quad (83)$$

Axial $$\qquad (v, \beta, vu, v\alpha, v\gamma, v\delta, \beta u, \beta\alpha, \beta\gamma, \beta\delta) \qquad (84)$$

* These are of course normally thought of as column vectors though we transpose them
here to row vectors.

The transfer matrices are now 17×17 (radial) and (10×10) axial, but the aberrations are confined to the upper two rows since the matrices have the following block structure:

Radial
$$\begin{pmatrix} \mathbf{R}_1 & \mathbf{R}_2 \\ \mathbf{R}_3 & \mathbf{R}_4 \end{pmatrix} \tag{85}$$

Axial
$$\begin{pmatrix} \mathbf{A}_1 & \mathbf{A}_2 \\ \mathbf{A}_3 & \mathbf{A}_4 \end{pmatrix} \tag{86}$$

In the radial transfer matrix, $\mathbf{R}_1$ is a 4×4 paraxial matrix; $\mathbf{R}_2$ contains the aberration coefficients, thus:

$$\mathbf{R}_2 = \begin{pmatrix} \text{aberrations of position} \\ \text{aberrations of slope} \\ 0 \\ 0 \end{pmatrix} \tag{87}$$

($\mathbf{R}_2$ has 17 columns, two nonzero rows, and two zero rows), $\mathbf{R}_3$ is null, and $\mathbf{R}_4$ codes the rules for combining individual matrices. In the axial transfer matrix, $\mathbf{A}_1$ is a 2×2 paraxial matrix, $\mathbf{A}_2$ has eight columns and two rows, containing the aberration coefficients, $\mathbf{A}_3$ is null, and $\mathbf{A}_4$ contains the rules for combining individual matrices. $\mathbf{R}_4$ and $\mathbf{A}_4$ are determined by $\mathbf{R}_1$ and $\mathbf{A}_1$, respectively. The resemblance between the structure of the matrices $\mathbf{R}$ and $\mathbf{A}$ and the corresponding matrices for round lenses ($\mathbf{M}$ in Eqs. 71–72) and quadrupoles ($\mathbf{M}$ and $\mathbf{N}$ in Eqs. 77–78) is obvious; we stress this point since one of the reasons for introducing the matrix formalism into aberration studies is precisely to simplify and unify the analysis of different types of components.

Formulas for all these matrix elements are given by Wollnik (1967a) for both magnetic and electrostatic sectors.

The same procedure can be used to establish the aberration matrices of next higher order. This calculation has been carried out by Matsuda and Wollnik (1970b) for the radial transfer matrices of the fringing fields of magnetic sectors; the radial matrix now has an additional 32 columns and rows, making a 49×49 matrix in all. In the same year, Matsuda and Wollnik (1970a) had already published formulas for the case of an inhomogeneous magnetic sector field with extended fringing fields; this case is further studied in Matsuo and Matsuda (1971). The electrostatic case, with toroidal fringing fields, is analyzed by Matsuda (1971) thus supplementing (and correcting) the earlier paper by Wollnik (1967a). Further studies on fringing fields have been made by Matsuda and Matsuo (1971) and Matsuda (1974). Recent papers by Taya (1978) and Taya *et al.* (1978) are of interest in this context.

C. *Combinations of Components*

The reason for expressing aberrations in matrix terminology is to facilitate the calculation of the aberrations of multiple-component systems, usually with a view to minimizing or eliminating some particularly undesirable defect. Once the individual matrix elements are known, those of the combination can be obtained by a "brute-force" method, allowing the computer to multiply the matrices and vary any free parameters in a search routine designed to reveal the optimal solution (or class of acceptable solutions). With complicated systems, however, this is not only liable to fail to find physically tolerable solutions but also gives little insight into the reason why the solution found is optimal and how sensitive it is to small variations in the parameters. It is therefore desirable to obtain explicit formulas for the matrix elements of two-component systems in terms of those of the two members; these can if necessary be incorporated into an iterative routine to bring in more components.

We therefore consider the matrix elements of pairs of lenses, pairs of quadrupoles, and (very briefly) pairs of sector fields.

1. *Round Lenses*

We have seen (Eq. 71) that the image vector $\mathbf{w}_m$ can be related to the object vector $\mathbf{w}_0$ by a matrix, $\mathbf{M}$:

$$\mathbf{w}_m = \mathbf{M}\mathbf{w}_0$$

Suppose now that a second lens (or lens combination) produces a subsequent image with magnification M'; the total magnification is then denoted by P,

$$P = MM' \tag{88}$$

Writing

$$\mathbf{w}_p = \mathbf{M}'\mathbf{w}_m \tag{89}$$

we see that

$$\mathbf{w}_p = \mathbf{M}'\mathbf{M}\mathbf{w}_0 = \mathbf{P}\mathbf{w}_0 \tag{90}$$

where the matrix $\mathbf{P} = \mathbf{M}'\mathbf{M}$ must clearly have the same block structure as that of $\mathbf{M}$ (or $\mathbf{M}'$). We find

$$\mathbf{P}_1 = \begin{pmatrix} P & 0 \\ c_p & \rho_p p \end{pmatrix} \tag{91}$$

in which

$$c_p = Mc' + p'cm' = D_p cc' \tag{92}$$

where

$$D_p = z'_{\text{Fo}} - z_{\text{Fi}} \tag{93}$$

and

$$\rho_p = \rho\rho' \tag{94}$$

The block matrix $\mathbf{P}_2$ now contains the aberrations of the combination; in conformity with Eq. (73), we write

$$\mathbf{P}_2 = \begin{pmatrix} Pp_{11} & Pp_{12} & Pp_{13} & Pp_{14} & Pp_{15} & Pp_{16} & Pp_{17} & Pp_{18} \\ p_{21} & p_{22} & p_{23} & p_{24} & p_{25} & p_{26} & p_{27} & p_{28} \end{pmatrix} \tag{95}$$

and

$$
\begin{aligned}
p_{11} &= m_{11} + M^2 m'_{11} + Mcm'_{12} + Mcm'_{13} + c^2 m'_{14} + c^2 m'_{15} + c^3 mm'_{16} \\
&= c_p^3(\kappa_p p + \mu_p/\rho_p + c_p/2 + i\psi_p) \\
p_{12} &= m_{12} + \rho m'_{12} + \rho cmm'_{14} + \rho c^2 m^2 m'_{16} \\
&= c_p^2\{\rho_p\kappa_p p^2 + (2\mu_p + \rho_p/2c_p)p + \lambda_p/\rho_p\} \\
p_{13} &= m_{13} + \rho m'_{13} + \rho cmm'_{14} + 2\rho cmm'_{15} + 2\rho c^2 m^2 m'_{16} \\
&= c_p^2\{2\rho_p\kappa_p p^2 + 2(2\mu_p + \rho_p/2c_p)p + \pi_p/\rho_p + i(2\rho_p\psi_p p + \tau_p)\} \\
p_{14} &= m_{14} + \rho^2 m^2 m'_{14} + 2\rho^2 cm^3 m'_{16} \\
&= 2c_p\{\rho_p^2\kappa_p p^3 + \rho_p(3\mu_p + \rho_p/2c_p)p^2 + (\lambda_p + \pi_p)p + \zeta_p/\rho_p\} \\
p_{15} &= m_{15} + \rho^2 m^2 m'_{15} + \rho^2 cm^3 m'_{16} \\
&= c_p\{\rho_p^2\kappa_p p^3 + \rho_p(3\mu_p + \rho_p/2c_p)p^2 \\
&\quad + (\lambda_p + \pi_p)p + \zeta_p/\rho_p + i(\rho_p^2\psi_p p^2 + \rho_p\tau_p p + \sigma_p)\} \\
p_{16} &= m_{16} + \rho^3 m^4 m'_{16} \\
&= \rho_p^3\kappa_p p^4 + \rho_p^2(4\mu_p + \rho_p/2c_p)p^3 \\
&\quad + 2\rho_p(\lambda_p + \pi_p)p^2 + (4\zeta_p + \rho_p/2c_p)p + \nu_p/\rho_p \\
p_{17} &= m_{17} + \rho m'_{17} + \rho cmm'_{18} = c_p^2(2\rho_p\psi_p p + \tau_p) \\
p_{18} &= m_{18} + \rho^2 m^2 m'_{18} = 2c_p(\rho_p^2\psi_p p^2 + \rho_p\tau_p p + \sigma_p)
\end{aligned}
\tag{96}
$$

The coefficients κ_p, λ_p, . . . , σ_p are as follows:

$$\kappa_p = \kappa' + 4\mu'C + 2(\lambda' + \pi')C^2 + 4\zeta'C^3 + (\kappa\rho' + \nu')C^4$$
$$+ (\rho'/2c')C(1 + C^2)$$

$$\lambda_p = \rho^2\lambda'C'^2 + \rho'\lambda C^2 + 2\rho^2\zeta'CC'^2 + 2\rho\rho'\mu C^2C'$$
$$+ \rho^2(\kappa\rho' + \nu')C^2C'^2 + (\rho^2\rho'/2c_p)CC'$$

$$\mu_p = \rho\mu'C' + \rho(\lambda' + \pi')CC' + 3\rho\zeta'C^2C' + \rho^2\mu C^3$$
$$+ \rho(\kappa\rho' + \nu')C^3C' + (\rho\rho'/2c_p)C^2$$

$$\nu_p = \rho'\nu + 4\rho\rho'\zeta C' + 2\rho^2\rho'(\lambda + \pi)C'^2 + 4\rho^3\rho'\mu C'^3$$
$$+ \rho^4(\kappa\rho' + \nu')C'^4 + (\rho^2\rho'/2c)C'(1 + \rho^2C'^2) \qquad (97)$$

$$\zeta_p = \rho'\zeta C + \rho\rho'(\lambda + \pi)CC' + \rho^3\zeta'C'^3 + 3\rho^2\rho'\mu CC'^2$$
$$+ \rho^3(\kappa\rho' + \nu')CC'^3 + (\rho^3\rho'/2c_p)CC'^2$$

$$\pi_p = \rho^2\pi'C'^2 + \rho'\pi C^2 + 4\rho^2\zeta'CC'^2 + 4\rho\rho'\mu C^2C'$$
$$+ 2\rho^2(\kappa\rho' + \nu')C^2C'^2 + (\rho^2\rho'/c_p)CC'$$

$$\psi_p = (\psi C + \sigma'C')C^2 + \tau'CC' + \psi'C'$$

$$\tau_p = 2\rho(\psi C + \sigma'C')CC' + \rho\tau'C'^2 + \tau C^2$$

$$\sigma_p = \rho^2(\psi C + \sigma'C')C'^2 + \rho\tau CC' + \sigma C$$

where $C = c/c_p$ and $C' = c'/c_p$.

2. Quadrupole Lenses

The procedure described in the preceding section, which yields the polynomial coefficients of a lens combination in terms of those of the individual components, is probably of most practical interest in connection with quadrupole lenses, which are almost invariably used in multiplets. The analysis proceeds exactly as in the case of round lenses, except that the expressions are more cumbersome. We refer to Hawkes (1970d), where the quadrupole counterparts of Eqs. (96)–(97) are listed.

3. Sector Fields

The aberration matrices mentioned in Section III,B,3 could be used to derive formulas for the aberrations of combinations of prisms or sector fields in general in terms of those of individual components. In the case of mass spectrometers it is also of interest to see how the aberrations of a single sector field arise—that is, which parts of the system contribute most to the most undesirable of the aberrations. Both questions have been studied. Wollnik (1967a) examined the problem of correcting the (second-order) aberrations of a magnetic sector and later (Wollnik, 1971) introduced the notion of a Q value for spectrometers, in order to facilitate the task of comparing the practical performance to be expected from different designs. More recently, Matsuda (1974) has considered mass spectrometers consisting of a toroidal electric field and a homogeneous magnetic field, for example, or a cylindrical electrostatic field, an electrostatic quadrupole, and again a homogeneous magnetic field. Still more complicated systems have been explored by Rose and others (Plies and Rose, 1971; Rose and Plies, 1973; Plies, 1973, 1974; Rose, 1978) in connection with the design and construction of an electron microscope corrected for the principal aberrations that limit resolution.

In 1971, Senoussi had examined the basic properties of an energy analyzer of the Ω type (see also Senoussi et al., 1971), the magnetic analog of the Castaing–Henry design in which an electrostatic mirror is employed (see Castaing et al.,1967). Further investigation by Rose and Plies (1974) revealed that such an analyzer can be designed in such a way that the aberrations are very low indeed. Wollnik et al. (1976) have explored this design further, including fringing fields in the calculation; this paper provoked a comment by Plies and Rose (1977), who observed that even with extended fringing fields, the aberration correction proposed in their earlier paper (Rose and Plies, 1974) should still be valid. (For details of the practical use of Ω filters, see Zanchi et al., 1975; Pearce-Percy, 1976; Pearce-Percy and Cowley, 1976; Kihn et al., 1976; Zanchi et al., 1977a, b; Pearce-Percy, 1978.) For further discussion of aberration correction, see Rose and Pejas (1979).

We note that the Ω configuration (or a related geometry that yields an S-shaped optic axis) has also been used as a particle monochromator (Plies and Hoppe, 1976). In this connection, we draw attention to recent suggestions by Plies (1978) for a wholly electrostatic energy filter and a monochromator. So far as the aberrations are concerned, this should be superior to the magnetic type and the fringing fields may well be more tractable. The filter again has an Ω-shaped optic axis, created entirely by electrostatic fields (Fig. 3a); the layout of the monochromator is shown schematically in Fig. 3b.

Before leaving this topic we note that a number of unusual electrostatic prism geometries have been studied by the group led by Kel'man in Alma Ata (e.g., Glikman et al., 1973a, b, c, 1976); for a thorough survey

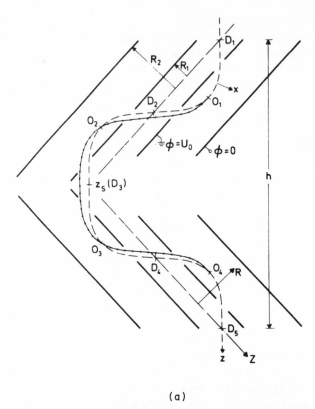

(a)

FIG. 3.   Energy filtering and monochromatization by means of electrostatic configurations. (a) An energy filter with small aberrations, having an Ω-shaped optic axis. (b) A monochromator with small aberrations; (left) chromatic effects; (right and below) geometrical effects. (Courtesy of Dr. E. Plies and the Microscopical Society of Canada.)

leaning heavily on their own work, see Kel'man *et al.* (1979). For a general account, not confined to Russian work but nevertheless giving a
useful survey of it, see Afanas'ev and Yavor (1978).

D. Computer Algebra Systems and Aberration Coefficients

It is a great deal easier to evaluate the formulas for the aberrations of a
system, once the potential or field distributions have been established,
than it is to establish the formulas: evaluation merely requires relatively
straightforward computer programming, calling upon subroutines that are
normally available in the library of any large computer. Deriving the formulas for all but the simplest cases, on the other hand, invariably requires
a vast amount of heavy algebra, of little intrinsic interest and needing

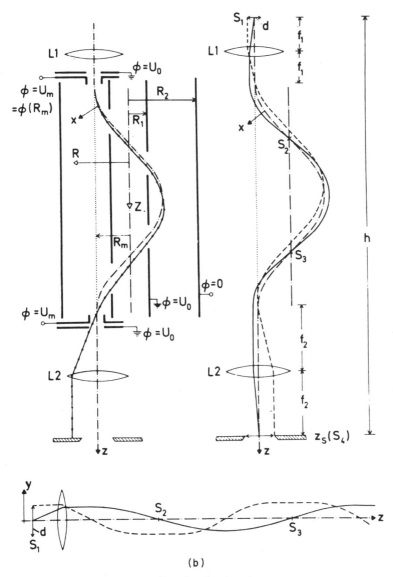

(b)

FIG. 3. *Continued.*

much patient checking to eliminate human error. Recently, however, various languages have become available for performing algebra (rather than arithmetic, with which computers are usually confronted) on computers. A comparison of such languages is to be found in Barton and Fitch

(1972); a full and extremely interesting account of recent developments is given in Ng (1979), in which we draw particular attention to a survey by Fitch (1979) and a description of a new language by Norman and Moore (1979). Here we give a brief description of one of these, CAMAL, in order to indicate the type of problem that can be solved in this way.

Calculation of most aberration coefficients follows a common pattern. First, the appropriate field expansions must be found; these are available in very general form and can hence usually be obtained easily. Then a refractive index or some other complicated function involving this field expansion, often as argument in a further series expansion, must be obtained. After this, a lower-order approximation has to be substituted in the expression derived. Finally, the resulting long and cumbersome structure has to be reorganized into aberration coefficients. The operations involved—series expansion, substitution, and rearrangement—are thus in themselves simple; they are laborious because the expressions involved are so unmanageable. Furthermore, the coefficients can usually be cast into various different forms, by partial integration; this is useful since it permits us to choose a form well-adapted to subsequent numerical evaluation. Partial integration of large unwieldy integrands is a further dull task, prone to mistake and it too can benefit from computer algebra.

How are these various operations represented in CAMAL? The case of the electrostatic lens has been studied in detail with the aid of CAMAL, and we use it to illustrate the type of programming required. The refractive index, from which all the properties are derived, is given by

$$\mu = \{\phi(1 + \epsilon\phi)(1 + x'^2 + y'^2)\}^{1/2}, \qquad \mathbf{E} = -\operatorname{grad} \phi(x, y, z)$$

into this we must substitute the series expansion for ϕ in terms of $\Phi(z) = \phi(0, 0, z)$ and $(x^2 + y^2)$ and also expand the square root, thus:

$$\mu = \{\Phi(1 + \epsilon\Phi)\}^{1/2} \left\{1 + \frac{\phi(1 + \epsilon\phi)(1 + x'^2 + y'^2) - \Phi(1 + \epsilon\Phi)}{\Phi(1 + \epsilon\Phi)}\right\}^{1/2} \tag{98}$$

It can readily be seen that the operations are extremely elementary whereas the operands rapidly become very large. Our first task is to translate the above expressions into a linear notation (i.e., not possessing subscripts and superscripts) and to replace Greek letters by Roman. We write

$$u\langle I\rangle = d^{(I)}\Phi(z)/dz^{(I)}, \qquad u\langle 0\rangle = \Phi(z)$$
$$b = x^2 + y^2, \qquad c = x'^2 + y'^2, \qquad e = \epsilon \tag{99}$$

and

$$f = 1/\{\Phi(1 + \epsilon\Phi)\}^{1/2} \tag{100}$$

Then the first definition of μ may be obtained by setting

$$F = A(1 + eA)(1 + c) \qquad (101)$$

with

$$A = u\langle 0 \rangle - (1/4)u\langle 2 \rangle b + (1/64)u\langle 4 \rangle b.2 \qquad (102)$$

A is thus the series expansion of ϕ; b.2 denotes b^2. The expansion of $\{...\}^{1/2}$ in Eq. (98) is obtained by writing

$$F = F - u\langle 0 \rangle(1 + eu\langle 0 \rangle), \qquad F = 1/f + (1/2)Ff - (1/8)F.2f.3 \quad (103)$$

Into this we wish to substitute the paraxial solutions $x(z)$ and $y(z)$. These occur as quadratic groups in the term responsible for aberrations and we therefore give names to $x^2 + y^2$ and $x'^2 + y'^2$. Writing the paraxial solutions as

$$x(z) = x_0 g(z) + x_0' h(z), \qquad y(z) = y_0 g(z) + y_0' h(z) \qquad (104)$$

we set

$$z\langle 0 \rangle = x_0^2 + y_0^2, \qquad z\langle 1 \rangle = x_0'^2 + y_0'^2, \qquad z\langle 2 \rangle = x_0 x_0' + y_0 y_0' \quad (105)$$

and

$$V = z\langle 0 \rangle g\langle 0 \rangle.2 + z\langle 1 \rangle h\langle 0 \rangle.2 + 2z\langle 2 \rangle g\langle 0 \rangle h\langle 0 \rangle \qquad (106)$$

The line

$$F = SUB(F, V, b) \qquad (107)$$

then substitutes this expression for b in F.

Similarly, $c = x'^2 + y'^2$ is replaced by writing

$$V = z\langle 0 \rangle g\langle 1 \rangle.2 + z\langle 1 \rangle h\langle 1 \rangle.2 + 2z\langle 2 \rangle g\langle 1 \rangle h\langle 1 \rangle$$
$$F = SUB(F, V, c) \qquad (108)$$

in which $g\langle 0 \rangle = g$, $h\langle 0 \rangle = h$, $g\langle 1 \rangle = g'$, and $h\langle 1 \rangle = h'$.

These few lines of program, accompanied by some preliminary material (declaration of arrays, statements to control the size of certain types of expression), text, and output instructions have essentially completed the difficult part of the calculation. It is nevertheless convenient to use CAMAL to rearrange the terms of F into the familar pattern of aberration coefficients and numerous special instructions are available for this type of reorganization.

The question of partial integration provides an interesting example of the flexibility of CAMAL. This language manipulates some functions correctly and can differentiate and integrate some types of expression, but it frequently happens that functions outside the basic repertoire are required. The rules for manipulating these can be "taught" to CAMAL by providing SET instructions, which might, for example, be used to ensure that the relations between Bessel functions of different orders are taken into account or to replace second derivatives of $g(z)$ or $h(z)$ by the expression given by the paraxial equation of motion. In the latter case, for example, we might write (nonrelativistically)

$$\text{SET} \quad dg\langle 1\rangle/dz = \rangle \; -u\langle 1\rangle g\langle 1\rangle/2u\langle 0\rangle \; - \; u\langle 2\rangle g\langle 0\rangle/4u\langle 0\rangle$$

which would be used by CAMAL to eliminate g'' as soon as it received the appropriate instruction. Partial integration is best performed by the systematic procedure devised by Seman (1951, 1954, 1955, 1958) and applied to a variety of cases by Hawkes (1966–1967, 1967); more recently, Kuyatt (1978) has used it to obtain convenient forms of the asymptotic aberration coefficients of round electrostatic lenses.* The complete program for performing such partial integration with the aid of CAMAL (46 lines including a change of notation, introduced merely for convenience, occupying 9 lines) is reproduced and discussed in Hawkes (1977b) and is therefore not described further here.

We have also used CAMAL to perform the simple but lengthy integrations that arise with the bell-shaped model, for round magnetic lenses or quadrupoles. The programming here is particularly straightforward for the SET facility is used to ensure that the integration routine only encounters functions that it can integrate in closed form after which all the simplification and collecting up is performed by CAMAL automatically; the limits of the definite integrals are inserted with the aid of SUB. The calculations that arise with a simple bell are not unduly lengthy, but as soon as we consider any more elaborate model—a rectangle terminated by half-bells for example—they very rapidly become tiresomely long; with CAMAL, however, the corresponding increase in programming is trivial though in practice, printing out the answers in a reasonably legible form does require some thought and the use of the full panoply of CAMAL's resources for sorting output into convenient groupings.

The amount of labor that can be saved by using one or other of the various algebra languages is particularly appreciable in electron optics; Ohiwa (personal communication) has used such a system in his work on

---

* It is worth pointing out that Kuyatt's comparison of his results with those of Sturrock (1955), from which he concludes that the latter are wrong, may well not be correct. The same comparison had been made earlier by Glaser (1952, end of note 160 on p. 676), who also concluded, wrongly, that Sturrock's (1951) earlier formulas contained a mistake. The reason for these misunderstandings is to be sought in Sturrock's use of reduced coordinates, to eliminate the term in dx/dz from the paraxial equation. If Sturrock's formulas are converted back into natural coordinates, the disagreement vanishes.

H[34] =   6u<1>fj<2>+24u<1>fj<1>-3u<1>fj<0>+12u<0>u<1>efj<2>+48u<0>u<1>efj<1>-6u<0>u<1>efj<0>

H[35] =   8j<0>/(f)
            - ((1/2)u<0>2f3+u<0>3ef3+(1/2)u<0>4e2f3)

H[36] =   (1/32)u<4>f+4u<4>fj<6>-(1/32)u<2>2f3+4u<2>2ft3j<8>-2u<2>2ft3j<3>+(1/8)u<2>2ef+4u<2>2efj<7>+
            4u<1>u<3>ft3j<8>-8u<1>u<3>ft3j<6>+4u<1>u<3>ef3j<7>+8u<1>u<3>ef3j<6>+12u<1>t2u<2>ft5j<9>-12u<1>t2u<2>ft5j<8>-
            2u<1>t2u<2>ft5j<4>+12u<1>t2u<2>ef3j<10>-4u<1>t2u<2>ef3j<7>-2u<1>t2u<2>ef3j<5>-20u<1>t4ft7j<9>-
            12u<1>t4ef5j<10>+8u<1>t4ef5j<9>+4u<1>t4ef3j<11>+(1/16)u<0>u<4>ef+8u<0>u<4>efj<6>-(1/8)u<0>u<2>2ef+3-
            8u<0>u<2>2ef+3j<3>-16u<0>u<3>ef3j<6>+24u<0>u<1>t2u<2>ef5j<9>-24u<0>u<1>t2u<2>ef5j<8>-4u<0>u<1>t2
            u<2>ef5j<4>+12u<0>u<2>2e2ft3j<3>+12u<0>u<1>t2u<2>e2ft3j<7>-4u<0>u<1>t2u<2>e2ft3j<5>-80u<0>u<1>t4ef7
            j<9>-12u<0>u<1>t4e2f5j<1>-24u<0>u<1>t4e2f5j<10>-(1/8)u<0>t2u<2>t2e2ft3+3-8u<0>t2u<2>2e2ft3j<3>-
            16u<0>t2u<3>e2ft3j<6>-80u<0>t2u<1>t4e2f7j<9>-24u<0>t2u<3>e2ft3j<3>-

H[37] =   12u<3>3fj<6>+6u<3>3fj<3>+12u<1>u<2>2ft3j<8>+12u<1>u<2>2ft3j<3>-(3/2)u<1>u<2>2ft3j<2>-
            6u<1>u<2>ft3j<1>+12u<1>u<2>ef3j<7>+12u<1>u<2>2ef3j<5>+12u<1>u<2>ef3j<3>+12u<1>3f+5j<9>-21u<1>3f+5j<4>+
            12u<1>t3ef3j<10>-9u<1>t3ef3j<5>+24u<0>u<3>ef3j<6>+12u<0>u<3>ef3j<3>-36u<0>u<1>u<2>2ef+3j<3>-6u<0>u<1>u<2>2ef3
            j<2>-24u<0>u<1>u<2>2ef3j<1>+24u<0>u<3>e2ft3j<3>+6u<0>u<1>u<2>ef5j<9>-4zu<0>u<1>t3ef5j<4>+12u<0>u<1>t3ef3j<11>-18u<0>u<1>t3et2
            f+3j<5>-36u<0>t2e2f+3j<3>-6u<0>t2u<2>2e2f+3j<2>-24u<0>t2u<2>2ef+3j<1>

H[38] =   -((1/4)u<2>2fj<3>-2u<2>2fj<2>-8u<2>2fj<0>-12u<1>t2ft3j<4>+4u<1>t2f+3j<2>+
            16u<1>t2f+3j<3>-12u<1>t2ef5j<5>-4u<1>t2ef3j<2>-16u<1>t2efj<1>-(1/8)u<0>u<2>2f+3+(1/2)u<0>u<2>2ft3-24u<0>u<2>ef
            j<3>-4u<0>u<2>2ef3j<2>-16u<0>u<3>u<2>2ef3j<2>+16u<0>u<1>t2e2ft3j<2>+64u<0>u<1>t2ef3j<1>-
            (3/8)u<0>t2u<2>2ef+3j<3>+16u<0>t2u<1>t2e2ft3j<1>-(1/4)u<0>t3u<2>2e2f3)

H[39] =   2u<1>fj<2>+8u<1>fj<1>-u<1>fj<0>+4u<0>u<1>efj<2>+16u<0>u<1>efj<1>-2u<0>u<1>efj<0>

FIG. 4. An example of CAMAL output, from which it is clear that the main obstacle to be overcome by the reader is the linear representation of indices and suffices.

4. THIRD-ORDER TRAJECTORY EQUATION AND ABERRATION COEFFICIENTS

Substituting (10) - (14) into (2) and retaining terms up to the third-order in w and W, we obtain the third-order trajectory equation, (with the following simplified notation: $F = \phi_F$, $G = \phi_G$, $P = \phi_P$, $Q = \phi_Q$, $R = \phi_R$, $f = \psi_F$, $g = \psi_G$, $p = \psi_P$, $q = \psi_Q$, $r = \psi_R$.)

(15) $w'' = w'\{(-1/2 \, \epsilon_2 F'/(\epsilon_1 F)) + in(f'/(\epsilon_1 F)^{1/2})\}$

$+ w\{(-1/4 \, \epsilon_2 F''/(\epsilon_1 F)) + in(1/2 \, f''/(\epsilon_1 F)^{1/2})\}$

$+ W\{(1/2 \, \epsilon_2 P/(\epsilon_1 F)) + in(-p/(\epsilon_1 F)^{1/2})\}$

$+ w^2\bar{w}\{(1/32 \, \epsilon_2 F''''/(\epsilon_1 F) - 1/16 \, \epsilon_3 F''^2/(\epsilon_1 F)^2)$

$+ in(-1/16 \, f''''/(\epsilon_1 F)^{1/2} + 1/16 \, \epsilon_2 F''f''/(\epsilon_1 F)^{3/2})\}$

$+ w\bar{w}w'\{(1/8 \, \epsilon_2 F'''/(\epsilon_1 F) - 1/8 \, \epsilon_3 F''F'/(\epsilon_1 F)^2)$

$+ in(-1/4 \, f'''/(\epsilon_1 F)^{1/2} + 1/8 \, \epsilon_2 F''f'/(\epsilon_1 F)^{3/2})\}$

$+ ww'\bar{w}'\{(-1/4 \, \epsilon_2 F''/(\epsilon_1 F)) + in(1/2 \, f''/(\epsilon_1 F)^{1/2})\}$

$+ \bar{w}w'^2\{ \qquad\qquad + in(-1/4 \, f''/(\epsilon_1 F)^{1/2})\}$

$+ w'^2\bar{w}'\{(-1/2 \, \epsilon_2 F'/(\epsilon_1 F)) + in(1/2 \, f'/(\epsilon_1 F)^{1/2})\}$

$+ w^2\bar{W}\{(-1/16 \, \epsilon_2 P''/(\epsilon_1 F) + 1/8 \, \epsilon_3 F''\bar{P}/(\epsilon_1 F)^2)$

$+ in(1/8 \, \bar{p}''/(\epsilon_1 F)^{1/2} - 1/8 \, \epsilon_2 \bar{P}f''/(\epsilon_1 F)^{3/2})\}$

(a)

FIG. 5.   Automatic production of a typescript, including formulas generated by a computer algebra language. (a) A page of the original typescript. (b) A page of the same article as published in *Optik,* including the text reproduced in Fig. 5a. (Courtesy of Dr. T. Soma and Wissenschaftliche Velagsgesellschaft.)

4. Third-order trajectory equation and aberration coefficients

Substituting (10)–(14) into (2) and retaining terms up to the third-order in w and W, we obtain the third-order trajectory equation, (with the following simplified notation: $F = \varphi_F$, $G = \varphi_G$, $P = \varphi_{\dot{P}}$, $Q = \varphi_{\dot{Q}}$, $R = \varphi_{\dot{R}}$, $f = \psi_F$, $g = \psi_G$, $p = \psi_{\dot{P}}$, $q = \psi_{\dot{Q}}$, $r = \psi_{\dot{R}}$)

$$
\begin{aligned}
w'' = &\; w' \left\{ (-1/2\, \varepsilon_2 F'/(\varepsilon_1 F)) + i\eta\, (f'/(\varepsilon_1 F)^{1/2}) \right\} \qquad (15) \\
&+ w \left\{ (-1/4\, \varepsilon_2 F''/(\varepsilon_1 F)) + i\eta\, (1/2\, f''/(\varepsilon_1 F)^{1/2}) \right\} \\
&+ W \left\{ (1/2\, \varepsilon_2 P/(\varepsilon_1 F)) + i\eta\, (-\, p/(\varepsilon_1 F)^{1/2}) \right\} \\
&+ w^2\bar{w}\left\{ (1/32\, \varepsilon_2 F''''/(\varepsilon_1 F) - 1/16\, \varepsilon_3 F''^2/(\varepsilon_1 F)^2) \right. \\
&\quad \left. + i\eta(-1/16\, f''''/(\varepsilon_1 F)^{1/2} + 1/16\, \varepsilon_2 F'' f''/(\varepsilon_1 F)^{3/2}) \right\} \\
&+ w\bar{w}w'\left\{ (1/8\, \varepsilon_2 F'''/(\varepsilon_1 F) - 1/8\, \varepsilon_3 F'' F'/(\varepsilon_1 F)^2) \right. \\
&\quad \left. + i\eta(-1/4\, f'''/(\varepsilon_1 F)^{1/2} + 1/8\, \varepsilon_2 F'' f'/(\varepsilon_1 F)^{3/2}) \right\} \\
&+ ww'\bar{w}\left\{ (-1/4\, \varepsilon_2 F''/(\varepsilon_1 F)) + i\eta(1/2\, f''/(\varepsilon_1 F)^{1/2}) \right\} \\
&+ \bar{w}w'^2\left\{ + i\eta(-1/4\, f''/(\varepsilon_1 F)^{1/2}) \right\} \\
&+ w^2\bar{w}'\left\{ (-1/2\, \varepsilon_2 F'/(\varepsilon_1 F)) + i\eta(1/2\, f'/(\varepsilon_1 F)^{1/2}) \right\} \\
&+ w^2\bar{W}\left\{ (-1/16\, \varepsilon_2 \bar{P}''/(\varepsilon_1 F) + 1/8\, \varepsilon_3 F'' \bar{P}/(\varepsilon_1 F)^2) \right. \\
&\quad \left. + i\eta(1/8\, \bar{p}''/(\varepsilon_1 F)^{1/2} - 1/8\, \varepsilon_2 \bar{P} f''/(\varepsilon_1 F)^{3/2}) \right\} \\
&+ w\bar{w}W\left\{ (-1/8\, \varepsilon_2 P''/(\varepsilon_1 F) + 1/4\, \varepsilon_3 F'' P/(\varepsilon_1 F)^2) \right. \\
&\quad + i\eta(1/4\, p''/(\varepsilon_1 F)^{1/2} - 1/8\, \varepsilon_2 P f''/(\varepsilon_1 F)^{3/2} \\
&\quad \left. - 1/8\, \varepsilon_2 F'' p/(\varepsilon_1 F)^{3/2}) \right\} \\
&+ ww'\bar{W}\left\{ (-1/4\, \varepsilon_2 \bar{P}'/(\varepsilon_1 F) + 1/4\, \varepsilon_3 F' \bar{P}/(\varepsilon_1 F)^2) \right. \\
&\quad + i\eta(1/2\, \bar{p}'/(\varepsilon_1 F)^{1/2} - 1/4\, \varepsilon_2 \bar{P} f'/(\varepsilon_1 F)^{3/2} \\
&+ \bar{w}w'W\left\{ (-1/4\, \varepsilon_2 P'/(\varepsilon_1 F) + 1/4\, \varepsilon_3 F' P/(\varepsilon_1 F)^2) \right. \\
&\quad \left. + i\eta(1/2\, p'/(\varepsilon_1 F)^{1/2} - 1/4\, \varepsilon_2 P f'/(\varepsilon_1 F)^{3/2}) \right\} \\
&+ w'^2\bar{W}\left\{ + i\eta(1/2\, \bar{p}/(\varepsilon_1 F)^{1/2}) \right\} \\
&+ w'\bar{w}'W\left\{ (1/2\, \varepsilon_2 P/(\varepsilon_1 F)) + i\eta(-\, p/(\varepsilon_1 F)^{1/2}) \right\} \\
&+ wW\bar{W}\left\{ (-1/4\, \varepsilon_3 P\bar{P}/(\varepsilon_1 F)^2 \right. \\
&\quad + 1/4\, \varepsilon_3 F'' G/(\varepsilon_1 F)^2 - 1/4\, \varepsilon_2 G''/(\varepsilon_1 F)) \\
&\quad + i\eta(1/4\, \varepsilon_2 \bar{P} p/(\varepsilon_1 F)^{3/2} - 1/4\, \varepsilon_2 G f''/(\varepsilon_1 F)^{3/2} \\
&\quad \left. + 1/2\, g''/(\varepsilon_1 F)^{1/2}) \right\} \\
&+ \bar{w}W^2\left\{ (-1/4\, \varepsilon_3 P^2/(\varepsilon_1 F)^2 + \varepsilon_2 Q/(\varepsilon_1 F)) \right. \\
&\quad \left. + i\eta(1/4\, \varepsilon_2 P p/(\varepsilon_1 F)^{3/2} - 2\, q/(\varepsilon_1 F)^{1/2}) \right\} \\
&+ w'W\bar{W}\left\{ (1/2\, \varepsilon_3 F' G/(\varepsilon_1 F)^2 - 1/2\, \varepsilon_2 G'/(\varepsilon_1 F)) \right. \\
&\quad \left. + i\eta(-1/2\, \varepsilon_2 G f'/(\varepsilon_1 F)^{3/2} + g'/(\varepsilon_1 F)^{1/2}) \right\}
\end{aligned}
$$

(b)

FIG. 5 *Continued.*

deflection systems (e.g., Ohiwa, 1978), and the present author is applying CAMAL to some unsolved problems and incompletely explored situations in aberration theory (see Hawkes, 1977a, c). Goto and Soma (1977) and Soma (1977) have used REDUCE (Hearn, 1973) to derive aberration formulas for the algebraically very complex case of combined focusing–deflection systems, allowing for both magnetic and electrostatic fields and for relativistic effects. A particularly interesting feature of their work concerns the output. In the case of CAMAL, the results are written out in linear form on the line printer, which must therefore be capable of printing upper- and lower-case characters and a wide range of mathematical symbols. Despite considerable efforts on the part of the designers of the language, such linear output is not easy to read. Figure 4 gives an example of CAMAL output. The IBM language SCRATCHPAD (Griesmer *et al.*, 1975) again uses the line printer, but subscripts and superscripts are now in their correct places; since the characters must be at least one line apart and different fonts are not available, formulas have a rather untidy scattered appearance but are certainly quite easy to read. At the Information Science Laboratory of the University of Tokyo, however, where REDUCE-2 is used, the output is transfered to a text-editing system (STEP), which is implemented on a dedicated minicomputer. The STEP provides flexible editing and, in particular, can handle special mathematical symbols and Greek characters. The minicomputer also manages the text formating system, which organizes the edited text into a form suitable for printing by means of an IBM Selectric typewriter interfaced to the minicomputer (Soma, private communication, 1978). Figure 5 shows a page of formulas from a paper by Soma (1977) in two forms: in Fig. 5a, as produced automatically on the IBM typewriter and in Fig. 5b, as printed in *Optik*. A direct interface connecting the minicomputer to a computer typesetting machine would simplify the process of publication ever further, by eliminating one source of human error. This is a distinct improvement over line printer output, even that of SCRATCHPAD, since Greek letters (and indeed, any characters available on the typewriter) are freely available, and bars or other diacritic marks can be placed over symbols if required (e.g., w and $\bar{w}$). Subscripts and superscripts can be written in small type but cannot nevertheless be closer than single spacing permits.

IV. OPTIMIZATION AND PARTIAL CORRECTION OF ABERRATIONS

In this section, we survey the various attempts that have been made in the past few years to combat the adverse effects of aberrations. Progress has been made both in the design of optimal systems—that is, systems in which the inherent aberrations are reduced as far as possible by improved design, not by introducing corrector units—and in the construction of correctors. We begin with an account of optimization, drawing attention in particular to the work of Moses on constrained minimization and that of Szilágyi on search procedures using dynamic programming. In this connection, we also briefly mention work on deflection systems and projector combinations. We then discuss aberration correction by means of quadrupole–octopole combinations, charged foils and space charge, high-frequency components, and mirrors.

A. System Optimization

1. Variational Techniques

Attempts to establish the lower bound, if any, on the principal aberration coefficients date from the early years of electron optics. The publication by Scherzer in 1936 of his celebrated positive definite integrand for C_s (rewritten in relativistically correct form by Rose in 1966–1967) provoked intermittent discussion* of the minimum attainable value of this coefficient and of C_c until Tretner's (1959) "Existenzbereiche rotationssymmetrischer Elektronenlinsen," the culmination of a series of earlier papers (Tretner, 1950, 1954, 1955, 1956), effectively solved the problem by setting out the relation between these minimum values and the lens geometry and excitation. In this paper, the results of which are related to those obtained in practice in the review of Mulvey and Wallington (1973), Tretner uses the calculus of variations to establish maximum and minimum values of the chromatic and spherical aberration coefficients of magnetic and electrostatic lenses. These extrema are constrained by requirements governing the focal length or magnification, the highest permissible electric or magnetic field on the axis and, in the electrostatic case, the maximum tolerable potential at object and image. Some of Tretner's results are reproduced in Fig. 6.

Central though Tretner's definitive study is to the design of optimal lenses, it leaves the question of how best to attain the minimum open, and it is clear from the comparisons made by Mulvey and Wallington (1973) that, as might be expected, more than one configuration comes very close to the minimum. Field distributions for which certain aberration coefficients are as low as possible have been obtained, again by variational methods, by Moses, who was initially concerned with quadrupole

---

* References can be found in the bibliographic Appendix to Hawkes (1980a); we draw attention to the papers of Seman (1953a, b), which are often overlooked in this context.

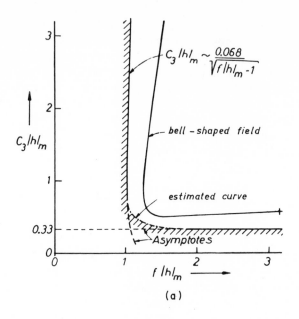

(a)

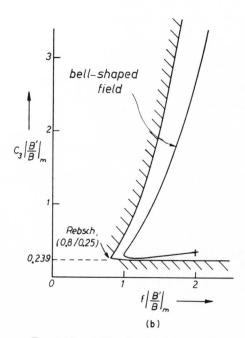

(b)

FIG. 6 (a) and (b).   See legend on p. 93.

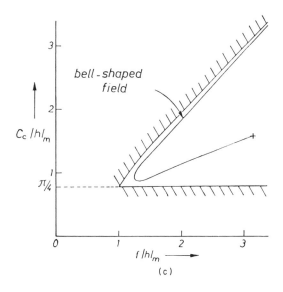
(c)

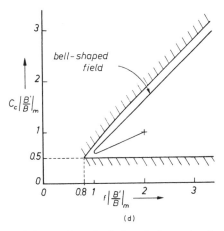
(d)

FIG. 6. The lower limits to the spherical and chromatic aberration coefficients of round magnetic lenses, subject to two different constraints: first, the magnetic field must not exceed some maximum value, $|h|_m$, $h = \eta B/2\Phi^{1/2}$, and, second, $B'(z)/B(z)$ must not exceed some maximum value, $|B'/B|_m$. (a) $C_s|h|_m$ as a function of $f|h|_m$, together with the corresponding curve for Glaser's bell-shaped field. (b) $C_s|B'/B|_m$ as a function of $f|B'/B|_m$, again showing the bell-shaped field curve and the extremum obtained by Rebsch (1938). (c) $C_c|h|_m$ as a function of $f|h|_m$, with the bell-shaped field curve for comparison. (d) $C_c|B'/B|_m$ as a function of $f|B'/B|_m$, together with the bell-shaped field curve. (Courtesy of Dr. W. Tretner and Wissenschaftliche Verlagsgesellschaft.)

systems (Moses, 1970, 1971a, b) but subsequently applied the same techniques to the design of magnetic round lenses free of coma, both isotropic and anisotropic, and having as little spherical aberration as possible (Moses, 1973). Rose and Moses (1973) derived a number of round and cylindrical magnetic lens fields having minimum spherical aberration, negligible field at the specimen, and, in the case of cylindrical lenses, no image rotation. As an illustration of Moses' technique, we describe his work on coma-free round lenses; for further details the interested reader is recommended to consult Moses (1973), Rose and Moses (1973), and Moses (1974).

It is convenient to use the complex rotating coordinate u, such that the paraxial equations of motion in a field $B(z)$ become

$$u'' + h^2 u = 0 \tag{109}$$

where

$$h(z) = (e/8mV)^{1/2} B(z) = \eta B/2V^{1/2} \tag{110}$$

and the rotation is $\chi(z)$,

$$\chi(z) = \int_{z_0}^{z} h\, dz \tag{111}$$

The linearly independent paraxial solutions are chosen to satisfy boundary conditions at the object plane ($z = z_0$) and the aperture plane ($z = z_a$); we adopt Moses' notation for the paraxial solutions, $u_\alpha(z)$ and $u_\gamma(z)$:

$$u_{\alpha 0} = u_{\gamma a} = 0, \qquad u'_{\alpha 0} = u_{\gamma 0} = 1 \tag{112}$$

so that a general ray has the form

$$u = w_a u_\alpha + u_0 u_\gamma, \qquad w_a = u_a/u_{\alpha a} \tag{113}$$

Coma and spherical aberration, referred back to the object plane, cause the ray to deviate from its paraxial path by a distance Δu_0:

$$\Delta u_0 = C_3 \overline{w}_a w_a^2 + \overline{B}_3 \overline{u}_0 w_a^2 + 2B_3 u_0 w_a \overline{w}_a \tag{114}$$

in which a bar indicates the complex conjugate and C_3, B_3 denote integrals from object to image (or exit plane, $z = z_e$, beyond which the value of B is negligible). The spherical aberration C_3 cannot of course vanish, but the isotropic coma, $\mathrm{Re}(B_3)$, can be eliminated by suitable choice of aperture plane. The anisotropic coma, $\mathrm{Im}(B_3)$, is represented by an integral of the form $\int hP\, dz$, where P is an everywhere positive function involving u_α and h; the integral cannot therefore vanish unless h changes sign within the lens system.

Any solution will be acceptable only if the lens is physically reasonable, that is, if certain practical constraints, on the maximum attainable field strength, for example, are respected. Moses requires that $|h|$ shall not exceed some maximum, h_m:

$$|h| \leq h_m \qquad (115)$$

which is convenient but does not really represent the physical limitations with sufficient flexibility.

We now write

$$C_3 = \int_{z_0}^{z_e} F(u_\alpha, u'_\alpha, h, h') \, dz \qquad (116a)$$

and

$$\text{Im}(B_3) = \frac{1}{4} \int_{z_0}^{z_e} K(u_\alpha, u'_\alpha, h) \, dz \qquad (116b)$$

Introducing Lagrange multipliers Γ and $\mu(z)$, we minimize C_3 subject to $\text{Im}(B_3) = 0$ and $u'' + h^2 u = 0$ by requiring that

$$\delta \int_{z_0}^{z_e} \{F + \Gamma K + \mu(u''_\alpha + h^2 u_\alpha)\} \, dz = 0 \qquad (117)$$

Setting $I = F + \Gamma K$, we obtain the Euler equations

$$\mu'' + h^2 \mu = -\frac{\partial I}{\partial u_\alpha} + \frac{d}{dz} \frac{\partial I}{\partial u'_\alpha}, \qquad \frac{\partial I}{\partial h} - \frac{d}{dz} \frac{\partial I}{\partial h'} + 2\mu h u_\alpha = 0 \quad (118)$$

with boundary conditions

$$\left[\frac{\partial I}{\partial h'} \, \delta h + \left(\frac{\partial I}{\partial u'_\alpha} - \mu' \right) \delta u_\alpha + \mu \delta u'_\alpha \right]_{z_0}^{z_e} = 0 \qquad (119)$$

After further discussion of the boundary conditions and imposition of the restriction on $|h|$, magnetic fields can be computed numerically for which C_3 is minimized subject to the various constraints. For details of the numerical techniques, see Moses (1973). Figures 7 and 8 show some of Moses' results, together with a projected lens design to create one of the field distributions obtained. Figures 9 and 10 show some fields calculated by Rose and Moses (1973), which give minimum spherical aberration with no magnetic field at the object. As Munro (1971) had found earlier, it is advantageous to use an asymmetric field distribution, steep on the object side and falling off more slowly on the image side; many earlier studies of asymmetric lenses had already established this result (see Mulvey and Wallington, 1973, for example, or Lenz, 1980), which emerged directly from Moses' calculations.

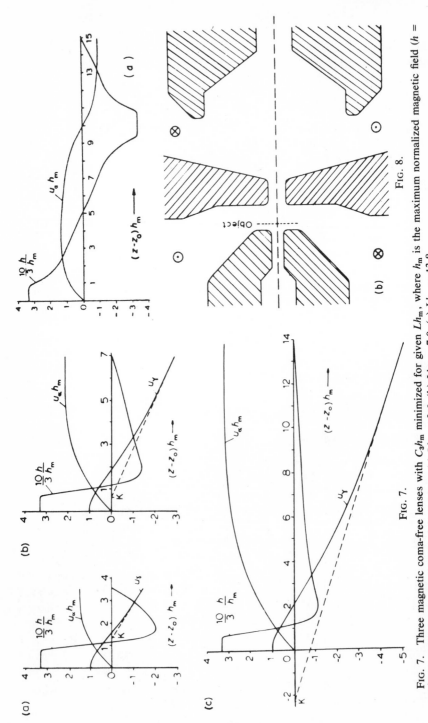

FIG. 7. Three magnetic coma-free lenses with $C_3 h_m$ minimized for given $L h_m$, where h_m is the maximum normalized magnetic field ($h = \eta B / 2\phi^{1/2}$) and L is the total length of the system. (a) $L h_m = 3.6$; (b) $L h_m = 7.0$; (c) $L h_m = 13.8$.

FIG. 8. Coma-free lenses with $C_3 h_m$ minimized for given $L h_m$ (cf. Fig. 7). (a) Field distribution and a paraxial ray in a dual-image lens; $L h_m = 15$. (b) Pole pieces of a single-image coma-free lens with $L h_m = 7$. (Figures 7 and 8 courtesy of Dr. R. W. Moses and Academic Press.)

96

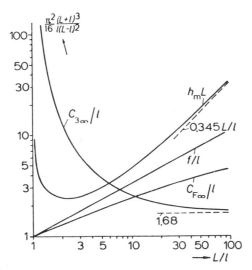

FIG. 9.   Variation of the high-magnification values of C_s and C_c, the focal length and the normalized maximum field of an optimized high-magnification magnetic lens with a field-free working distance l as a function of L/l, where L and l are the distances from object to exit plane and from the object plane to the plane of entry into the magnetic field (see Fig. 10).

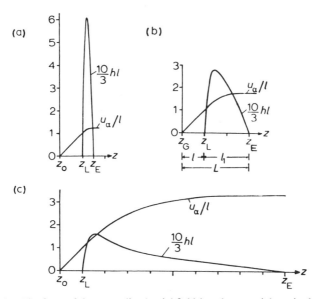

FIG. 10.   The form of the normalized axial field h and a paraxial ray in three magnetic lenses with minimum spherical aberration and different lengths. (a) $L/l = 1.5$; (b) $L/l = 3$; (c) $L/l = 10$. (Figures 9 and 10 courtesy of Drs. H. Rose and R. W. Moses and Wissenschaftliche Verlagsgesellschaft.)

97

2. Dynamic Programming

A very different technique has been explored by Szilágyi (1977a), who has combined the search routines developed for "dynamic programming" with a very simple electrostatic or magnetic lens model. The method generates vast numbers of field distributions corresponding to a minimum of some function, the spherical aberration coefficient, for example. From among these, distributions can be selected that satisfy some practical constraint: that the magnification must take some preset value, for example. The function to be minimized, S, will be in the form of an integral between two values of z, which we now denote z_n and z_0 (i.e., z_n is the exit plane labelled z_e above or the image plane z_i). We divide the distance $z_n - z_0$ into n equal regions, so that $z_n - z_0 = n \, \Delta z$ and write

$$S = \Delta z \sum_{1}^{n} F_k \tag{120}$$

where

$$F_k = \{F(z_{k-1}) + F(z_k)\}/2 \tag{121}$$

and S represents $\int F \, dz$ from z_0 to z_n. The field function $h(z)$ (Eq. 110) is replaced by a sequence of linear segments,

$$h(z) = H_0 + H_1 z \tag{122}$$

for which the paraxial ray equation can be solved explicitly in terms of Bessel functions (Szilágyi, 1969):

$$\begin{pmatrix} r_k \\ r_k' \end{pmatrix} = \frac{\pi \{H_0(H_0 + H_1 \Delta z)\}^{1/2}}{2\sqrt{2} H_1} \, \mathbf{R} \begin{pmatrix} r_{k-1} \\ r_{k-1}' \end{pmatrix} \tag{123}$$

The elements of the 2×2 matrix $\mathbf{R}$ are as follows:

$$R_{11} = \pm H_0 \{J_{3/4}(w_0)J_{1/4}(w) + J_{-3/4}(w_0)J_{-1/4}(w)\}$$

$$R_{12} = J_{-1/4}(w_0)J_{1/4}(w) - J_{1/4}(w_0)J_{-1/4}(w)$$

$$R_{21} = (H_0 + H_1 \, \Delta z)H_0 \{J_{3/4}(w_0)J_{-3/4}(w) - J_{-3/4}(w_0)J_{3/4}(w)\} \tag{124}$$

$$R_{22} = \pm (H_0 + H_1 \, \Delta z) \{J_{-1/4}(w_0)J_{-3/4}(w) + J_{1/4}(w_0)J_{3/4}(w)\}$$

with

$$w_0 = H_0^2/2|H_1|, \qquad w = (H_0 + H_1 \, \Delta z)^2/2|H_1| \tag{125}$$

Simpler expressions, listed by Szilágyi (1977a), are obtained for the special cases $H_0 = 0$ and $H_1 = 0$. In Eqs. (124), the plus signs are to be used when H_1 is positive, the minus signs when it is negative.

Denoting the maximum value of $h(z)$ by h_m, we divide the total range over which the field can vary into steps Δh, so that

$$M \Delta h = h_m \tag{126}$$

The value of $h(z)$ at the point $z_k = k \Delta z$ is then characterized by a matrix element h_{ik} such that

$$h(z_k) = h_{ik} = i \Delta h \tag{127}$$

where i may take any integral value such that $-M \leq i \leq M$. It is to be emphasized that the suffices of h_{ik} characterize very different quantities: field (i) and distance along the optic axis (k). From Eq. (122), it is immediately clear that, for the axial zone between z_{k-1} and z_k,

$$H_0 = h_{j,k-1} = j \Delta h \tag{128}$$

and

$$H_1 = \frac{h_{ik} - h_{j,k-1}}{\Delta z} = (i - j) \frac{\Delta h}{\Delta z} \tag{129}$$

As for i, $-M \leq j \leq M$.

The ray $r(z)$ can now be calculated across the kth axial zone, assuming that the preceding zones have already been evaluated, using the matrix **R**. This will generate two new *arrays* of values, one for r and one for r', corresponding to the $(2M + 1)$ values of i and j. Equation (121) is then used to calculate the *array* of possible values of the integrand for the kth axial zone:

$$(F_k)_{ij} = \frac{1}{2} F \left((r_{k-1})_{ij}, (r'_{k-1})_{ij}, j \Delta h, (i - j) \frac{\Delta h}{\Delta z} \right)$$
$$+ \frac{1}{2} F \left((r_k)_{ij}, (r'_k)_{ij}, i \Delta h, (i - j) \frac{\Delta h}{\Delta z} \right) \tag{130}$$

If $G_{j, k-1}$ denotes the optimum field configuration for the first $k - 1$ axial zones, therefore, we obtain G_{ik}, the optimum for the first k zones, by varying j until $(F_k)_{ij} + G_{j, k-1}$ is minimized:

$$G_{ik} = \min \{ (F_k)_{ij} + G_{j, k-1} \} \tag{131}$$

Setting out from z_0, this process is performed iteratively until the endpoint z_n is reached. The result is a set of optimum values of H_0 and H_1 which may be represented graphically as line segments as we shall illustrate below. For each axial zone, $z_{k-1} \leq z \leq z_k$, an optimum pair (H_0, H_1) is associated with each initial value of h, $h = i \Delta h$, that is, with each value of h in the plane $z = z_{k-1}$. Figure 11 shows the optimum linear field seg-

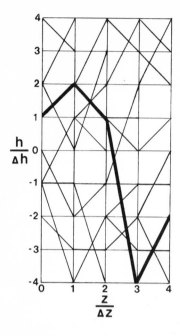

Fig. 11. The pattern of branching lines showing how minimum values of the integral of interest are generated for various values of the field as the distance is advanced step by step. The heavy line shows a relatively smooth—and hence physically realistic—distribution.

ments for $-4 \leq h/\Delta h \leq 4$ and $0 \leq z/\Delta z \leq 4$. We see that for each value of $z = k \, \Delta z$, a field line sets out from each value of $h = i \, \Delta h$. These are the optimum field segments for each axial zone as a function of the value of the field at the beginning of the axial zone in question.

Our choice from among these numerous optima is guided by boundary conditions—requirements on r_n and r'_n, for example—and by practical considerations. The field must not exhibit variations that cannot be produced to a reasonably good approximation by means of pole pieces of acceptable shape.

This procedure has been applied to magnetic lenses (Szilágyi, 1977b) and electrostatic immersion lenses (Szilágyi, 1978a), in both cases with a view to minimizing the spherical aberration (see also Szilágyi, 1978c). The choice of M, n, and $\delta = \Delta h$. Δz is important in obtaining the full range of possible solutions, as Szilágyi (1977b) discusses and illustrates in considerable detail. Figures 12a, 13a, and 14a show the complete arrays for various values of the parameters, and Figs. 12b, 13b, and 14b show some physically interesting special cases extracted from them. Figure 12b is the type of field obtained by Glaser by solving the differential equation obtained by setting the integrand of C_S equal to zero (Glaser, 1940) and later used by Siegbahn (1942) for a focal-separation β-ray spectrometer lens (see too Marton and Bol, 1947). Figure 13b (dotted line) is especially interesting

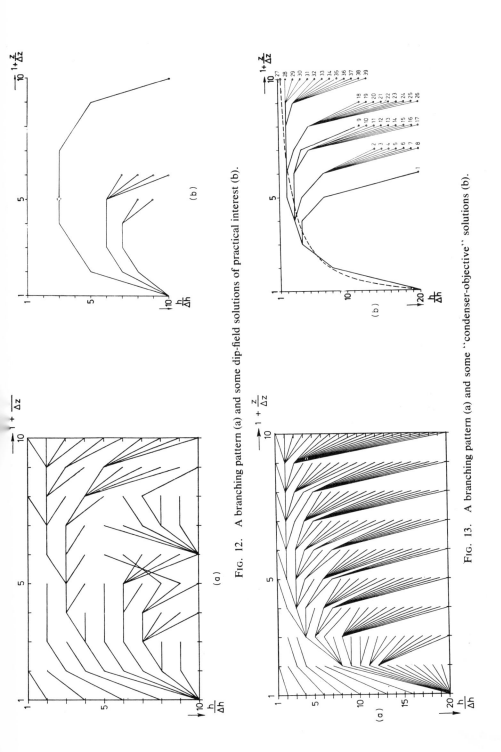

FIG. 12. A branching pattern (a) and some dip-field solutions of practical interest (b).

FIG. 13. A branching pattern (a) and some "condenser-objective" solutions (b).

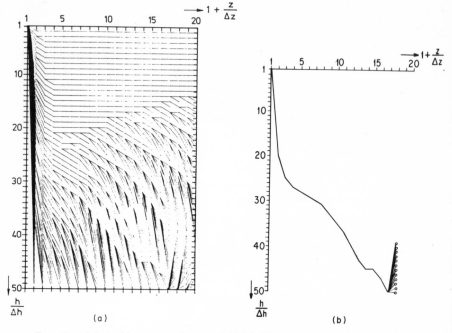

FIG. 14. A branching pattern for zero initial field (a) and a practical field distribution taken from it (b). (Figures 11–14 courtesy of Dr. M. Szilágyi and Wissenschaftliche Verlagsgesellschaft.)

in that it represents a distribution with high field at the object, low field at the image, and very low spherical aberration. The advantages of such condenser–objective operation were established long ago, using the bell-shaped model, and Szilágyi's approach should enable us to establish the optimum rate of falloff of the field.

Finally, we recall that in Szilágyi's companion paper (1978a), electrostatic immersion lens geometries are found for which the spherical aberration coefficient is least. As in the magnetic case, numerous interesting configurations arise, some familiar but many new.

3. Scanning Systems

Deflection aberrations have recently attracted considerable attention owing to their role in the design of microfabrication systems and scanning transmission electron microscopes (STEMs). These topics are dealt with in detail in Supplement B, and we therefore touch on them only very briefly;

they do, however, provide a very good example of system optimization, and of the advisability of devoting considerable effort to this before embarking on the usually much more difficult (and costly) task of correction.

The study and avoidance of deflection aberrations have a long history which is traced succinctly but thoroughly in the extremely detailed study of deflection aberrations made by Kaashoek (1968). This long paper marks the beginning of the modern treatment of these defects, which leans heavily on the computer and from which have emerged many new designs and valuable theoretical results. Apart from the applications already mentional, an example of the exploitation of these results is the large-area electron film writer, built by Rao and Nixon (1978). The most important of the earlier studies is that of Haantjes and Lubben (1957, 1959).

One approach that has been extensively studied involves virtual displacement of the objective lens and has therefore been named Moving Objective Lens (MOL) by Ohiwa *et al.* (1971). In this arrangement, a deflection field is superimposed on a rotationally symmetric focusing field: the axial flux distribution is chosen in such a way that the round lens appears displaced laterally. The aberrations of such a system have been very thoroughly studied (Ohiwa, 1970; Ohiwa *et al.*, 1971; Soma, 1977; Goto and Soma, 1977; Ohiwa, 1977a, b, 1978, 1979).

A systematic comparative study of the aberrations of prelens deflection coils and postlens deflection systems, with microfabrication in mind, has been made by Owen and Nixon (1973), which shows clearly which configurations are preferable. Suitable measures of the effect of aberrations are discussed by Mauer (1978; see also Mauer *et al.*, 1977). For further discussion of deflection aberrations, see Amboss and Wolf (1971), Der-Shvarts (1974), Thomson (1975), Amboss (1975, 1976), and Ritz (1979).

As a result of this activity in scanning coil design, formulas for the aberration coefficients of superimposed deflection and magnetic lens fields have now been derived (see the chapter by Munro in Part B of this Supplement for a full account). The formulas of Munro (1974) were generalized by Goto and Soma (1977) and still further extended by Soma (1977); we recall that Soma used a computer algebra system for this (see Section III,D). They have been investigated for a practical system by Speidel *et al.* (1979–1980).

Finally, we draw attention to the work of Crewe and Parker (1976), who show how, by using dynamic focusing, it should in principle be possible to eliminate all the aberrations in a scanning electron microscope, apart from the sperical aberration. This is described in detail by Parker *et al.* (1976a,b, 1978, 1979). Corrected postspecimen optical systems for the STEM are discussed by Crewe (1977).

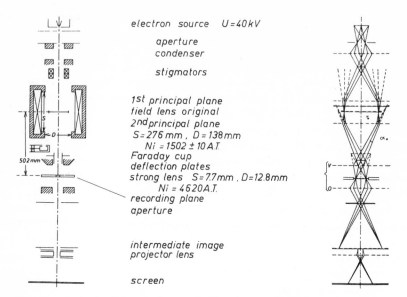

electron source   U = 40 kV

aperture
condenser

stigmators

1st principal plane
field lens original
2nd principal plane
   S = 276 mm , D = 138 mm
     Ni = 1502 ± 10 A.T.
Faraday cup
deflection plates
strong lens   S = 7.7 mm , D = 12.8 mm
     Ni = 4620 A.T.
recording plane
aperture

intermediate image
projector lens

screen

502 mm

FIG. 15. A demagnifying electron projection system with reduced aberrations, containing a long magnetic lens and a short strong lens.

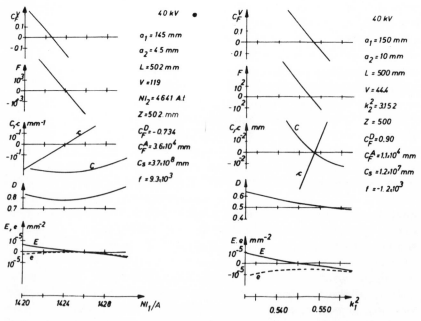

FIG. 16. Characteristics and aberration coefficients for two-lens demagnifying systems as a function of NI_1, the excitation of the long lens (left) or as a function of k_1^2 (right; the bell-shaped model is used for this example). The half-widths of the lens fields are denoted by a_1 and a_2 and the strong lens is labeled by the suffix 2. The isotropic and anisotropic chromatic field aberrations are denoted by C_F^V and C_F^D respectively and the axial chromatic aberration by C_F^A. For further details, see Koops (1973a).

4. *Special Lens Combinations*

The object of the work on aberration matrices of lens combinations, described in Section III,C, was to find lens combinations for which some particular coefficient or set of coefficients lies within certain bounds, and very flexible computer programs were written by Maclachlan to implement this (Machlachlan and Hawkes, 1970; Machlachlan, 1971). Independently, several other lens combinations have been devised that satisfy constraints that are particularly desirable for some specific application. We now draw attention to some examples.

The work of Koops on improving the resolution of electron beam systems used for microminiaturization shows that a great improvement can be achieved by replacing a single demagnifying lens by a suitably chosen doublet. The practical details of the basic instrument (Fig. 15) are described in (Koops, 1972a). The aberrations are studied in a separate note (Koops, 1972b) and in two later papers (Koops, 1973a, b), in which the author shows that for a particular choice of the excitations of the two magnetic lenses, the coefficients of isotropic distortion, isotropic chromatic field aberration, isotropic coma, isotropic astigmatism, and anisotropic astigmatism all vanish; for the same excitations, the field curvature and anisotropic distortion coefficients pass through minima. The remaining coefficients—the spherical aberration, axial chromatic aberration, anisotropic coma, and anisotropic chromatic field aberration—are relatively insensitive to the excitation. The variation of the aberration coefficients shown in Fig. 16 illustrates this optimum situation. With this system, it was possible to obtain 2280 resolved lines per frame at a resolution of 100 nm. In an improved design (Koops and Bernhard, 1975), it was possible also to eliminate the anisotropic chromatic field aberration by using a rotation-free lens comination. A full calculation of the maximum number of lines per frame then showed that the system could be improved by using weaker lenses and lower demagnification, at the expense of lengthening the system. Figures 17 and 18 show the recommended system and the dominant aberration coefficients. With such systems, it is possible to attain 10,000 lines per frame with a resolution of 0.1 μm.

The other study of lens combinations that we examine here is concerned with reduction of the distortion in electron microscope projector systems. This subject has a long history (see Kynaston and Mulvey, 1963, for early papers, and the bibliographic appendix in Hawkes, 1980a), largely devoted to the radial or isotropic distortion. It is now known how to reduce the latter to a negligible level whereas little attention has been paid to the spiral or anisotropic distortion. The reasons why this aberration has proved resistant to attempts to eliminate it are discussed very

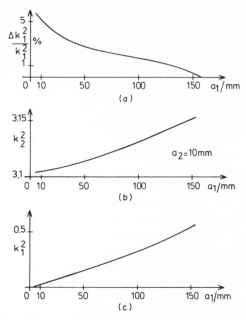

FIG. 17.   Further results on low-aberration electron projection systems. (a) The relative range, $\Delta k_1^2 / k_1^2$, within which the aberration coefficients E, C, c, F, and C_F^v pass through zero, while e and D are minimal. (b) and (c) The values of k_2^2 and k_1^2 for which seven aberration coefficients vanish as functions of the half-width a_1.

clearly by Marai and Mulvey (1977): the principal reason is that magnetic lenses of traditional design cannot be placed close enough together. In the past few years, however, there has been a quiet revolution in ideas concerning magnetic lens design, largely due to the various highly original proposals of Mulvey for exploiting modern technological developments, particularly in the design of highly stabilized power supplies. Mulvey has pointed out that the traditional bulky magnetic lens occupying considerable column space could often be replaced to great advantage by a flatter design, operating at a higher current density. These ideas have important repercussions on the design of many electron optical devices, though a certain resistance, or hesitancy at least, on the part of designers accustomed to the traditional type of lens still remains to be overcome. An example is the subject of this paragraph, the spiral distortion, which can indeed be compensated if single pole piece lenses are adopted (Fig. 19). Experimental verification of this is described by Lambrakis et al. (1977) and Elkamali and Mulvey (1980). A practical application of these lenses in field emission gun design is to be found in Cleaver (1978–1979, 1980).

The properties of rotation-free magnetic doublets have been explored by Juma and Mulvey (1974, 1975, 1978); such doublets have also been an-

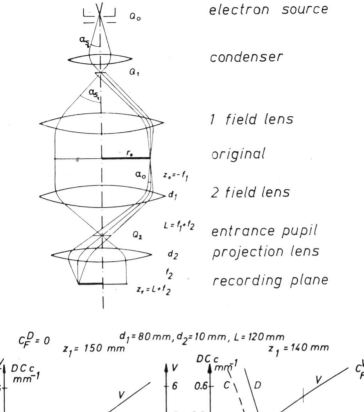

FIG. 18.   An electron projection system containing two weak magnetic lenses (Koops and Bernhard, 1975). (a) Lens system. (b) The variation of the principal aberration coefficients with the position of the master or template, z_0; V denotes the demagnification. (Figures 15–18 courtesy of Drs. H. Koops and W. Bernhard and the American Vacuum Society.)

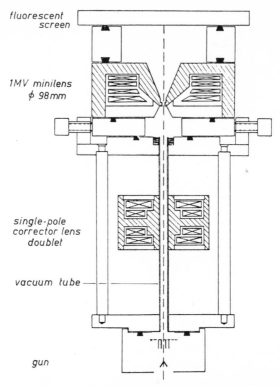

FIG. 19. Arrangement for correcting spiral (anisotropic) distortion. The single-pole corrector lens is very strongly excited and its spiral distortion cancels that of the 1-MV mini-lens. (Courtesy of E. Lambrakis, F. Z. Marai, and T. Mulvey and the Institute of Physics.)

analyzed in great detail by Baba *et al.* (1978) and Baba and Kanaya (1979), using the field model

$$H(z) = \pm \frac{H_0 C |z/a|^{m-1}}{1 + |z/a|^{2m}} \tag{132}$$

in which the plus sign corresponds to $z \geq 0$, the minus sign to $z \leq 0$; this model reduces to that used by Lenz (1956a) if we set $m = 2$.

Mulvey's work on unconventional magnetic lens design has recently been surveyed (Mulvey, 1980), and we shall therefore not describe it further here. We wish to stress nevertheless that future generations of electron microscopes and related devices are likely to be very profoundly affected once Mulvey's new designs become incorporated into commercial instruments. We take this opportunity of mentioning another way of reducing the bulk of magnetic lenses, of particular interest at high voltage. By using an anisotropic material for the yoke, a high flux density can be maintained everywhere inside it, so that no superfluous metal is employed (Balladore and Murillo, 1977; Balladore et al., 1977; Murillo, 1978).

B. Aberration Correction

Although the feeling that computer image processing has as good a chance of producing better electron images as the introduction of complicated correcting devices (see Section V) is gaining ground, a number of interesting studies, mostly concerned with the reduction of spherical and chromatic aberration, have been published since the last full survey of this topic appeared (Septier, 1966). In the present section, we draw attention to a number of studies of the various methods of combating spherical and chromatic aberration; a concerted long-term attempt to produce a highly corrected microscope is considered in Section IV,C.

We recall that spherical and/or chromatic aberration can in principle be eliminated by abandoning rotational symmetry (quadrupoles and octopoles), by introducing charged foils or controlled space charge, by employing catadioptric systems (mirrors and lenses in combination) or by incorporating high-frequency fields (microwave cavity lenses). We briefly consider each of these in turn.

1. Foil Lenses and Space Charge

Despite the danger that the insertion of a foil or free charge distribution into the path of the beam may create problems comparable with those the corrector is intended to obviate, work has continued on these methods of correcting spherical aberration. Indeed, they have been supplemented by a method in which current flows in a superconductor placed in the path of the electron beam.

Before examining these various studies separately, we recall an attempt by Le Poole (1972) to correct spherical aberration by injecting slow electrons from a conventional gun at about 30° to the axis of a long coil magnetic lens; these slow electrons then spiral down the field, creating a supposedly beneficial space charge potential. For reasons that need not concern us here, unexpected drawbacks were encountered and Le Poole (1972) concluded, "Careful evaluation of all results obtained throws grave doubts on their usefulness but some very useful by-products were obtained by these investigations" (p. 130). This melancholy remark could well form the epigraph to most (though happily not all) practical attempts to correct spherical aberration.

The correction of spherical aberration by means of thin foils or gauzes has been studied by several groups, in Holland, Germany, Japan, and the United States and in an early paper by Seman (1952). We now give a succinct summary of the results obtained.

Foil lenses, in which the opening in the central electrode of an electrostatic lens is covered with a thin foil, are notoriously difficult to use in practice, mainly because of scattering in the foil, and the idea of replacing the foil by gauze is therefore tempting. The small holes in the gauze perturb the lens field (e.g., Verster, 1963), but, as the calculations and preliminary experimental results of Rus (1965) showed, this perturbation can be tolerated if the gauze lens is designed to have negative spherical aberration and is used to cancel the positive spherical aberration of a conventional lens. Barth (1967) demonstrated that the adverse effects of the holes in the gauze can be reduced by the use of several gauzes. All these attempts to develop foil or gauze lenses were made in the Technological University of Delft in the Laboratory of Le Poole, who, with Dekkers (Dekkers and Le Poole, 1968), then had the idea of using a superconducting coil carrying a persistent current. (This recalls an earlier proposal of Marton, 1967, in which a superconducting body is placed on the axis, which in turn reminds us of the correction scheme of Dungey and Hull, 1947). This idea was very thoroughly explored by Dekkers (1969), who found that the foil thickness necessary to carry sufficient persistent current for correction was probably excessive. Conversely, a superconducting zone plate, designed so that the persistent current improved the shape of the phase contrast transfer function in the open rings, seemed very promising. Figure 20 shows the calculated transfer function for the objective lens of a Philips EM 300 microscope ($C_s = 1.57$ mm, $f = 1.59$ mm), in the case of perfect coherence. The difficulties associated

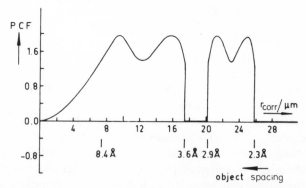

Fig. 20. The theoretical phase contrast transfer function (PCF) for a Philips EM 300 objective lens fitted with an annular corrector, assuming perfectly coherent illumination. (Courtesy of Dr. N. H. Dekkers.)

with both foils and zone plates can be avoided by using superconducting gauze. Dekkers' work concludes with an account of his measurements of the aberrations of a lens equipped with current-carrying superconducting gauze: for different currents, he was able to obtain overcorrection and undercorrection.

A careful study of the possibility of achieving spherical and chromatic correction by means of space charge or the introduction of charged foils or gauzes has also been made by Typke. In a preliminary study (Typke, (1968–1969), the theoretical possibilities of correction were analyzed by examining the form of the integral for C_s:

$$
\begin{aligned}
C_s = \frac{1}{16\Phi_0^{1/2}} \int_{z_0}^{z_i} &\left[\frac{5}{4} \left(\frac{\Phi''}{\Phi} + \frac{\Phi' h'}{\Phi h} - \frac{\Phi'^2}{\Phi^2} \right)^2 + \frac{\Phi'^2}{\Phi^2} \left(\frac{h'}{h} + \frac{7\Phi'}{8\Phi} \right)^2 + \frac{1}{64} \frac{\Phi'^4}{\Phi^4} \right. \\
&+ \frac{2\eta^2}{\Phi} \left(B' + B \frac{h'}{h} - \frac{5}{4} B \frac{\Phi'}{\Phi} \right)^2 + \frac{2\eta^2 B^2}{\Phi} \left(\frac{h'}{h} + \frac{\Phi'}{4\Phi} \right)^2 \\
&+ \frac{\eta^4 B^4}{\Phi^2} + \frac{\eta^2 B^2 \Phi'^2}{8\Phi^3} - \frac{\rho_2}{2\epsilon_0 \Phi} + \frac{\rho_0}{\epsilon_0 \Phi} \left(\frac{9}{4} \frac{\Phi''}{\Phi} + \frac{\rho_0}{\epsilon_0 \Phi} - \frac{\Phi'^2}{16\Phi^2} + \frac{5\Phi' h'}{\Phi h} \right. \\
&\left. \left. + 4 \frac{h'^2}{h^2} + \frac{2\eta^2 B^2}{\Phi} \right) \right] \Phi^{1/2} h^4 \, dz
\end{aligned}
\tag{133}
$$

The first group of terms, not containing ρ, form Scherzer's positive-definitive expression for C_s in the absence of charge, while the remaining terms, involving ρ_2 and ρ_0, are the additional terms due to charge. The meaning of these terms may be seen from the general potential expansion

$$
\phi(r, z) = \Phi(z) - \frac{1}{4} r^2 \{\Phi'' + \rho_0(z)/\epsilon_0\}
$$

$$
+ \frac{1}{64} r^4 \left\{ \Phi'''' + \frac{\rho_0''(z) + \rho_2(z)}{\epsilon_0} \right\} - \cdots
\tag{134a}
$$

and

$$
\rho(r, z) = \rho_0(z) - \tfrac{1}{4} r^2 \rho_2(z) + \cdots
\tag{134b}
$$

Typke discusses in some detail the suitability of the terms in ρ_0 and ρ_2 for canceling C_s without converting the overall system into a diverging lens. In a later paper (Typke, 1972a), the design of a spherically corrected magnetic lens containing a gauze (Fig. 21) is analyzed in detail; some results are shown in Figs. 22 and 23. Finally (Typke, 1972b), the possibility of simultaneous chromatic and spherical correction was explored but unfortunately, the conclusions drawn proved overoptimistic (Typke, 1976).

A paper by Hoch et al. (1976) supplements this work, in that the pri-

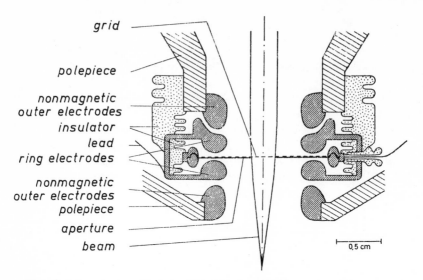

FIG. 21.   A corrector grid situated between the pole pieces of a magnetic lens.

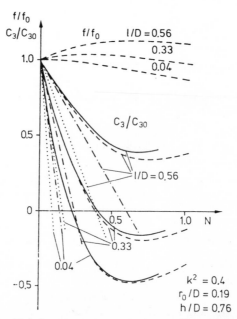

FIG. 22.   The focal length and spherical aberration coefficient of the lens of Fig. 21 as functions of the grid voltage $N\Phi_\infty$, where Φ_∞ denotes the accelerating voltage. The curves are normalized with respect to the values at $N = 0$ and correspond to three values of l/D, for $k^2 = 0.4$, $\sigma_0/D = 0.19$, and $h/D = 0.76$; r_0 denotes distance of the field-free point on the foil from the axis, h the half-width of the magnetic field, l the width of the ring electrodes, and D their bore radius.

112

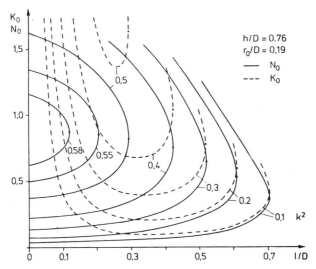

Fig. 23. The variation of the correction voltage on the grid, $N_0\Phi_\infty$, and the voltage on the ring electrodes, $K_0\Phi_\infty$, with ring width l for $r_0 = 0.19D$ and $h = 0.76D$ and various values of k^2 (cf. Fig. 21). (Figures 21–23 courtesy of Dr. D. Typke and Wissenschaftliche Verlagsgesellschaft.)

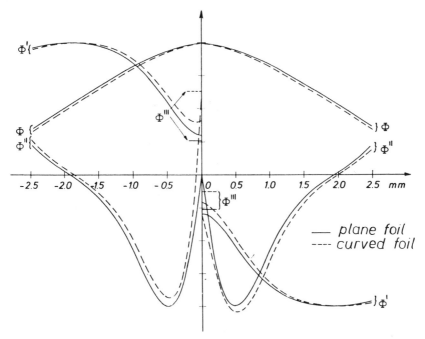

Fig. 24. Correction of spherical and chromatic aberration by means of charged foils. Distribution of potential Φ and its first and second derivatives in the neighborhood of the foil.

113

mary spherical aberration and paraxial chromatic aberration of electro-static foil lenses with curved foils are calculated numerically. Figure 24 shows the axial potential distribution and its first three derivatives for plane and curved foils in the vicinity of the latter for a foil radius of curvature of -1.875 mm; the bore diameter of the inner electrode is 0.5 mm and of the outer electrodes of the symmetric einzel lens studied, 1 mm. The center of the outer electrodes is 4 mm from the symmetry plane. Some results are reproduced in Fig. 25a and b from which we conclude that there is an optimum voltage ratio, for which C_s vanishes, for each value of the radius of curvature of the foil. Since it it usually not possible to choose the radius, which is determined by the electrical and mechanical forces acting on the foil in any given case, these results allow us to estimate the sensitivity of the device when used for aberration correction.

During much the same period, Maruse, Ichihashi, and others in the University of Nagoya were also studying spherical correction by means of thin conducting foils. In their first paper (Maruse *et al.*, 1970a,b), they suggest that the undesirable effects of scattering in the foil could be avoided by using the specimen itself or the supporting grid as the corrector and they present measurements of C_s for a hemispherical foil and for a plane foil close to a small aperture, in conjunction with a magnetic lens. Much more detailed results, indicating that the spherical aberration of the magnetic lens can be successfully compensated over a wide angle, were presented by Ichihashi and Maruse (1971). The further theoretical studies of Ichihashi and Maruse (1973) have been extended by Hibino and Maruse (1976), who discuss in detail the configuration of Fig. 26. They found that the third- and fifth-order spherical aberrations were not corrected at the same foil potential with the result that compensation of the third-order aberration of the magnetic lens slightly increased its fifth-order aberration. The latter is however negligible up to angles of 25 mrad. Furthermore, the residual fifth-order spherical aberration varies with the geometry, and the authors believe that it should be possible to find a configuration for which the angle can be appreciably increased. Conversely, the chromatic aberration is slightly worse with the foil corrector in action. The simultaneous correction of third- and fifth-order spherical aberration is shown by Hibino *et al.* (1977), who contemplated using a foil corrector in a 400 kV STEM. Figure 27 shows the variation of the fifth-order aberration (C_5) at the foil voltage for which C_s is effectively canceled. For subsequent developments, see Hibino *et al.* (1978).

We now turn to the work of Thomson (Thomson and Jacobsen, 1971; Thomson, 1973), who estimated the properties of a double foil corrector, and of Munro and Wittels (1977), who derived formulas for all the third-order aberration coefficients of electrostatic and magnetic lenses

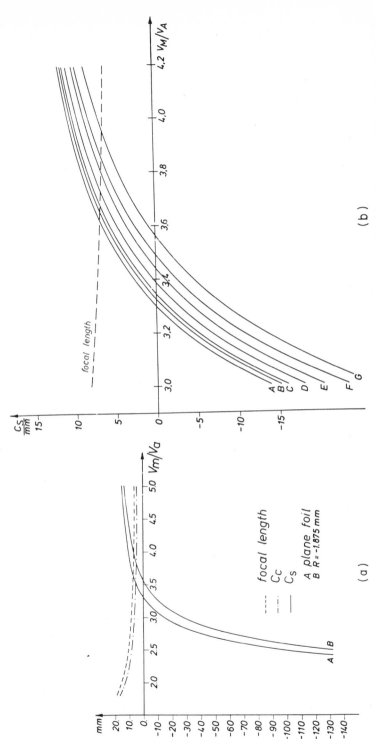

Fig. 25. Correction of spherical and chromatic aberration by means of charged foils. (a) Variation of focal length, f, C_s, and C_c with the voltage ratio V_m/V_a, where V_m and V_a denote the potentials on the central and outer electrodes. (b) Variation of C_s with V_m/V_a for various radii of curvature, R, of the foil (A) Plane foil; (B) $R = 6.5$ mm; (C) $R = -6.5$ mm; (D) $R = 2.5$ mm; (E) $R = -2.5$ mm; (F) $R = 1.875$ mm; (G) $R = -1.875$ mm. (Figures 24 and 25 courtesy of Drs. H. Hoch, E. Kasper, and D. Kern and Wissenschaftliche Verlagsgesellschaft.)

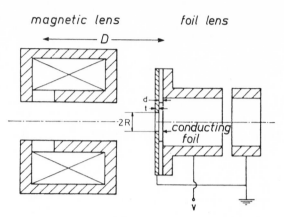

FIG. 26. The foil lens corrector studied by Hibino and Maruse (1976). In the experimental lens, $2R = 0.5$ mm and $t = 0.1$ mm.

containing charged foils. The object of much of this work was the design of a new device, a high-resolution Auger electron microscope, in which a foil lens is used to correct spherical aberration after acceleration of the slow Auger electrons (King *et al.*, 1978). The electron optics of this instrument contains many features of interest as Fig. 28 shows. In particular, an electrostatic lens plays a dual role, focusing the exciting electrons, for which it acts as a lens and reflecting the Auger electrons emitted, for which it acts as a mirror. Figure 29a shows the mirror-objective and foil

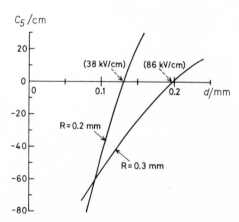

FIG. 27. Variation of the coefficient of fifth-order spherical aberration with spacing between aperture and foil (d) for two values of R at the foil lens voltage for which third-order spherical aberration is canceled. (Figures 26 and 27 courtesy of Dr. M. Hibino and S. Maruse and the Japanese Society of Electron Microscopy.)

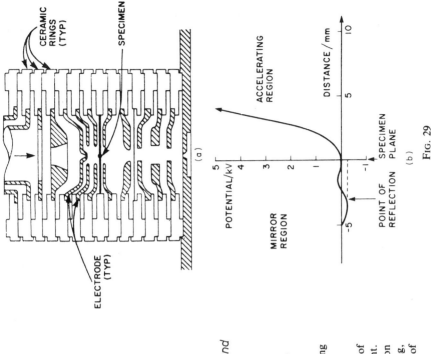

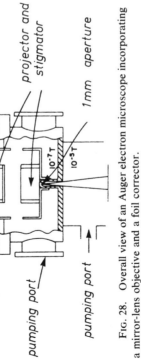

FIG. 28. Overall view of an Auger electron microscope incorporating a mirror-lens objective and a foil corrector.

FIG. 29. Details of the objective region of the Auger microscope of Fig. 28. (a) Mirror-lens objective accelerating structure and foil element. (b) Typical axial potential distribution corresponding to an earlier version of the system shown above. (Figures 28 and 29 courtesy of Drs. J. G. King, J. W. Coleman, and E. M. Jacobsen and the New York Academy of Sciences.)

lens unit and Fig. 29b the axial potential distribution in the specimen region. Energy analysis, in addition to that provided rather crudely by the mirror, is effected with the aid of a Castaing–Henry analyzer (see Castaing *et al.*, 1967, or the review by Metherell, 1971, or Hawkes, 1972 for an elementary account or the chapter by Ballu in Part B of this supplement); the energy window of the mirror is typically 50 eV wide for electron energies up to 0.7 keV, while the Castaing–Henry analyzer combines a spatial resolution said to be better that 1 Å with an energy resolution of the order of 0.1 eV. Returning to the subject of this section, the foil will consist of a carbon film, some 10 nm thick; its role is of course to correct the spherical aberration of the accelerating lens, which is high since the collection angle of the mirror objective is extremely large.

Finally, we mention the recent work of van der Merwe (1978a,b,c, 1979), who has calculated the potential distribution in a variety of foil lenses, in preparation for further studies on the optical properties of both single-foil and double-foil geometries.

2. *High-Frequency Lenses*

We have already mentioned the role of microwave cavities as electron lenses in Section II,A, where we were concerned with methods of solving the equations of motion and computing cardinal elements and aberration coefficients characteristic of such lenses. We recall that such lenses were, however, first discussed in the context of chromatic and spherical aberration correction, and it is this aspect of their behavior that we consider here. The original reasons for considering microwave cavities were simple: first, Scherzer's theorem does not apply to them; furthermore, it seems reasonable to suppose that, if a burst of electrons is allowed to fall on a field, the intensity of which decreases with time, the later arrivals will be focused less. These later arrivals will be the peripheral electrons if the burst sets out from the neighbourhood of the axis, so that spherical aberration, which causes peripheral electrons to be focused more strongly than axial electrons, can apparently be counteracted. If, however, we estimate the orders of magnitude involved, we find that for electrons of some tens of kilovolts, frequencies in the gigahertz range are necessary. The transit time of the electrons through the field is then comparable with the period (less than a nanosecond) of the microwave field. This in turn vitiates our simple picture of the correction, but it is intuitively reasonable to expect that electrons falling on a microwave cavity excited at high frequency will experience a converging or diverging lens action, depending on the phase of the microwave field when the electrons arrive, and there is no reason to suppose that C_s will not likewise change sign; frequencies of a few gigahertz may be expected to be suitable.

Considerable experimental and theoretical work has been performed on the electron optical properties of small microwave cavities, particularly in the past decade. Four distinct lines of research have emerged: a series of attempts by Vaidya and colleagues to correct the spherical aberration of a magnetic lens by means of a "synklysmotron," a combination of two cavities, one acting as a buncher, the other as a corrector (Vaidya and Hawkes, 1970; Vaidya, 1972, 1975a,b; Garg and Vaidya, 1974; Vaidya and Garg, 1974; Pandey and Vaidya, 1976, 1977, 1978); derivation of formulas for many of the aberration coefficients by Matsuda and Ura (1974a,b,c); a thorough study of the fields inside reentrant cavities and of their paraxial properties by Oldfield (1971, 1973a,b, 1974, 1976); and a proposal for a high-voltage electron microscope incorporating high-frequency lenses and superconducting lenses (Dietrich *et al.*, 1975; Passow, 1976a,b,c; Dietrich, 1976, 1978). The last proposal is a natural development of the experimental attempts of Watanabe *et al.* (1974) and Anazawa *et al.* (1975) to couple a pulsed field-emission gun to a linear accelerator for microscopy in the 5–10-MV range.

The progress made by Vaidya and colleagues in the design of synklysmotron lenses for various applications—electrostatic or magnetic objective and probe-forming lenses—has culminated in the development of a corrected high-voltage system to be placed between the final condenser and the objective of a 5-MV microscope (Pandey and Vaidya, 1977). The geometry is shown schematically in Fig. 30; operating at a frequency of about 38.5 GHz, Pandey and Vaidya found that the spherical aberration coefficient of the corrector remained at a suitable negative value for a phase variation of some 20° and that the other factors involved were also favorable in this range. The authors estimate that such a corrector could improve the resolution of a 5-MV microscope to better than 0.1 nm, if C_s is the only limitation.

In the papers of Matsuda and Ura (1974a,b,c), lists of aberration coefficients are given for the primary and secondary aberrations of microwave cavity lenses. The present author is at present examining these further, with the aid of the computer algebra language discussed in Section III,D (Hawkes, 1977a,c), in the hope that simpler forms will emerge than those obtained by Matsura and Ura (who incidentally used the trajectory method, whereas the new calculations will be based on the eikonal technique). The later work of these authors in the field of microwave electron optics is concerned with very fast deflection and is not considered here. In this connection, we draw attention to the papers of Plows and Nixon (1968), Robinson (1971), Ura and Morimura (1973), Gopinath and Hill

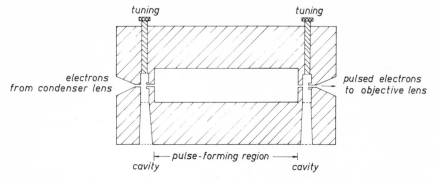

FIG. 30.   Design for a 5-MV synklysmotron lens. The bore diameter is 1.076 mm, the gap width 2.69 mm, and the pulse-forming region 150 mm long. The operating frequency is between 38 and 39 GHz. (Courtesy of Dr. N. C. Vaidya and the Japanese Society of Electron Microscopy.)

(1973a,b, 1974, 1977), Hill and Gopinath (1974), Oldfield (1976), Hosokawa *et al.*, (1977a,b), Fujioka *et al.* (1978), Ura *et al.* (1978), Gopinathan and Gopinath (1978), and Feuerbaum and Otto (1978); see too the surveys by Menzel and Kubalek (1978, 1979).

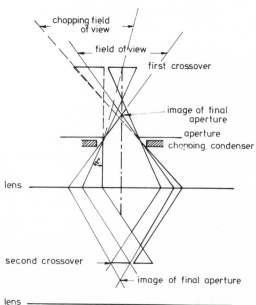

FIG. 31.   A versatile electron beam chopping system with an additional lens; the chopping structure is situated between the electron gun and this lens. (Courtesy of Drs. E. Menzel and E. Kubalek and Verlag R. A. Remy, Münster.)

Oldfield has made an extremely full study of the paraxial properties of microwave cavities, based on full calculation of the field in the cavity by means of an iterated relaxation technique. The variation of the space and time cardinal elements is discussed at length and illustrated with numerous graphs and tables. These show clearly, in the frequency range considered (around 3 GHz), the conditions in which cavity lenses will be divergent and convergent and the sensitivity of the various characteristics to changes. A rotationally symmetric chopper capable of providing picosecond pulses was designed on the basis of this (Oldfield, 1976). The beam choppers at present in use have been criticized by Menzel and Kubalek (1978) on the grounds that each is only suitable for its own particular application. A more versatile system is proposed (Fig. 31) and its performance analysed.

Finally, we turn to the very ambitious project described by Dietrich *et al.* (1975) and further discussed by Passow (1976a,b,c, 1977), Dietrich (1978), and Strojnik and Passow (1978a,b). The suggestion here is that the technology already developed in the field of particle accelerators (e.g., Hartwig and Passow, 1975) should be combined with recent work on superconducting lens design (Dietrich, 1976, 1978; Bonjour, 1976; Hawkes and Valdrè, 1977) to produce a very high-voltage pulsed-beam electron microscope. (The paper by Strojnik and Passow, 1978a, considers what conventional lenses for such a microsope would be like.) The overall preliminary design is shown in Fig. 32. This projected instrument is discussed briefly in the context of other new or avant-garde machines by Riecke (1977), Herrmann (1978), and Cosslett (1978a); it is, however, really too early to comment usefully on its potential performance, except to observe that the restrictive relation between geometry, microwave frequency, and accelerating voltage is likely to be a major inconvenience, unless some way of circumventing it emerges.

3. *Quadrupoles and Octopoles*

For many years, and especially during the 1960s when many research groups were concerned with these components, it was widely believed that combinations of quadrupoles and octopoles would soon solve the aberration problems of electron microscopes. Although a few attempts are still being made to improve objectives or probe-forming lenses with correctors of this type, there has been a marked swing away from this method in favor of computer image processing, perhaps because none of the systems that emerged from so much effort managed to convince the manufacturers of its commercial viability. Nevertheless, there is no doubt that some reduction of the spherical and chromatic aberration, to widen

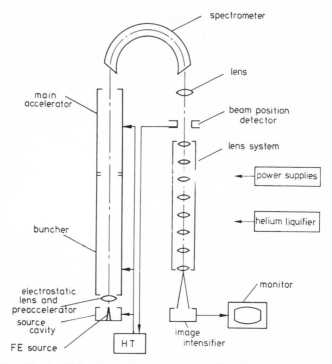

FIG. 32.   The ultrahigh-voltage microscope proposed by Dietrich *et al.* (1975), incorporating a microwave accelerator and superconducting lenses. (Courtesy of Drs. I. Dietrich, K.-H. Herrmann, and C. Passow and Wissenschaftliche Verlagsgesellschaft.)

the first zone of the phase contrast transfer function, would be very welcome indeed for high-resolution work. The case for preferring quadrupole–octople correctors to foils or gauzes, in which the electrons are scattered, or high-frequency devices, which have chromatic problems and entail jettisoning much of the beam, is a strong one, and hope of building a practically convenient and optically successful unit has not therefore been abandoned. The most elaborate attempt at correction is being made in the Technische Hochschule of Darmstadt: this is dealt with separately in Section IV,C. Here we mention some of the other attempts to use quadrupole correction that have appeared since the survey by Hawkes (1970f) and also indicate some of the principal trends in quadrupole studies in the 1970s.

    A determined effort has been made for several years in the Laboratory of A. V. Crewe in the University of Chicago to design and build a quadrupole quadruplet corrector for the probe-forming lens of a STEM, operating at 100 kV. The project was first announced by Crewe *et al.*

(1968), and a computer study of the aberrations was made by Thomson (1972). The configuration chosen, an antisymmetric quadrupole quadruplet with an octople between each quadrupole, was excited in the telescopic mode (Fig. 33a); the geometry is illustrated in Fig. 33b. The corrector is placed above the objective scanning coils (Fig. 34) so that, of the geometrical aberrations, only the spherical aberration is important. Progress with this corrector is described by Beck and Crewe (1974, 1976), and the latest results are to be found in Beck (1977, p. 90): "Recently a number of experiments have been carried out on a STEM which included a multipole corrector for primary spherical aberration. The results of these experiments indicate that the correction of primary spherical aberration with magnetic multipoles is beset with very serious difficulties related to hysteresis." Despite the care given to the choice of pole-piece material (Permendur 4 V) and the inclusion of trim coils, it proved impossible to center and align the corrector satisfactorily, even through the mechanical precision was extremely high, typically 2 μm. In spite of this disappointing outcome of so much effort, Crewe's group has not "lost hope because we found numerous reasons why the system would not work other than the correction itself" (Crewe, 1978, p. 204), and a new design is planned (Crewe, 1978–1979). An ingenious proposal has been made by Beck (1979), who noticed that one of the secondary aberrations of a pair of sextupoles is effectively of the same type as the spherical aberration of round lenses (a point that is mentioned in passing by Hawkes, 1965); since the coefficient can be negative for sextupoles, Beck suggests using a sextupole doublet to cancel C_s. A much fuller discussion is given by Crewe and Kopf (1980), and although it is not quite clear whether the lower order effects can be made to vanish satisfactorily, if this can indeed be achieved, the suggestion is a very attractive one.

The Leningrad group led by S. Ya. Yavor has continued to contribute to many aspects of quadrupole studies (earlier work is reviewed by Yavor, 1968, and Hawkes, 1970f). Space does not permit an account of all their work and we therefore draw attention to a theoretical study of the benefit to be gained by correcting the spherical aberration of the probeforming lenses in various commercial and experimental instruments (Lyubchik and Fishkova, 1974a,b), taking the fifth-order spherical aberration into account (Lyubchik et al., 1971; Yavor et al., 1972) and to various original quadrupole geometries. The five-electrode lens (Fig. 35) has the advantage that a round lens field, a quadrupole field and an octopole field can all be created easily in a single component; its properties are studied in (Ovsyannikova et al., 1972; Petrov et al., 1972; Petrov et al., 1974; Petrov and Shpak, 1975). It is a natural evolution of earlier work on three-electrode lenses consisting of two arcs inside a cylinder and quadru-

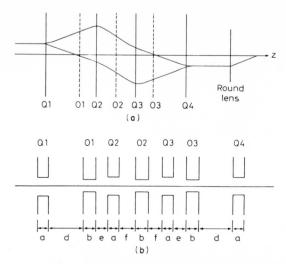

FIG. 33.   A quadrupole–octopole corrector unit proposed for use in a STEM. (a) Paraxial ray diagram showing the trajectories in the two principal sections. (b) Details of the geometry. $a = 7.4$ mm, $b = 8.4$ mm, $d = 24.2$ mm, $e = 8.1$ mm, $f = 10.8$ mm. The quadrupole bore radius is 3 mm and that of the octopoles, 2 mm. The total length of the corrector is 141 mm. (Courtesy of Dr. M. G. R. Thomson and Wissenschaftliche Verlagsgesellschaft.)

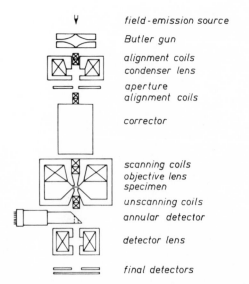

FIG. 34.   Diagram showing where the corrector of Fig. 33 is incorporated in a STEM. (Courtesy of Drs. V. Beck and A. V. Crewe and the Electron Microscopy Society of America.)

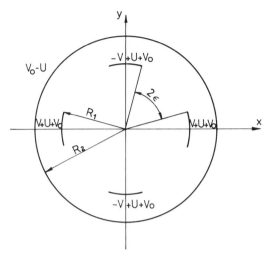

FIG. 35.   The geometry and excitation of a five-electrode multipole lens, capable of producing round, quadrupole, and octopole components. (After Petrov *et al.* 1972.)

poles with electrodes in the form of concave arcs (e.g., Baranova *et al.*, 1972; Koltay *et al.*, 1972; Bosi, 1974).

More recently, Petrov, Yavor, and Baranova have studied three-electrode einzel lenses, with rectangular openings instead of round holes in the plane electrodes (Petrov, 1976; Petrov and Yavor, 1976; Petrov *et al.*, 1978; Baranova *et al.*, 1978). These are rather easy to build and align, but their main interest resides in the behavior of their spherical aberration. Unless the rectangles reduce to squares, these "crossed lenses" (Fig. 36a) have planes of electrical and geometrical symmetry but not planes of antisymmetry midway between these.* They may be pictured as a superposition of an electrostatic einzel lens, quadrupoles, and octopoles (and of course higher-order multipoles); the quadrupole components form a symmetric triplet as do the octopoles. It is therefore not surprising that a combination of aperture shapes and excitation can be found for which the aperture aberration coefficient in (angle)^3 in the converging plane of the crossed lens vanishes. This very interesting result was demonstrated by Petrov and Yavor (1975) and further evidence is presented by Petrov and Yavor (1976). It is natural to enquire whether two such crossed lenses can be combined to achieve simultaneous cancellation of two of the aperture aberration coefficients. Such a combination (Petrov, 1977) could be con-

---

* In another extreme case, the crossed lens reduces to a two-dimensional einzel lens or cylindrical lens; working curves for a number of such lenses have been published by Afanas'ev *et al.* (1975a,b).

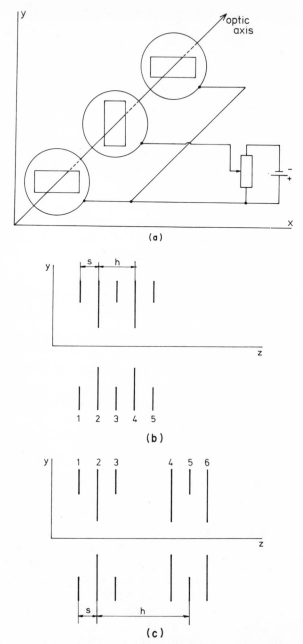

FIG. 36. Crossed lenses. (a) A crossed lens, consisting of three electrodes, excited as in an einzel lens but containing rectangular rather than round openings. (b) A five-electrode crossed-lens doublet; the central electrode is common to both elements of the doublet. (c) A six-electrode crossed-lens doublet; the final electrode of the first lens no longer coincides with the first electrode of the second lens.

structed using five electrodes, in which case the central electrode is common to both members, or six electrodes (Fig. 36b,c). The measurements of Petrov *et al.* (1978), also mentioned in Baranova *et al.* (1978), indicate that the aperture aberration coefficient in (angle)^3 in the converging–diverging plane of a stigmatic (six-electrode) doublet vanishes for certain values of the parameters, but it proved impossible in those experiments to measure the corresponding coefficient in the diverging–converging plane. Numerical calculations of the optical properties of crossed lenses are described by Afanas'ev *et al.* (1979), using the method of Gritsyuk and Lachashvili (1976) for the potential determination.

In view of the large number of geometries and voltage ratios that can be imagined for these lenses—the openings could of course have more complicated shapes such as slits with curved ends, for example—it seems very reasonable to hope that configurations with low aberrations will be found.

Various other topics in multipole theory have been examined, including the deliberate distortion of particle beams (Yavor, 1971; Baranova and Yavor, 1972), for example, by means of sextupoles (Baranova, 1972). Szilágyi (1978b) has pointed out that it is possible to design a quadrupole lens that is "ideal," in the sense that its potential expansion contains only a term in 2θ (where θ denotes the angle in a cylindrical polar coordinate system): we have only to divide a cylinder into arcs, without of course destroying the quadrupole symmetry, and excite these in such a way that higher harmonics in θ are eliminated. Some further work has appeared on quadrupole aberration coefficients, evaluated for the rectangular and bell-shaped models (Szilágyi *et al.*, 1973, 1974). Quadrupole triplet properties are discussed by Ueda *et al.* (1969, 1970, 1971, 1973) and Ueda and Nagami (1975). Wollnik (1972) comments on the general question of correction by multipoles. Amboss and Jennings (1970) examine the aberrations caused by small asymmetries in air–cored solenoids (see Hawkes, 1966 and 1970f, for references to earlier work on parasitic aberrations).

A very old idea of Klemperer (1953, patented 1942–1945; see Hawkes, 1966) has been revived by Andreev, Glikman, and Iskakova, who have explored the properties of astigmatic two-tube electrostatic lenses.* These are lenses consisting of two coaxial rotationally symmetric tubes, separated by a narrow gap that is not perpendicular to the common axis of the tubes but nevertheless leaves the system with quadrupole symmetry. In the case studied by Andreev *et al.*, the line of separation is defined by a third cylinder, or rather cylindrical arc, the axis of which is perpendicular

---

* We note that a considerable amount of information on the paraxial properties and aberrations of multielectrode tubular lenses has been published by Glikman *et al.* (1973a,d), Nurmanov (1975), and Glikman and Nurmanov (1976).

to the lens axis.* The curve of intersection of this cylinder (of radius R', say) and a cylinder (radius R) centered on the optic axis defines the gap. The paraxial properties of such lenses are studied by Andreev *et al.* (1975a) for various values of R'/R and voltage ratio; the aberrations are examined by Andreev *et al.* (1975b). In two later papers, Glikman and Is- kakova (1976a,b) tabulate parameters characterizing the aperture aberra- tion coefficients again for a range of geometries and excitations; these parameters, which are similar to those described in Section III,A, are independent of object position.

Finally, we draw attention to two studies of beam emittance in quadru- pole systems. Shpak (1978) considers the distortions of the emittance caused by the quadrupole aberrations. In an interesting analysis of the growth of the emittance of a beam guided by a quadrupole system, Tanguy and Durand (1978) have shown that, if the mean-square emit- tances are examined, rather than the emittances themselves (Lapostolle, 1970), the variations are frequently determined only by the elements of the paraxial transfer matrices and are independent of the aberration coef- ficients; whether or not this is the case depends on the initial particle den- sity distribution in phase space. The same authors have also given explicit formulas for the aberration coefficients between nonconjugate planes, using the rectangular model (Durand and Tanguy, 1977).

4. *Mirror Correctors*

Although the possibility of using electron optical systems containing mirrors to reduce spherical aberration has not been entirely neglected (see Zworykin *et al.*, 1945, for example, for some early proposals, recapitu- lated in Septier, 1966), it has received very much less attention than the various other correction techniques. One new design has been proposed, however, in which both magnetic and electrostatic fields are used, and which appears to avoid the problems that rendered the earlier proposals impractical (Kasper, 1968–1969).

It is known that electrostatic mirrors producing real images generally have large spherical and chromatic aberration coefficients, which is unsat- isfactory if the mirror is used alone, even though these coefficients are negative. The situation can, however, be quite different if the mirror field is superimposed on a magnetic field (in such a way that rotational sym- metry is maintained, of course).

---

* The original cylinder may be pictured as being cut by an apple corer, except that the cutting edge is only semicircular.

In particular, let us consider (following Kasper) an electrostatic potential $\Phi(r, z)$,

$$\Phi(r, z) = U + \tfrac{1}{2}Q(\tfrac{1}{2}r^2 + a^2 - z^2) \tag{135}$$

and a uniform magnetic field, $B_z = B$, the other components of which are zero. The origin of potential is chosen so that U denotes the accelerating voltage of the electrons incident on the mirror. On the axis, therefore, electrons will be reflected at the plane $z = (a^2 + 2U/Q)^{1/2}$. Writing

$$\omega_E = (eQ/m)^{1/2} = \eta(2Q)^{1/2}, \qquad \omega_M = eB/2m = \eta^2 B$$
$$\omega = (\omega_M^2 - \omega_E^2/2)^{1/2} \tag{136}$$

we have

$$u = u_0 \cos \omega t + (1/\omega)\dot{u}_0 \sin \omega t$$
$$z = a \cos \omega_E t + (1/\omega_E)\dot{z}_0 \sin \omega_E t \tag{137}$$

where

$$u = r \exp\{i(\phi - \phi_M)t\} = (x + iy) \exp(-i\omega_M t)$$

and the initial conditions are $u = u_0$, $\dot{u} = \dot{u}_0$, $z = a$, $\dot{z} = \dot{z}_0$ at $t = 0$; dots indicate differentiation with respect to t. In the paraxial approximation, $\dot{z}_0 = v = (2eU/m)^{1/2} = 2\eta U^{1/2}$.

All the electrons from some point $P_0(u_0, z_0)$ will be focused to a point $P_1(u_1, z_1)$, in the plane z_1 for which

$$z_1 = a \cos(\pi\omega_E/\omega) + (2U/Q)^{1/2} \sin(\pi\omega_E/\omega) \tag{138}$$

with $t_1 = \pi/\omega$ and $u_1 = -u_0$. The plane $z = a$ is thus focused with unit magnification, and image rotation χ,

$$\chi = \omega_M t_1 - \pi = \pi(\omega_M/\omega - 1) \tag{139}$$

Can we arrange that z_1 is also equal to a? From Eq. (138), we see that this will occur if

$$\sin\left(\frac{\pi\omega_E}{2\omega}\right) = \frac{1}{a}\left(\frac{2U}{Q}\right)^{1/2} \cos\left(\frac{\pi\omega_E}{2\omega}\right) \tag{140}$$

or

$$\cot\left(\frac{\pi\omega_E}{2\omega}\right) = a\left(\frac{Q}{2U}\right)^{1/2} \tag{141}$$

This is equivalent to Eq. (11) of Kasper (1968–1969). For this particular imaging condition, the only aberrations that deteriorate the image are spherical aberration, field curvature and axial chromatic aberration (both the magnification and the image rotation are independent of electron energy). Kasper finds that

$$C_s = C_c = - \frac{a}{1 + Qa^2/2U} \tag{142}$$

and since a and Q are positive, both C_s and C_c are negative; the fifth-order spherical aberration and the secondary axial chromatic aberration coefficients are both equal to $C_s/4$. A geometry that could be used in practice to achieve these imaging conditions is shown in Fig. 37.

In mirror systems, some arrangement must be made to separate the incident beam from the reflected beam: outside the objective area, a magnetic prism can be used but in the objective-mirror zone itself, where the incident beam, which traverses the specimen, must be separated from the reflected beam, which does not, Kasper proposes an ingenious novel solution. The principle is illustrated in Fig. 38. The axis of the lens preceding the objective is tilted slightly with respect to that of the latter, and so placed that the axis of the incident beam passes through the focus of the (magnetic) objective. Owing to the image rotation of this lens, the electrons reach the principal plane at a different azimuth (H in Fig. 38) after which they pass through the object and an image having unit magnification is then formed by the mirror; the object (O) is placed slightly off-axis and the mirror image will therefore be formed opposite to it, at O'. With proper adjustment, the image rotation will bring the point H' in the principal plane back to H (Fig. 38) and the returning electrons will follow the same path as the incident beam, having traversed the specimen only once, however. From the geometry of this arrangement, we see that the separation s between O and O' is related to the lens focal length f_L, the angle of tilt θ and the rotation χ_L by

$$s = 2f_L \theta \sin \chi_L \tag{143}$$

so that we must arrange that $\chi_L \approx \pi/2$.

The final step is to choose the magnification and the magnitudes of the aberration coefficients in such a way that both the chromatic and spherical aberration are compensated. Kasper shows that this is perfectly possible and concludes that such a system should pose no particular intrinsic problems: it is in principle capable of forming an image of very high resolution directly on the final screen; conversely, it will be extremely prone to parasitic aberrations, due to vibrations, ac magnetic fields, and similar disturbances. If these can be kept sufficiently small, there seems no reason why the system should not work, but, so far, it has not been tested experimentally.

A very different, electrostatic mirror system for which the aperture

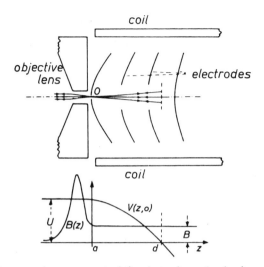

FIG. 37.   The general arrangement of the electrodes and pole pieces in mirror corrector of magnetic lens spherical aberration. (Top) pole piece, magnetic coil, and electrodes.
(Bottom) axial potential distribution and magnetic field. The object is situated at the point O,
where $z = a$, $r = 0$.

aberration can in principle be removed has been analyzed by Bimurzaev
(Bimurzaev *et al.*, 1976; Bimurzaev, 1976a,b,c); here two-dimensional
fields are used (so that the lenses and mirror in question are cylindrical as
opposed to rotationally symmetric, or "spherical"). The general appearance of the unit and typical trajectories are shown in Fig. 39; as shown in
Fig. 39a, the complete unit consists of three pairs of plane electrodes
forming a mirror (electrodes 2 and 3) and a lens (electrodes 2 and 1) and

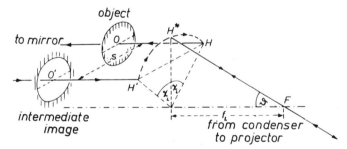

FIG. 38.   Separation of the incident beam from the returning beam in the corrected objective of Fig. 37. The rotation due to the coil magnetic field twists the incident beam away
from H^* to H, after which the beam traverses the object and is reflected by the mirror. An
intermediate image is formed (O') and the returning beam is twisted from H' back to H^*
after which it retraces its original path and enters the projector system. (Figures 37 and 38
courtesy of Dr. E. Kasper and Wissenschaftliche Verlagsgesellschaft.)

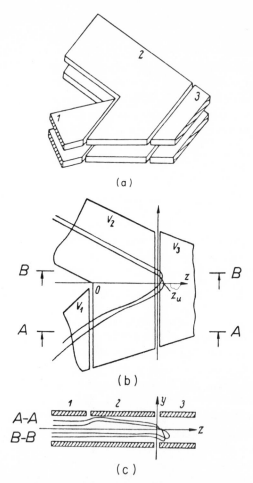

(a)

(b)

(c)

FIG. 39. A telescopic electrostatic system with mirror action for which spherical aberration can vanish. (a) Electrode geometry. (b) Typical trajectories projected onto the plane midway between the electrodes and parallel to them (the x–z plane). (c) Typical trajectories projected onto the plane perpendicular to the electrodes (the y–z plane). The trajectories correspond to the Sections A–A and B–B. (After Bimurzaev, 1976a.)

Bimurzaev plots various paraxial parameters and aberration coefficients as a function of voltage ratio. Such a system is intended for use in a mass or electron spectrometer, in order to improve resolution and luminosity.

C. The Darmstadt High-Resolution Project

The attainment of very high resolution has long preoccupied designers—and of course users—of electron optical instruments. At present, opinion is divided into two camps, one of which believes that it is possible to generate high-resolution images directly by building corrected microscopes, the other that the effort involved would be better spent on correcting images, optically or digitally, obtained with existing instruments; the latter already offer resolutions of the order of 0.2 nm, depending on the definition of resolution and on the mode of operation. It is only fair to add that most members of both groups expect that the ultimate resolutions will be obtained by a judicious combination of better instruments and computer image processing.

Those who are concerned with improved instrument design are themselves divided into two schools of thought, one advocating higher voltage, the other lower aberrations. Our concern here is with the latter, but we must stress that the need for higher-voltage operation (probably with some aberration correction) has also been argued most persuasively. The case is most clearly stated in the work of Riecke (1971, 1974). We note that most of the high-voltage microscopes built so far have been intended for increased penetration at moderate resolution, and neither their optics nor their mechanical construction is particularly well adapted to high-resolution operation; the latter is not necessarily excluded, (see, for example, Dorignac and Jouffrey, 1976) but cannot be regarded as a routine mode. Recently, however, high-voltage microscopes specifically conceived for high resolution have been built (Kobayashi *et al.*, 1974; Cosslett, 1977a,b, 1978a; Krivanek *et al.*, 1977; Horiuchi *et al.*, 1977a,b, 1978; Cleaver, 1977a,b; Catto, 1977; Nixon *et al.*, 1977, 1978; further references are to be found in the Proceedings of the various conferences devoted to high-voltage electron microscopy and in the review by Herrmann, 1978), and the Cambridge instrument has already (autumn, 1977) produced images of better resolution than any commercial high-voltage microscope.* Nevertheless, the final stages in the approach to the ultimate theoretical performance of these sensitive instruments are inevitably long and difficult (Cosslett, 1980b).

The attainment of high resolution by correcting all the resolution-limiting aberrations of a microscope operating in the conventional voltage range has been systematically pursued for several years in the Technische Hochschule in Darmstadt, under the overall guidance of O. Scherzer, until his recent retirement. Scherzer's interest in particular correction systems dates back to the earlier years of electron optics (Scherzer, 1936,

---

* For further developments, and in particular, for early high-voltage high-resolution images taken with this microscope, see Cosslett *et al.* (1979), Jefferson *et al.* (1979), Cosslett and Smith (1978–1979), Jefferson *et al.* (1980), Freeman *et al.* (1980), Fryer *et al.* (1980), Smith and Gaskell (1980), and Nixon *et al.* (1980). The volume by Kihlborg (1979) gives a good idea of the state of high-resolution studies at that date (see in particular Horiuchi, 1978–1979; Uyeda, 1978–1979). The subject is surveyed by Hashimoto (1979).

1946, 1947, 1948, 1949, 1950, among others), but it is with developments in the 1970s that we are concerned here. The theoretical papers of Rose (1966–1967, 1967, 1967–1968, 1968, 1968–1969; Rose and Petri, 1971) on the paraxial properties and aberrations of systems with straight axes, irrespective of their symmetry, may be regarded as forerunners; in these, to which we cannot unfortunately do justice here for reasons of space, Rose establishes an eikonal-based formalism which, although inevitably complicated, permits us to calculate the primary and secondary aberrations of complex systems of multipole components. The generality of the approach has the advantage that the study of parasitic aberrations, due to misalignments, for example, is incorporated naturally, whereas previous studies of these defects had been of a piecemeal nature.

The first practical design to emerge from these studies was a magnetic objective, corrected for spherical aberration and for axial chromatic aberration; this was a particularly complicated unit, since quadrupoles were situated within a rotationally symmetric magnetic field and their poles had therefore to be twisted to match the rotation associated with the round lens field (Reichenbach and Rose, 1968–1969). In the following years, designs for apochromats, achromats, and aplanatic lenses were published. We briefly consider each of these in turn.

An apochromat is a lens for which the chromatic aberration is such that three wavelengths are imaged sharply and intermediate wavelengths with little aberration. The system proposed by Rose (1970) consists of four mixed electrostatic and magnetic quadrupoles, the geometry and excitation of which are such that they form an antisymmetric quadruplet (cf. Hawkes, 1970f). Rose shows that the desired correction can be obtained with such a unit; he also considers the chromatic aberration of magnification, and Fig. 40 shows a system in which this aberration should be negligible also. In the same year, a design for an apochromat was proposed by Schiske (1970).

In the following year, Rose (1971a) described a spherically corrected apochromat, again consisting of a round magnetic lens followed by a quadrupole quadruplet, operating in the telescopic mode. The contributions of the various aperture aberrations are analyzed very fully, and Rose illustrates his conclusions with a specific quadrupole–octopole corrector, which should be capable of imaging about 100 image points with a resolution of 50 pm at an electron wavelength of 5 pm ($\approx$ 60 kV). This small field of view is clearly a very severe restriction, and in order to increase the number of image points to a more realistic figure, an aplanat is required, by which we mean a lens in which not only are primary chromatic aberration, third-, and fifth-order spherical aberration well corrected but also the aperture dependence of the magnification is eliminated; the latter

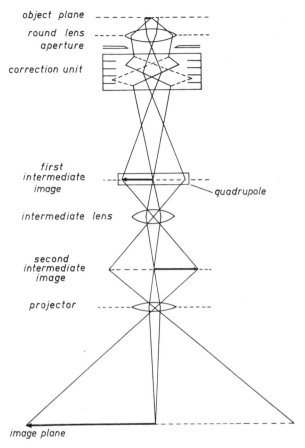

object plane

round lens

aperture

correction unit

first intermediate image

quadrupole

intermediate lens

second intermediate image

projector

image plane

FIG. 40.   Ray diagram in an electron microscope equipped with an apochromat.

requirement implies correction or balancing of the third-order coma and of the threefold astigmatism. In a later paper by Rose (1971b), which is central for an understanding of the subsequent experimental work, this problem is essentially solved, though with a very considerable increase in the complexity of the system. The number of image points should then increase to 2000 per diameter. Figure 41 shows the arrangement of multipoles required, and Table I lists the roles of the various elements; the performances to be expected of various designs, including the semiaplanat of Bastian *et al.* (1971), are listed in Table II. The need for dodecapoles to reduce fifth-order spherical aberration is clear.

The possibilities of these aplanats and apochromats were further studied in two papers by Pöhner (1976, 1977); in the first of these, the author

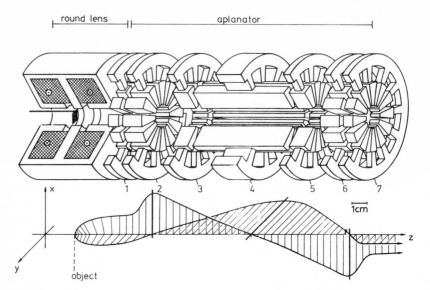

FIG. 41. General appearance of a high-resolution aplanat and typical rays in the two principal sections. (Figures 40 and 41 Courtesy of Dr. H. Rose and Wissenschaftliche Verlagsgesellschaft.)

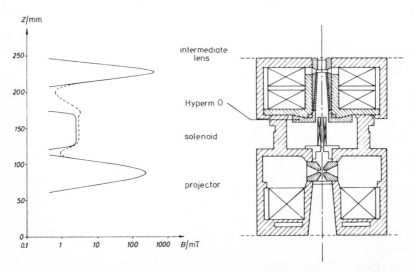

FIG. 42. Cancellation of the chromatic aberration of magnification and of rotation (the isotropic and anisotropic chromatic field aberrations) in an electron microscope. (Right) cross section of part of the column of a Siemens Elmiskop I incorporating a solenoid and a new pole piece plate of Hyperm 0. (Left) The measured (dotted curve) and calculated (full curve) axial field distribution of the triple lens combination shown. (Courtesy of Drs. W. Bernhard and H. Koops and Wissenschaftliche Verlagsgesellschaft.)

TABLE I

ROLES OF THE COMPONENTS OF THE UNIT SHOWN IN FIG. 41

Component	Role
Magnetic quadrupoles (1, 7)	Creating or cancelling paraxial astigmatism
Electrostatic–magnetic quadrupoles (2, 4, 6)	Focusing the astigmatic beam in one direction and correcting first-order chromatic spread
Third-order corrector (all)	Correction of radial component of third-order aperture aberration (1, 2, 4, 6, 7) and balancing of the third- and fifth-order aperture dependence of magnification
Fifth-order corrector (all)	Correction of fifth-order aperture aberration (1 or 7, 2 or 6, 3 or 5, and 4) and partial correction of the aperture dependence of magnification (fifth order)
Zero-order deflection unit	Straightening of the axis (all) and exploring the object (1 or 3)
First-order stigmator (1 or 3 or 5 or 7)	Correction of first-order axial astigmatism
Second-order stigmator (all)	Correction of axial astigmatism, axial coma (second order) and second-order aperture dependence of magnification
Third-order stigmator (1 or 7, 3 or 5)	Correction of azimuthal components of third-order aperture aberration
Fourth-order stigmator (1 or 7, 2 or 6, 3 or 5, 4)	Correction of axial aligment errors of fourth order

shows that fifth-order spherical aberration can be canceled with the aid of the dodecapole field component produced by quadrupoles without anay loss of the lower-order correction. In the second, Rose's (1971a) aplanat is reconsidered, to see whether it can function as an apochromat. The result is a five-element corrector capable of correcting primary and secondary (axial) chromatic aberration, third-order spherical aberration and coma, and the chromatic aberration of magnification. Pöhner points out that the lens could be useful in low-energy scanning electron microscopy: a scanning spot 1 nm in diameter should be attainable at 0.5 kV.

The correction of chromatic aberration has been tested experimentally by Bernhard, Koops, Kuck, and Scherzer (Bernhard and Koops, 1977; Koops *et al.*, 1977; Koops, 1978a,b). The first of these papers (Bernhard and Koops, 1977) is in fact not concerned directly with the systems described above but with a simple means of canceling the chromatic aberration of magnification and the anisotropic chromatic aberration by inserting a solenoid between the intermediate and projector (Fig. 42). This would then be used in conjunction with the objective–corrector complex.

TABLE II

PERFORMANCES OF CORRECTED OBJECTIVES

System	Round lens	Aplanat fields	Nominal resolution (Å)	Number of image points	Smallest object visible
Semiaplanat	Conventional magnetic lens	Two electrostatic or magnetic quadrupoles, three combined electrostatic–magnetic quadrupoles, five octopoles, deflection fields, two-, three-, and fourfold stigmator fields	0.8	600–800	Medium atoms
Aplanat without dodecapoles	Magnetic lens with no third-order azimuthal coma		1	$\approx 10^4$	Heavy atoms
Aplanat with dodecapoles	Magnetic lens with no third-order azimuthal coma	As above plus seven dodecapoles and a fivefold stigmator field	0.4	2000	Atoms such that $Z \geqslant 6$

The imaging quality of a three-quadrupole chromatic corrector has been investigated experimentally by Koops *et al.* (1977), who obtained a resolution of 140 nm with the corrector and projector lenses alone, that is, with no objective. With an objective lens in the system, the effect of chromatic aberration on the resolution should be negligible, since this resolution figure allowed rms variations in accelerating voltage as high as 3.5×10^{-3}. A Rose-type aplanator has been tested by Koops and Bernard (1978), who combined it with a 2-mm focal length condenser–objective and concluded that, if spherical and parasitic aberrations can be reduced sufficiently, a resolution of 0.1 nm should be attainable.

These results are summarized and further details set out in surveys by Koops (1978a,b). The next stage, in which the possibility of obtaining simultaneous correction of chromatic and spherical aberration is tested experimentally, is likely to be of very considerable interest. A very important requirement is a systematic and accurate alignment and adjustment procedure; a practical solution has been found by Kuck (1979), who has tested the five-component corrector needed to give a resolution of 0.1 nm at 60 kV. An additional multipole component will be needed to reach the target of 40 pm. Suitable magnetic screening is considered by Pejas (1978) and the design of very highly stabilized power supplies by Fey (1980).

During the same period, Plies and Rose (Plies and Rose, 1971; Rose and Plies, 1973, 1974; Plies, 1973, 1974) have been analyzing the properties of magnetic deflection systems with curved optic axes, as we mentioned in Section III,C,3, and have shown that systems free of spherical aberration and astigmatism can be designed, using multipole components. A system with a high degree of correction—and of complexity—is described in Rose and Plies (1973) and Plies (1974).

It seems appropriate to end this section with some remarks of Scherzer (1978), who has dryly observed that however meticulous the electron optical calculations may be, there is a further limitation on attainable resolution: "There are three troublesome limitations for the resolving power of electron microscopes: electron diffraction, radiation damage, and money" (p. 123). After discussing the first two of these, Scherzer turns to the expense that high-resolution work incurs:

As Dr. Koops reported in his contribution to this Congress (Toronto: Koops, 1978a), we built a corrected electron microscope at Darmstadt. In our attempts to make use of its benefits, we had only one serious problem: the mechanical stability of so many correcting electrodes and pole pieces. The stability is necessary to get the resolution limit down to the theoretical expectation and to make our results reproducible. Many of the commercially available microscopes have the necessary stability. As Dr. Dietrich described in her contribution to this Congress (Dietrich, 1978), the stability of the mechanical and magnetic devices becomes even better, if liquid-helium temperatures are applied. But the combination of our success in lens correction with the experience of the commercial microscope builders and of the cryo-specialists will cost several million dollars. Up to the present we have found no one who is honestly willing to pledge such a high sum (p. 127).

After some further discussion, Scherzer concludes, "In all these cases, the resolution is clearly limited by the inavailability of the necessary funds" (p. 127).

V. CONCLUDING REMARKS

We have attempted to give some account of the progress that has been made in the past decade in the general field of aberration studies and correction, with some indication of the numerical methods that are found most helpful. Electron image improvement by digital or optical processing has not been included, partly because surveys of this topic are already available (see Saxton, 1978, for a text entirely devoted to digital image processing, Hawkes, 1978b, for a literature survey, a very practical study by Kübler *et al.*, 1978, the multiauthor volumes edited by Hawkes, 1980b, Hoppe and Mason, 1979, and Baumeister, 1980, and a book by Misell, 1978, on analog and digital electron image processing) but also because it does not fall naturally within the device-oriented framework of this volume. This is not however true of some of the hardware that is being developed to ease the practical, as opposed to the theoretical, side of digital image processing, and we therefore indicate where further information on this can be found. We are not concerned with the microdensitometers and film writers, often directly interfaced to computers, that are available commercially (to those for whom Scherzer's third limitation is not too restrictive) but with specially designed links for transferring images directly from the image plane of the electron microscope to the main memory or backing store (magnetic tape or disk) of a computer.

A. Special-Purpose Digital Processing Equipment

The problem is very different in the cases of scanning and fixed-beam electron microscopes, for the obvious reason that the image is already available as a sequence of electrical signals in scanning microscopes, whereas fixed-beam images have to be read off, pixel by pixel, via a suitable analog-to-digital unit.

The early literature on the design of suitable links between scanning microscopes and computers is listed without comment by Hawkes (1978a); an extremely balanced survey of mainly recent developments in both theory and hardware, and of course results, has been prepared by

Jones and Smith (1978), which is probably the best point of departure for further exploration of the literature taken in conjunction with a discussion of instrumental image processing in the scanning transmission electron microscope by Isaacson *et al.* (1980). Some applications of optical processing of scanning images is discussed by Tovey and Wong (1978).

In the case of the conventional transmission electron microscope, the image must be either recorded on film as usual and digitized in a subsequent step or some specially designed interface must be built, connecting the microscope image to some bulk storage element. Relatively early systems were described by Glaeser *et al.* (1971) and Goldfarb and Siegel (1973, 1975; Goldfarb, 1976), and suitable designs have recently been examined very thoroughly by Herrmann *et al.* (1976, 1978a,b; Brüders *et al.*, 1976; Rust *et al.*, 1978; Herrmann, 1978). The object of their efforts was to achieve so high a detector quantum efficiency (DQE) that images obtained with very few electrons, to minimize radiation damage, could be measured accurately prior to subsequent processing. The general scheme proposed by Herrmann *et al.* (1978a) is shown in Fig. 43 and a convenient variant, permitting rapid image accumulation in memory, is described in Rust *et al.* (1978); in the latter scheme, a slave DEC PDP 11/03 is used as well as the PDP 10. Figure 43 is reasonably self-explanatory, and we therefore simply point out that various modes of operation are possible: an analog mode, suitable for reasonably bright pictures and a single-electron mode, for minimum-exposure images. The former can be used to store one or several images, depending on the number of bits required per pixel (bright images require more than dim ones). The possible real-time applications of such a scheme are legion: among the more straightforward, successive minimum-dose images may be subtracted, to show the onset of radiation damage, and simultaneously superimposed to improve the signal-to-noise ratio.

Last, we mention that a number of links for transferring the electron image to an optical processing unit have been built. For details, see the appropriate section of the bibliography compiled by Hawkes (1978b) and in particular, the papers by Bonhomme *et al.* (1976), Downing *et al.* (1977), Dumont *et al.* (1977), Herrmann and Krahl (1976), and Kübler and Waser (1973). For more recent developments, see Herrmann *et al.* (1980) and Beorchia *et al.* (1980).

B. Final Observations

Underlying all the efforts to combat aberrations in the microscope and with the aid of the computer is the desire to apply electron microscopy to types of specimen that have so far proved recalcitrant: those containing

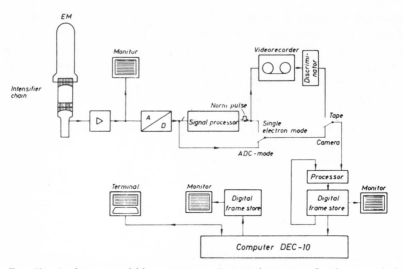

FIG. 43. An image acquisition, storage, and processing system for the transmission electron microscope. Although particularly well suited for very dim images, it has an operating mode capable of handling images with a wide contrast range. (Courtesy of Dr. K.-H. Herrmann and North-Holland Publishing Co.)

high-resolution information that is easily destroyed by the electron beam. The problems of radiation damage have been a major preoccupation of many microscopists during recent years (Cosslett, 1978b, 1980a) and are likely to overshadow the subject of electron microscopy for many years to come. This is naturally having repercussions on electron microscope design, with a view to facilitating minimum-exposure operation and image accumulation at least. A very recent finding by Dietrich et al. (1979) extended by Dubochet and Knapek (1978–1979) and Knapek and Dubochet (1980), suggests that one of the possible ways of increasing specimen resistance to radiation damage, namely reducing the temperature, is indeed extremely effective provided that the true specimen temperature is low enough. By using a superconducting microscope, they could be sure that the temperature of the specimen environment remained at 4 K and their preliminary experiments indicate that a range of biological specimens can tolerate far higher doses (as indicated by electron diffraction pattern decay) at 4 K than at even slightly higher temperatures. Further details are given by Dietrich and Dubochet in Baumeister (1980).

In the related fields discussed here, designers may be governed by other criteria, but these are often interrelated. The work of Kern, Kurz, Kasper and Hauke on guns will no doubt be useful in the field of microfabrication as well as that of Owen and Nixon, Soma, and Ohiwa on deflection coils. We hope that this survey of recent progress in selected branches of particle optics, with particular reference to aberrations, gives an idea of what has already been achieved, what still needs to be done, and helps to promote cross-fertilization between adjoining but sometimes regrettably disjoint domains.

REFERENCES

Afanas'ev, V. P., and Yavor, S. Ya (1978). "Elektrostaticheskie Energoanalizatory dlya Puchkov Zaryazhennykh Chastits" [Electrostatic energy analyzers for charged particle beams]. Nauka, Moscow.
Afanas'ev, V. P., Glukhoi, Yu. O., and Yavor, S. Ya (1975a). Zh. Tekh. Fiz. 45, 1526; Sov. Phys. Tech. Phys. 20, 969.
Afanas'ev, V. P., Glukhoi, Yu. O., and Yavor, S. Ya. (1975b). Zh. Tekh. Fiz. 45, 1973; Sov. Phys. Tech. Phys. 20, 1240.
Afanas'ev, V. P., Gritsyuk, N. P., Lachashvili, R. A., and Yavor, S. Ya. (1979). Zh. Tekh. Fiz. 49, 1498; Sov. Phys. Tech. Phys. 24, 833.
Amboss, K. (1975). J. Vac. Sci. Technol. 12, 1152.
Amboss, K. (1976). Scanning Electron Microsc. 1976 699.
Amboss, K., and Jennings, J. C. E. (1970). J. Appl. Phys. 41, 1608.
Amboss, K., and Wolf, E. D. (1971). Rec. Symp. Electron Ion Laser Beam Technol., 11th p. 195.
Anazawa, N., Aihara, R., and Ohta, S. (1975). J. Phys. E: Sci. Instr. 8, 971.
Andersen, W. H. J. (1967). Brit. J. Appl. Phys. 18, 1573.
Andersen, W. H. J., and Le Poole, J. B. (1970). J. Phys. E: Sci. Instr. 3, 121.
Andreev, Yu. A., Glikman, L. G., and Iskakova, Z. D. (1975a). Zh. Tekh. Fiz. 45, 1604; Sov. Phys. Tech. Phys. 20, 1024.
Andreev, Yu. A., Glikman, L. G., and Iskakova, Z. D. (1975b). Zh. Tekh. Fiz. 45, 2043; Sov. Phys. Tech. Phys. 20, 1289.
Baba, N., and Kanaya, K. (1979). J. Phys. E: Sci. Instr. 12, 525.
Baba, N., Ito, Y., and Kanaya, K. (1978). Proc. Int. Cong. Electron Microsc., 9th Toronto 1, 32.
Balladore, J. L., and Murillo, R. (1977). J. Microsc. Spectrosc. Electron. 2, 211,
Balladore, J. L., Murillo, R., Trinquier, J., and Jouffrey, B. (1977). In "High Voltage Electron Microscopy 1977" (T. Imura and H. Hashimoto, eds.), p. 41. Japanese Society of Electron Microscopy, Tokyo.
Banford, A. P. (1966). "The Transport of Charged Particle Beams." Spon, London.
Baranova, L. A. (1972). Radiotekh. Elektron. 17, 2642; Radio. Eng. Electron. Phys. 17, 2130.
Baranova, L. A., and Yavor, S. Ya. (1972). Radiotekh. Elektron. 17, 2639; Radio. Eng. Electron. Phys. 17, 2128.
Baranova, L. A., Ovsyannikova, L. P., and Yavor, S. Ya. (1972). Zh. Tekh. Fiz. 42, 210; Sov. Phys. Tech. Phys. 17, 170.
Baranova, L. A., Petrov, I. A., and Yavor, S. Ya. (1978). Proc. Int. Cong. Electron Microsc., 9th Toronto 1, 28.
Barth, J. E. (1967). Electrostatic correction of the spherical aberration of electron lenses. Dissertation, University of Arizona.

Barton, D., and Fitch, J. P. (1972). *Rep. Prog. Phys.* **35,** 235.

Bastian, B., Spengler, K., and Typke, D. (1971). *Optik* **33,** 591.

Baumeister, W., ed. (1980). "Electron Microscopy in Molecular Dimensions. State of the Art and Strategies for the Future." Springer-Verlag, Berlin and New York.

Beck, V. (1977). *Proc. Ann. Meeting EMSA, 35th (Boston)* p. 90.

Beck, V. D. (1979). *Optik* **53,** 241.

Beck, V., and Crewe, A. V. (1974). *Proc. Annual Meeting EMSA, 32nd. (St. Louis)* p. 426.

Beck, V., and Crewe, A. V. (1976). *Proc. Annual Meeting EMSA, 34th (Miami Beach)* p. 578.

Bell, A. E., and Swanson, L. W. (1979). *Phys. Rev.* **B19,** 3353.

Beorchia, A., Bonhomme, P., and Bonnet, N. (1980). *Optik* **55,** 11.

Bernhard, W., and Koops, H. (1977). *Optik* **47,** 55.

Bimurzaev, S. (1976a). *Zh. Tekh. Fiz.* **46,** 1580; *Sov. Phys. Tech. Phys.* **21,** 909.

Bimurzaev, S. (1976b). *Zh. Tekh. Fiz.* **46,** 2292; *Sov. Phys. Tech. Phys.* **21,** 1350.

Bimurzaev, S. (1976c). *Zh. Tekh. Fiz.* **46,** 2299; *Sov. Phys. Tech. Phys.* **21,** 1354.

Bimurzaev, S., Kel'man, V. M., and Yakushev, E. M. (1976). *Zh. Tekh. Fiz.* **46,** 452, 460; *Sov. Phys. Tech. Phys.* **21,** 258, 262.

Bonhomme, P., Beorchia, A., Meunier, B., Dumont, F., and Rossier, D. (1976). *Optik* **45,** 159.

Bonjour, P. (1976). *Proc. Eur. Congr. Electron Microscopy, 6th, Jerusalem* **1,** 73.

Bosi, G. (1974). *Rev. Sci. Instr.* **45,** 1260.

Broers, A. N. (1979). *Scanning Electron Microsc. 1979* **I,** 1.

Brouwer, W. (1957). The use of matrix algebra in geometrical optics, dissertation, Delft.

Brouwer, W. (1964). "Matrix Methods in Optical Instrument Design." Benjamin, New York and Amsterdam.

Brouwer, W., and Walther, A. (1967). *In* "Advanced Optical Techniques" (A. C. S. van Heel, ed.), p. 503. North-Holland, Amsterdam.

Brown, K. L. (1968). *In* "Advances in Particle Physics" (R. L. Cool and R. E. Marshak, eds.), Vol. 1, p. 71. Wiley-Interscience, New York and London; distributed as SLAC Report No. 75, 105 pp. (1967).

Brown, K. L., Belbeoch, R., and Bounin, P. (1964). *Rev. Sci. Instr.* **35,** 481.

Brüders, R., Herrmann, K.-H., Krahl, D., and Rust, H.-P. (1976). *Proc. Eur. Cong. Electron Microscopy, 6th, Jerusalem* **1,** 318.

Bulirsch, R., Grigorieff, R. D., and Schröder, J., eds. (1978). "Numerical Treatment of Differential Equations," *Lecture Notes in Mathematics,* Vol. 631. Springer-Verlag, Berlin and New York.

Castaing, R., Hennequin, J. F., Henry, L. and Slodzian, G. (1967). *In* "Focusing of Charged Particles" (A. Septier, ed.), Vol. 2, p. 265. Academic Press, New York.

Catto, C. J. D. (1977). In "Developments in Electron Microscopy and Analysis, 1977" (D. L. Misell, ed.), p. 21. Institute of Physics, Bristol.

Cleaver, J. R. A. (1975). *Int. J. Electron.* **38,** 513, 531.

Cleaver, J. R. A. (1977a). *Optik* **48,** 95.

Cleaver, J. R. A. (1977b). In "Developments in Electron Microscopy and Analysis, 1977 (D. L. Misell, ed.), p. 17. Institute of Physics, Bristol.

Cleaver, J. R. A. (1978–1979). *Optik* **52,** 293.

Cleaver, J. R. A. (1980). *In* "Electron Microscopy and Analysis 1979" (T. Mulvey, ed.), p. 55. Institute of Physics, Bristol.

Collins, R. E. (1973). *J. Vac. Sci. Technol.* **10,** 1106.

Cosslett, V. E. (1977a). In "Developments in Electron Microscopy and Analysis, 1977" (D. L. Misell, ed.), p. 1. Institute of Physics, Bristol.

Cosslett, V. E. (1977b). In "High Voltage Electron Microscopy, 1977" (T. Imura and H. Hashimoto, eds.), p. 87. Japanese Society of Electron Microscopy, Tokyo.

Cosslett, V. E. (1978a). Proc. Int. Congr. Electron Microsc., 9th, Toronto 3, 163.

Cosslett, V. E. (1978b). J. Microsc. 113, 113.

Cosslett, V. E. (1980a). In "Electron Microscopy and Analysis 1979" (T. Mulvey, ed.), p. 277. Institute of Physics, Bristol.

Cosslett, V. E. (1980b). Proc. Roy. Soc. (London) A370, 1.

Cosslett, V. E., and Smith, D. J. (1978–1979). Chem. Scr. 14, 39.

Cosslett, V. E., Camps, R. A., Saxton, W. O., Smith, D. J., Nixon, W. C., Ahmed, H., Catto, C. J. D., Cleaver, J. R. A., Smith, K. C. A., Timbs, A. E., Turner, P. W., and Ross, P. M. (1979). Nature 281, 49.

Crewe, A. V. (1970). Q. Rev. Biophys. 3, 137.

Crewe, A. V. (1973). Prog. Opt. 11, 223.

Crewe, A. V. (1977). Optik 47, 299, 371.

Crewe, A. V. (1978). Proc. Int. Cong. Electron Microscopy, 9th, Toronto, 3, 197.

Crewe, A. V. (1978–1979). Chem. Scr. 14, 17.

Crewe, A. V., and Kopf, D. (1980). Optik 55, 1.

Crewe, A. V., and Parker, N. W. (1976). Optik 46, 183.

Crewe, A. V., Wall, J., and Welter, L. M. (1968). J. Appl. Phys. 39, 5861.

Daumenov, T. D., Sapargaliev, A. A., and Yakushev, E. M. (1978). Zh. Tekh. Fiz. 48, 2447; Sov. Phys. Tech. Phys. 23, 1400.

Dekkers, N. H. (1969). Correction of spherical aberration, dissertation, Delft.

Dekkers, N. H., and Le Poole, J. B. (1968). Proc. Eur. Reg. Conf. Electron Microsc., 4th, Rome 1, 167.

Der-Shvarts, G. V. (1974). Izv. Akad. Nauk SSSR (Ser. Fiz.) 38, 1505; Bull. Acad. Sci. USSR (Phys. Ser.) 38, No. 7, 136.

Dietrich, I. (1976). "Superconducting Electron-Optic Devices." Plenum, New York and London.

Dietrich, I. (1978). Proc. Int. Cong. Electron Microscopy, 9th, Toronto 3, 173.

Dietrich, I., Herrmann, K.-H., and Passow, C. (1975). Optik 42, 439.

Dietrich, I., Formanek, H., Fox, F., Knapek, E., and Weyl, R. (1979). Nature 277, 380.

Dorignac, D., and Jouffrey, B. (1976). In "Microscopie électronique à haute tension, 1975" (B. Jouffrey and P. Favard, eds.), p. 143. Société Française de Microscopie Electronique, Paris.

Downing, K. H., Kübler, O., and Noble, M. (1977). Proc. Annual Meeting EMSA, 35th (Boston) 76.

Dubochet, J., and Knapek, E. (1978–1979). Chem. Scr. 14, 267.

Dumont, F., Rossier, D., Bonhomme, P., Beorchia, A., and Meunier, B. (1977). J. Phys. E: Sci. Instr. 10, 520.

Dungey, J. W., and Hull, C. R. (1947). Proc. Phys. Soc. London 59, 828.

Durand, A., and Tanguy, P. (1977). Nucl. Instr. Methods 143, 561.

Elkamali, H. H., and Mulvey, T. (1980). In "Electron Microscopy and Analysis 1979" (T. Mulvey, ed.), p. 63. Institute of Physics, Bristol.

Enge, H. A. (1967). In "Focusing of Charged Particles" (A. Septier, ed.), Vol. 2, p. 203. Academic Press, New York.

Engel, W., Kunath, W., and Krause, S. (1974), Proc. Int. Cong. Electron Microscopy, 8th, Canberra 1, 118.

Feuerbaum, H. P., and Otto, J. (1978). J. Phys. E: Sci. Instr. 11, 529.

Fey, G. (1980). Optik 55, 55.

Fitch, J. P. (1979). In "Symbolic and Algebraic Computation" (E. W. Ng, ed.), p. 30. Springer-Verlag, Berlin and New York.

146   P. W. HAWKES

Foster, A. (1968). Correction of aperture aberrations in magnetic lens spectrometers. Thesis, London.

Freeman, L. A., Smith, D. J., and Fisher, R. M. (1980). In "Electron Microscopy and Analysis 1979" (T. Mulvey, ed.), p. 439. Institute of Physics, Bristol.

Fryer, J. R., Cleaver, J. R. A., and Smith, D. J. (1980). In "Electron Microscopy and Analysis 1979" (T. Mulvey, ed.), p. 287. Institute of Physics, Bristol.

Fujioka, H., Hosokawa, T., Kanda, Y., and Ura, K. (1978). Scanning Electron Microsc. 1978 I, 755.

Galejs, A., and Kuyatt, C. E. (1978). J. Vac. Sci. Technol. 15, 865.

Garg, R. K., and Vaidya, N. C. (1974). Proc. Int. Cong. Electron Microscopy, 8th, Canberra 1, 154.

Glaeser, R. M., Kuo, I., and Budinger, T. F. (1971). Proc. Annual Meeting EMSA, 29th (Boston) p. 466.

Glaser, W. (1940). Z. Physik 116, 19.

Glaser, W. (1952). "Grundlagen der Elektronenoptik." Springer, Vienna.

Glaser, W. (1956). In "Handbuch der Physik" (S. Flügge, ed.), Vol. 33, p. 123. Springer-Verlag, Berlin and New York.

Glikman, L. G., and Iskakova, Z. D. (1976a). Zh. Tekh. Fiz. 46, 1171; Sov. Phys. Tech. Phys. 21, 666.

Glikman, L. G., and Iskakova, Z. D. (1976b). Zh. Tekh. Fiz. 46, 1182; Sov. Phys. Tech. Phys. 21, 672.

Glikman, L. G., and Nurmanov, M. Sh. (1976). Zh. Tekh. Fiz. 46, 1582; Sov. Phys. Tech. Phys. 21, 911.

Glikman, L. G., Kel'man, V. M., and Nurmanov, M. Sh. (1973a). Zh. Tekh. Fiz. 43, 1358; Sov. Phys. Tech. Phys. 18, 864.

Glikman, L. G., Kel'man, V. M., and Fedulina, L. V. (1973b). Zh. Tekh. Fiz. 43, 1793; Sov. Phys. Tech. Phys. 18, 1139.

Glikman, L. G., Kel'man, V. M., and Fedulina, L. V. (1973c). Zh. Tekh. Fiz. 43, 2017; Sov. Phys. Tech. Phys. 18, 1273.

Glikman, L. G., Kel'man, V. M., and Nurmanov, M. Sh. (1973d). Zh. Tekh. Fiz. 43, 2278; Sov. Phys. Tech. Phys. 18, 1441.

Glikman, L. G., Kel'man, V. M., Pavlichkova, O. V., and Spivak-Lavrov, I. F. (1976). Zh. Tekh. Fiz. 46, 1810, 1821, 1978; Sov. Phys. Tech. Phys. 21, 1055, 1060, 1153.

Goldfarb, W. (1976). Proc. Eur. Cong. Electron Microsc., 6th, Jerusalem 1, 316.

Goldfarb, W., and Siegel, B. M. (1973). Proc. Annual Meeting EMSA, 31st (New Orleans) p. 264.

Goldfarb, W., and Siegel, B. M. (1975). Proc. Annual Meeting EMSA, 33rd (Las Vegas) p. 124.

Gopinath, A., and Hill, M. S. (1973a), Scanning Electron Microsc. 1973 p. 197.

Gopinath, A., and Hill, M. S. (1973b), IEEE Trans. Electron Devices ED-20, 610.

Gopinath, A., and Hill, M. S. (1974). Scanning Electron Microsc. 1974 235.

Gopinath, A., and Hill, M. S. (1977). J. Phys. E: Sci. Instr. 10, 229.

Gopinathan, K. G., and Gopinath, A. (1978). J. Phys. E: Sci. Instr. 11, 229.

Goto, E., and Soma, T. (1977), Optik 48, 255.

Griesmer, J. H., Jenks, R. D. and Yun, D. Y. Y. (1975). "SCRATCHPAD User's Manual." IBM, Yorktown Heights.

Gritsyuk, N. P., and Lachashvili, R. A. (1976). Zh. Tekh. Fiz. 46, 2486; Sov. Phys. Tech. Phys. 21, 1470.

Grivet, P. (1972). "Electron Optics." Pergamon, Oxford and New York.

Guckenberger, R., and Heil, H. (1972). Proc. Eur. Cong. Electron Microsc., 5th, Manchester 112.

Haantjes, J., and Lubben, G. J. (1957). *Philips Res. Rept.* **12**, 46.
Haantjes, J., and Lubben, G. J. (1959). *Philips Res. Rept.* **14**, 65.
Hahn, E. (1961). *Jenaer Jahrbuch* Pt. II, 325.
Hahn, E. (1964). *Jenaer Jahrbuch* 217.
Hahn, E. (1965). *Jenaer Jahrbuch* 107.
Hahn, E. (1966). *Jenaer Jahrbuch* 145.
Hahn, E. (1969–1970). *Jenaer Jahrbuch* 175.
Hahn, E. (1971). *Wiss. Z. Tech. Univ. Dresden* **20**, 361.
Hahn, E. (1975). *Proc. VIII Arbeitstagung "Elektronenmikroskopie,"* Berlin p. 249.
Hainfeld, J. F. (1977). *Scanning Electron Microsc. 1977* **I**, 591.
Hairer, E. (1978). *J. Inst. Maths. Appl.* **21**, 47.
Hanszen, K. J. (1971). *Adv. Opt. Electron Microsc.* **4**, 1.
Harting, E., and Read, F. H. (1976). "Electrostatic Lenses." Elsevier, Amsterdam, Oxford, and New York.
Hartwig, W. R., and Passow, C. (1975). In "Applied Superconductivity" (V. L. Newhouse, ed.), Vol. 2, p. 541. Academic Press, New York and London.
Hashimoto, H. (1979). *J. Electron Microsc.* **28** (Suppl.), S-1.
Hauke, R. (1977). Theoretische Untersuchungen rotationssymmetrischer Elektronenstrahlerzeugungssysteme unter Berücksichtigung von Raumladung. Dissertation, Tübingen.
Hawkes, P. W. (1965). *Phil. Trans. R. Soc. London* **A257**, 479.
Hawkes, P. W. (1966). "Quadrupole Optics." Springer-Verlag, Berlin and New York.
Hawkes, P. W. (1966–1967). *Optik* **24**, 252, 275.
Hawkes, P. W. (1967). *J. Microsc.* **6**, 917.
Hawkes, P. W. (1968a). *J. Phys. D: Appl. Phys.* **1**, 131.
Hawkes, P. W. (1968b). *J. Phys. D: Appl. Phys.* **1**, 1549.
Hawkes, P. W. (1970a). *Optik* **31**, 213.
Hawkes, P. W. (1970b). *Optik* **31**, 302.
Hawkes, P. W. (1970c). *Optik* **31**, 592.
Hawkes, P. W. (1970d). *Optik* **32**, 50.
Hawkes, P. W. (1970e). *J. Microsc.* **9**, 435.
Hawkes, P. W. (1970f). "Quadrupoles in Electron Lens Design." Academic Press, London and New York.
Hawkes, P. W. (1972). "Electron Optics and Electron Microscopy." Taylor and Francis, London.
Hawkes, P. W. (1973). *Comput. Aided Des.* **5**, 200.
Hawkes, P. W. (1977a). *Ultramicroscopy* **2**, 179.
Hawkes, P. W. (1977b). *Optik* **48**, 29.
Hawkes, P. W. (1977c). In "High Voltage Electron Microscopy 1977" (T. Imura and H. Hashimoto, eds), p. 57. Japanese Society of Electron Microscopy, Kyoto.
Hawkes, P. W. (1978a). In "Principles and Techniques of Electron Microscopy" (M. A. Hayat, ed.), Vol. 8, p. 262. Van Nostrand-Reinhold, Princeton, New Jersey.
Hawkes, P. W. (1978b). *Comput. Graph. Image Proc.* **8**, 406.
Hawkes, P. W. (1980a). In "Magnetic Electron Lens Properties" (P. W. Hawkes, ed.), Chapter 1. Springer-Verlag, Berlin and New York.
Hawkes, P. W., ed. (1980b). "Computer Processing of Electron Microscope Images." Springer-Verlag, Berlin and New York.
Hawkes, P. W., and Valdrè, U. (1977). *J. Phys. E: Sci. Instr.* **10**, 309.
Hearn, A. C. (1973). "REDUCE 2 User's Manual." University of Utah Symbolic Computation Group Rep. No. UCP-19.
Heritage, M. B. (1972). *Proc. Eur. Cong. Electron Microsc., 5th, Manchester* p. 88.

Heritage, M. B. (1973). In "Image Processing and Computer-Aided Design in Electron Optics" (P. W. Hawkes, ed.), p. 324. Academic Press, London and New York.

Herrmann, K.-H. (1978). *J. Phys. E: Sci. Instr.* **11**, 1076.

Herrmann K.-H., and Krahl, D. (1976). *Optik* **45**, 231.

Herrmann, K.-H., Krahl, D., Rust, H.-P., and Ulrichs, O. (1976). *Optik* **44**, 393.

Herrmann, K.-H., Krahl, D., and Rust, H.-P. (1978a). *Proc. Int. Cong. Electron Microsc., 9th, Toronto* **1**, 100.

Herrmann, K.-H., Krahl, D., and Rust, H.-P. (1978b). *Ultramicroscopy* **3**, 227.

Herrmann, K.-H., Krahl, D., and Rust, H.-P. (1980). *In* "Electron Microscopy in Molecular Dimensions" (W. Baumeister, ed.). Springer-Verlag, Berlin and New York.

Herrmannsfeldt, W. B. (1973). "Electron trajectory program." SLAC Report No. 166, 83 pp.

Hibino, M., and Maruse, S. (1976). *J. Electron Microsc.* **25**, 229.

Hibino, M., Sugiyama, S., Hanai, T., and Maruse, S. (1977). In "High Voltage Electron Microscopy 1977" (T. Imura and H. Hashimoto, eds.), p. 49. Japanese Society of Electron Microscopy, Tokyo.

Hibino, M., Sugiyama, S., Hanai, T., and Maruse, S. (1978). *J. Electron Microsc.* **27**, 259.

Hicks, W. W., Keller, J. H., Benner, R. H., Winnard, J. R., Puzak, T. R., and Schmidt, S. (1976). *Nucl. Instr. Methods* **139**, 25.

Hill, M. S., and Gopinath, A. (1974). *J. Phys. D: Appl. Phys.* **7**, 69.

Hoch, H., Kasper, E., and Kern, D. (1976). *Optik* **46**, 463.

Hoch, H., Kasper, E., and Kern, D. (1978). *Optik* **50**, 413.

Hoppe, W. and Mason, R., eds. (1979). "Unconventional Electron Microscopy for Molecular Structure Determination." *Adv. Structure Res. Diffraction Methods* **7**.

Horiuchi, S. (1978–1979). *Chem. Scr.* **14**, 75.

Horiuchi, S., Matsui, Y., Bando, Y., Sekikawa, Y., and Sakaguchi, K. (1977a). In "High Voltage Electron Microscopy, 1977" (T. Imura and H. Hashimoto, eds.), p. 91. Japanese Society of Electron Microscopy, Tokyo.

Horiuchi, S., Kikuchi, T., and Goto, M. (1977b). *Acta Cryst.* **A33**, 701.

Horiuchi, S., Matsui, Y., Bando, Y., Katsuta, T., and Matsui, I. (1978). *J. Electron Microsc.* **27**, 39.

Hosokawa, T., Fujioka, H., and Ura, K. (1977a). *Appl. Phys. Lett.* **31**, 340.

Hosokawa, T., Fujioka, H., and Ura, K. (1977b). *Trans. Inst. Elec. Commun. Eng. Japan* **60-B**, 55.

Ichihashi, M., and Maruse, S. (1971). *J. Electron Microsc.* **20**, 167.

Ichihashi, M., and Maruse, S. (1973). *J. Electron Microsc.* **22**, 321.

Isaacson, M., Utlaut, M., and Kopf, D. (1980). *In* "Computer Processing of Electron Microscope Images" (P. W. Hawkes, ed.), p. 257. Springer-Verlag, Berlin and New York.

Jefferson, D. A., Thomas, J. M., Smith, D. J., Camps, R. A., Catto, C. J. D., and Cleaver, J. R. A. (1979). *Nature* **281**, 51.

Jefferson, D. A., Thomas, J. M., Mallinson, L. G., and Smith, D. J. (1980). *In* "Electron Microscopy and Analysis 1979" (T. Mulvey, ed.), p. 101. Institute of Physics, Bristol.

Jones, A. V., and Smith, K. C. A. (1978). *Scanning Electron Microsc. 1978* **I**, 13.

Juma, S. M., and Mulvey, T. (1974). *Proc. Int. Cong. Electron Microscopy, 8th, Canberra* **1**, 134.

Juma, S. M., and Mulvey, T. (1975). In "Developments in Electron Microscopy and Analysis" (J. A. Venables, ed.), p. 45. Academic Press, London and New York.

Juma, S. M., and Mulvey, T. (1978). *J. Phys. E: Sci. Instr.* **11**, 759.

Kaashoek, A. (1968). *Philips Res. Rept. Suppl.* **11**, 114 pp.

Kamminga, W. (1973). In "Image Processing and Computer-Aided Design in Electron Optics" (P. W. Hawkes, ed.), p. 400. Academic Press, London and New York.

Kamminga, W., and Francken, J. C. (1971). *Optik* 33, 375.

Kasper, E. (1968–1969). *Optik* 28, 55.

Kasper, E. (1980). In "Magnetic Electron Lens Properties" (P. W. Hawkes, ed.). Springer-Verlag, Berlin and New York.

Kel'man, V. M., Fedulina, L. V., and Yakushev, E. M. (1971a). *Zh. Tekh. Fiz.* 41, 1489, 1832; *Sov. Phys. Tech. Phys.* 16, 1171, 1449.

Kel'man, V. M., Fedulina, L. V., and Yakushev, E. M. (1971b). *Zh. Tekh. Fiz.* 41, 2016; *Sov. Phys. Tech. Phys.* 16, 1598.

Kel'man, V. M., Fedulina, L. V., and Yakushev, E. M. (1972a). *Zh. Tekh. Fiz.* 42, 297; *Sov. Phys. Tech. Phys.* 17, 238.

Kel'man, V. M., Sapargaliev, A. A., and Yakushev, E. M. (1972b). *Zh. Tekh. Fiz.* 42, 2001; *Sov. Phys. Tech. Phys.* 17, 1607.

Kel'man, V. M. Sekunova, L. M., and Yakushev, E. M. (1972c). *Zh. Tekh. Fiz.* 42, 2279; *Sov. Phys. Tech. Phys.* 17, 1786.

Kel'man, V. M., Sapargaliev, A. A., and Yakushev, E. M. (1973a). *Zh. Tekh. Fiz.* 43, 52; *Sov. Phys. Tech. Phys.* 18, 33.

Kel'man, V. M., Sekunova, L. M., and Yakushev, E. M. (1973b). *Zh. Tekh. Fiz.* 43, 1799, 1807; *Sov. Phys. Tech. Phys.* 18, 1142, 1147.

Kel'man, V. M., Karetskaya, S. P., Manabaev, Kh., Fedulina, L. V., and Yakushev, E. M. (1973c). *Zh. Tekh. Fiz.* 43, 2238, 2463; *Sov. Phys. Tech. Phys.* 18, 1418, 1552.

Kel'man, V. M., Nazarenko, L. M., and Yakushev, E. M. (1974a). *Zh. Tekh. Fiz.* 44, 830; *Sov. Phys. Tech. Phys.* 19, 523.

Kel'man, V. M., Sapargaliev, A. A., and Yakushev, E. M. (1974b). *Zh. Tekh. Fiz.* 44, 928, 938; *Sov. Phys. Tech. Phys.* 19, 592, 597.

Kel'man, V. M., Karetskaya, S. P., Fedulina, L. V., and Yakushev, E. M. (1979). "Elektronno-opticheskie Elementy Prizmennykh Spektrometrov Zaryazhennykh Chastits" (Electron optical elements of prism spectrometers for charged particles). Nauka, Alma-Ata (Kazakh SSR).

Kern, D. (1978). Theoretische Untersuchungen an rotationssymmetrischen Strahlerzeugungssystemen mit Feldemissionsquelle, Dissertation, Tübingen.

Kern, D., Kurz, D., and Speidel, R. (1978). *Optik* 52, 61.

Kihlborg, L., ed. (1979). "Direct Imaging of Atoms in Crystals and Molecules". Royal Swedish Academy of Sciences, Stockholm, 1979. (Also published as *Chemica Scripta* 14, 1978–1979.)

Kihn, Y., Zanchi, G., Sevely, J., and Jouffrey, B. (1976). *J. Microsc. Spectr. Electron.* 1, 363.

King, J. G., Coleman, J. W. and Jacobsen, E. M. (1978). *Ann. N.Y. Acad. Sci.* 306, 75.

Klemperer, O. (1953). "Electron Optics." Chambridge University Press, Cambridge, England.

Knapek, E., and Dubochet, J. (1980). *In* "Electron Microscopy and Analysis 1979" (T. Mulvey, ed.), p. 283. Institute of Physics, Bristol.

Knauer, W. (1979). *Optik* 54, 211.

Kobayashi, K., Suito, E., Uyeda, N., Watanabe, M. Yanaka, T., Etoh, T., Watanabe, H., and Moriguchi, M. (1974). *Proc. Int. Cong. Electron Microscopy, 8th, Canberra* 1, 30.

Koltay, E., Kish, I., Baranova, L. A., and Yavor, S. Ya. (1972). *Radiotekh. Elektron.* 17, 1906; *Radio Eng. Electron Phys.* 17, 1518.

Koops, H. (1972a). *Optik* 36, 93.

Koops, H. (1972b). *Proc. Eur. Cong. Electron Microscopy, 5th, Manchester* p. 126.

Koops, H. (1973a). *J. Vac. Sci. Technol.* 10, 909.

Koops, H. (1973b). *Optik* 38, 246.

150   P. W. HAWKES

Koops, H. (1978a). *Proc. Int. Cong. Electron Microscopy, 9th, Toronto* **3**, 185.
Koops, H. (1978b). *Optik* **52**, 1.
Koops, H., and Bernhard, W. (1975). *J. Vac. Sci. Technol.* **12**, 1141.
Koops, H., and Bernhard, W. (1978). *Proc. Int. Cong. Electron Microscopy, 9th, Toronto* **1**, 36.
Koops, H., Kuck, G., and Scherzer, O. (1977). *Optik* **48**, 225.
Krivanek, O. L., Isoda, S., and Kobayashi, K. (1977). *Phil. Mag.* **36**, 931.
Kübler, O., and Waser, R. (1973). *Optik* **37**, 425.
Kübler, O. Hahn, M., and Seredynski, J. (1978). *Optik* **51**, 171 and 235.
Kuck, G. (1979). Erprobung eines elektronenoptischen Korrektivs für Farb- und Öffnungs-fehler, Dissertation, Darmstadt.
Kunath, W. (1972). *Proc. Eur Cong. Electron Microsc., 5th, Manchester* p. 70.
Kunath, W. (1976). *Proc. Eur. Cong. Electron Microsc., 6th, Jerusalem* **1**, 340.
Kuroda, K. (1974). Analysis and design of accelerating lens system for field emission scanning electron microscope, *Rep. Dept. Appl. Phys., Osaka University*, 78 pp.
Kuroda, K., and Suzuki, T. (1972). *Japan. J. Appl. Phys.* **11**, 1222, 1382, and 1390.
Kuroda, K., and Suzuki, T. (1974a). *J. Appl. Phys.* **45**, 1436.
Kuroda, K., and Suzuki, T. (1974b). *Japan. J. Appl. Phys.* **13**, 1636.
Kuroda, K., and Suzuki, T. (1974c). *Appl. Phys. Lett.* **25**, 23.
Kuroda, K., and Suzuki, T. (1975). *J. Appl. Phys.* **46**, 454.
Kuroda, K., Ebisui, H., and Suzuki, T. (1974a). *J. Appl. Phys.* **45**, 2336.
Kuroda, K. Shingu, Y., and Suzuki, T. (1974b). *Japan. J. Appl. Phys.* **13**, 2033.
Kurz, D. (1979). Untersuchungen an einem Elektronenstrahlerzeugungssystem mit Feld-emissionskathode. Dissertation, Tübingen.
Kuyatt, C. E. (1978). *J. Vac. Sci. Technol.* **15**, 861.
Kuyatt, C. E., Di Chio, D., and Natali, S. V. (1973). *J. Vac. Sci. Technol.* **10**, 1124.
Kuyatt, C. E., Di Chio, D., and Natali, S. V. (1974). *Rev. Sci. Instr.* **45**, 1275.
Kynaston, D., and Mulvey, T. (1963). *Brit. J. Appl. Phys.* **14**, 199.
Lambert, J. D. (1977). "The State of the Art in Numerical Analysis" (D. Jacobs, ed.), p. 451. Academic Press, London and New York.
Lambrakis, E., Marai, F. Z., and Mulvey, T. (1977). In "Developments in Electron Microscopy and Analysis, 1977" (D. L. Misell, ed.), p. 35. Institute of Physics, Bristol.
Lapostolle, P. (1970). CERN Rep. ISR/DI/70-36.
Lauer, R. (1980). *Adv. Opt. Electron Microsc.* **8**.
Lee-Whiting, G. E. (1969). *Nucl. Instr. Methods* **76**, 305.
Lee-Whiting, G. E. (1970). *Nucl. Instr. Methods* **83**, 232.
Lee-Whiting, G. E. (1972). *Nucl. Instr. Methods* **99**, 609.
Lenz, F. (1956a). *Z. Angew. Phys.* **8**, 492.
Lenz, F. (1956b). *Proc. Eur. Conf. Electron Microscopy, 1st, Stockholm* p. 48 [published 1957].
Lenz, F. (1957). *Optik* **14**, 74.
Lenz, F. (1973). In "Image Processing and Computer-Aided Design in Electron Optics" (P. W. Hawkes, ed.), p. 274. Academic Press, London and New York.
Lenz, F. (1980). *In* "Magnetic Electron Lens Properties" (P. W. Hawkes, ed.). Springer-Verlag, Berlin and New York.
Le Poole, J. B. (1972). *Proc. Eur. Cong. Electron Microscopy, 5th, Manchester* p. 130.
Lyubchik, Ya. G., and Fishkova, T. Ya (1974a). *Izv. Akad. Nauk. SSSR (Ser. Fiz.)* **38**, 1484; *Bull. Acad. Sci. USSR (Phys. Ser.)* **38**, No. 7, 116.
Lyubchik, Ya. G., and Fishkova, T. Ya. (1974b). *Zh. Tekh. Fiz.* **44**, 2272; *Sov. Phys. Tech. Phys.* **19**, 1403.

Lyubchik, Ya. G., Mokhnatkin, A. V., Chentzov, Yu. V., and Yavor, S. Ya. (1971). *Optiko-Mekh. Prom.* **38**, No. 11,7; *Sov. J. Opt. Technol.* **38**, 652.

Maclachlan, M. E. C. (1971). *In* "Electron Microscopy and Analysis" (W. C. Nixon, ed.), p. 98. Institute of Physics, London.

Maclachlan, M. E. C., and Hawkes, P. W. (1970). *Proc. Int. Cong. Electron Microscopy, 7th, Grenoble* **2**, 23.

Manabaev, Kh. Kh. (1976). *Zh. Tekh. Fiz.* **46**, 947, 953; *Sov. Phys. Tech. Phys.* **21**, 554, 558.

Marai, F. Z., and Mulvey, T. (1977). *Ultramicroscopy* **2**, 187.

Martin, J. P. (1972). Höchstauflösung im Elektronen-Rastermikroskop, Dissertation, Tübingen.

Marton, L. (1967). *Rev. Sci. Instr.* **38**, 130.

Marton, L., and Bol, K. (1947). *J. Appl. Phys.* **18**, 522.

Maruse, S., Hiratake, S., and Ichihashi, M. (1970a). *Japan. J. Appl. Phys.* **9**, 1549.

Maruse, S., Ichihashi, M., and Hiratake, S. (1970b). *Proc. Int. Cong. Electron Microscopy, 7th, Grenoble* **2**, 1.

Matsuda, H. (1971). *Nucl. Instr. Methods* **91**, 637.

Matsuda, H. (1974). *Int. J. Mass Spectrom. Ion Phys.* **14**, 219.

Matsuda, H., and Matsuo, T. (1971). *Int. J. Mass Spectrom. Ion Phys.* **6**, 385.

Matsuda, H., and Wollnik, H. (1970a). *Nucl. Instr. Methods* **77**, 40.

Matsuda, H., and Wollnik, H. (1970b). *Nucl. Instr. Methods* **77**, 283.

Matsuda, H., and Wollnik, H. (1972). *Nucl. Instr. Methods* **103**, 117.

Matsuda, J.-I., and Ura, K. (1974a). *Optik* **40**, 179.

Matsuda, J.-I., and Ura, K. (1974b). *Optik* **40**, 284.

Matsuda, J.-I., and Ura, K. (1974c). *Trans. Inst. Elec. Commun. Eng. Japan* **57B**, 273.

Matsuo, T., and Matsuda, H. (1971). *Int. J. Mass Spectrom. Ion Phys.* **6**, 361.

Mauer, J. L. (1978). *J. Vac. Sci. Technol.* **15**, 853.

Mauer, J. L., Pfeiffer, H. C., and Stickel, W. (1977). *IBM J. Res. Develop.* **21**, 514.

Mel'nikov, S. L., and Kossovskaya, E. D. (1975). *Zh. Tekh. Fiz.* **45**, 705; *Sov. Phys. Tech. Phys.* **20**, 447.

Menzel, E., and Kubalek, E. (1978). *Beiträge elektronenmikrosk. Direktabbildung Oberflächen* **11**, 47.

Menzel, E., and Kubalek, E. (1979). *Scanning Electron Microsc. 1979* **I**, 305.

Metherell, A. J. F. (1971). *Adv. Opt. Electron. Microsc.* **4**, 263.

Miller, J. C. P. (1966) In "Numerical Analysis, an Introduction" (J. Walsh, ed.), p. 63. Academic Press, London and New York.

Misell, D. L. (1978). "Image Analysis, Enhancement and Interpretation." North Holland, Amsterdam.

Moses, R. W. (1970). *Rev. Sci. Instr.* **41**, 729.

Moses, R. W. (1971a). *Rev. Sci. Instr.* **42**, 828.

Moses, R. W. (1971b). *Rev. Sci. Instr.* **42**, 832.

Moses, R. W. (1973). In "Image Processing and Computer-aided Design in Electron Optics" (P. W. Hawkes, ed.), p. 250. Academic Press, London and New York.

Moses, R. W. (1974). *Proc. Roy. Soc. (London)* **A339**, 483.

Mulvey, T. (1980). In "Magnetic Electron Lens Properties" (P. W. Hawkes, ed.). Springer-Verlag, Berlin and New York.

Mulvey, T., and Wallington, M. J. (1973). *Rept. Prog. Phys.* **36**, 347.

Munro, E. (1971). In "Electron Microscopy and Analysis" (W. C. Nixon, ed.), p. 84. Institute of Physics, London.

Munro, E. (1972). *Proc. Eur. Cong. Electron Microscopy, 5th, Manchester* p. 22.

152   P. W. HAWKES

Munro, E. (1973). In "Image Processing and Computer-Aided Design in Electron Optics" (P. W. Hawkes, ed.), p. 284. Academic Press, London and New York.
Munro, E. (1974). *Scanning Electron Microsc. 1974*, 35.
Munro, E., and Wittels, N. D. (1977). *Optik* **47**, 25.
Murillo, R. (1978). Contribution à l'étude des lentilles magnétiques utilisées en microscopie électronique à très haute tension. Thèse, Toulouse.
Natali, S., Di Chio, D., and Kuyatt, C. E. (1972a). *J. Res. Natl. Bur. Stand.* **76A**, 27.
Natali, S., Di Chio, D., Uva, E., and Kuyatt, C. E. (1972b). *Rev. Sci. Instr.* **43**, 80.
Ng, E. W., ed. (1979). "Symbolic and Algebraic Computation," *Lecture Notes in Computer Science*, Vol. 72. Springer-Verlag, Berlin and New York.
Nixon, W. C., Ahmed, H., Catto, C. J. D., Cleaver, J. R. A., Smith, K. C. A., Timbs, A. E., Turner, P. W., and Ross, P. M. (1977). In "Developments in Electron Microscopy and Analysis" (D. L. Misell, ed.), p. 13. Institute of Physics, Bristol.
Nixon, W. C., Ahmed, H., Catto, C. J. D., Cleaver, J. R. A., Smith, K. C. A., Timbs, A. E., and Turner, P. W. (1978). *Proc. Int. Cong. Electron Microscopy, 9th, Toronto* **1**, 10.
Nixon, W. C., Ahmed, H., Catto, C. J. D., Cleaver, J. R. A., Smith, K. C. A., Timbs, A. E., and Turner, P. W. (1980). In "Electron Microscopy and Analysis 1979" (T. Mulvey ed.), p. 443. Institute of Physics, Bristol.
Norman, A. C., and Moore, P. M. A. (1979). In "Symbolic and Algebraic Computation" (E. W. Ng, ed.), p. 258. Springer-Verlag, Berlin and New York.
Noven, H. (1963). *Naturwissenschaften* **50**, 469.
Noven, H. (1965). *Z. Angew. Phys.* **18**, 329.
Nurmanov, M. Sh. (1975). *Zh. Tekh. Fiz.* **45**, 242; *Sov. Phys. Tech. Phys.* **20**, 155.
Ohiwa, H. (1970). Elimination of third order aberrations in electron beam scanning systems, dissertation, Tokyo.
Ohiwa, H. (1977a). *J. Phys. D: Appl. Phys.* **10**, 1437.
Ohiwa, H. (1977b). In "High Voltage Electron Microscopy 1977" (T. Imura and H. Hashimoto, eds.), p. 61. Japanese Society of Electron Microscopy, Kyoto.
Ohiwa, H. (1978). *J. Vac. Sci. Technol.* **15**, 849.
Ohiwa, H. (1979). *Optik* **53**, 63.
Ohiwa, H., Goto, E., and Ono, A. (1971). *Electron. Commun. Japan* **54B**, No. 12, 44.
Oldfield, L. C. (1971). In "Electron Microscopy and Analysis" (W. C. Nixon, ed.), p. 94. Institute of Physics, London.
Oldfield, L. C. (1973a). Microwave cavities as electron lenses, dissertation, Cambridge.
Oldfield, L. C. (1973b). In "Image Processing and Computer-Aided Design in Electron Optics" (P. W. Hawkes, ed.), p. 370. Academic Press, London and New York.
Oldfield, L. C. (1974). *Proc. Int. Cong. Electron Microscopy, 8th, Canberra* **1**, 152.
Oldfield, L. C. (1976). *J. Phys. E: Sci. Instr.* **9**, 455.
Orloff, J., and Swanson, L. W. (1979). *Scanning Electron Microsc. 1979* **I**, 39.
Ovsyannikova, L. P., Utochkin, B. A., Fishkova, T. Ya, and Yavor, S. Ya. (1972). *Radiotekh. Elektron.* **17**, 1062; *Radio Eng. Electron. Phys.* **17**, 825.
Owen, G., and Nixon, W. C. (1973). *J. Vac. Sci. Technol.* **10**, 983.
Pandey, A. K., and Vaidya, N. C. (1976). In "Microscopie électronique à haute tension, 1975" (B. Jouffrey and P. Favard, eds.), p. 51. Société Française de Microscopie Electronique, Paris.
Pandey, A. K., and Vaidya, N. C. (1977). In "High Voltage Electron Microscopy 1977" (T. Imura and H. Hashimoto, eds.), p. 53. Japanese Society of Electron Microscopy, Tokyo.
Pandey, A. K., and Vaidya, N. C. (1978). *Bull. Electron Micr. Soc. India* **2**, No. 2.
Parker, N. W., Golladay, S. D., and Crewe, A. V. (1976a). *Proc. Annual Meeting EMSA, 34th (Miami Beach)* p. 464.

Parker, N. W., Golladay, S. D., and Crewe, A. V. (1976b). *Scanning Electron Microsc. 1976* 37.
Parker, N. W., Utlaut, M., and Isaacson, M. S. (1978). *Optik* **51**, 333.
Parker, N. W., Utlaut, M., and Isaacson, M. S. (1979). *Proc. Annual Meeting EMSA, 37th (San Antonio)*, p. 578.
Passow, C. (1976a). *Optik* **44**, 427.
Passow, C. (1976b). *Optik* **46**, 501.
Passow, C. (1976c). *Proc. Eur. Cong. Electron Microscopy, 6th, Jerusalem*, **1**, 375.
Passow, C. (1977). *Optik* **47**, 351.
Pearce-Percy, H. T. (1976). *J. Phys. E: Sci. Instr.* **9**, 135.
Pearce-Percy, H. T. (1978). *Scanning Electron Microsc. 1978* I, 41.
Pearce-Percy, H. T., and Cowley, J. M. (1976). *Optik* **44**, 273.
Pegis, R. J. (1961). *Prog. Opt.* **1**, 1.
Pejas, W. (1978). *Optik* **50**, 61.
Petrov, I. A. (1976). *Zh. Tekh. Fiz.* **46**, 1085; *Sov. Phys. Tech. Phys.* **21**, 640.
Petrov, I. A. (1977). *Zh. Tekh. Fiz.* **47**, 1380; *Sov. Phys. Tech. Phys.* **22**, 792.
Petrov, I. A., and Shpak, E. V. (1975). *Zh. Tekh. Fiz.* **45**, 191; *Sov. Phys. Tech. Phys.* **20**, 125.
Petrov, I. A., and Yavor, S. Ya. (1975). *Pis'ma Zh. Tekh. Fiz.* **1**, 651; *Sov. Phys. Tech. Phys. Lett.* **1**, 289.
Petrov, I. A., and Yavor, S. Ya. (1976). *Zh. Tekh. Fiz.* **46**, 1710; *Sov. Phys. Tech. Phys.* **21**, 985.
Petrov, I. A., Shpak, E. V., and Yavor, S. Ya. (1972). *Izv. Akad. Nauk SSSR (Ser. Fiz.)* **36**, 1922; *Bull. Acad. Sci. USSR (Phys. Ser.)* **36**, 1699.
Petrov, I. A., Shpak, E. V., and Yavor, S. Ya. (1974). *Izv. Akad. Nauk SSSR (Ser. Fiz.)* **38**, 1502; *Bull. Acad. Sci. USSR (Phys. Ser.)* **38**, No. 7, 133.
Petrov, I. A., Baranova, L. A., and Yavor, S. Ya. (1978). *Zh. Tekh. Fiz.* **48**, 408; *Sov. Phys. Tech. Phys.* **23**, 242.
Plies, E. (1973). *Optik* **38**, 502.
Plies, E. (1974). *Optik* **40**, 141.
Plies, E. (1978). *Proc. Int. Cong. Electron Microscopy, 9th, Toronto* **1**, 50.
Plies, E., and Hoppe, W. (1976). *Optik* **46**, 75.
Plies, E., and Rose, H. (1971). *Optik* **34**, 171.
Plies, E., and Rose, H. (1977). *Optik* **47**, 365.
Plows, G. S., and Nixon, W. C. (1968). *J. Phys. E: Sci. Instr.* **1**, 595.
Pöhner, W. (1976). *Optik* **45**, 443.
Pöhner, W. (1977). *Optik* **47**, 283.
Rao, V. R. M., and Nixon, W. C. (1978). *Proc. Int. Cong. Electron Microscopy, 9th, Toronto* **1**, 96.
Rauh, H. (1971). *Z. Naturforsch.* **26a**, 1667.
Rauh, H., and Kern, D. (1978). *Z. Naturforsch.* **33a**, 910.
Recknagel, A. (1936). *Z. Tech. Phys.* **17**, 643.
Recknagel, A. (1937). *Z. Physik* **104**, 381.
Reichenbach, M., and Rose, H. (1968–1969). *Optik* **28**, 475.
Riddle, G. H. N. (1978). *J. Vac. Sci. Technol.* **15**, 857.
Riecke, W. D. (1971). *Phil. Trans. Roy. Soc. London* **B261**, 15.
Riecke, W. D. (1974). *Proc. Int. Cong. Electron Microscopy, 8th, Canberra* **1**, 236.
Riecke, W. D. (1977). In "High Voltage Electron Microscopy, 1977" (T. Imura and H. Hashimoto, eds.), p. 73. Japanese Society of Electron Microscopy, Tokyo.
Ritz, E. F. (1979). *Adv. Electron. Electron. Phys.* **49**, 299.
Robinson, G. Y. (1971). *Rev. Sci. Instr.* **42**, 251.

Rose, H. (1966–1967). *Optik* **24**, 36.

Rose, H. (1967). *Optik* **25**, 587.

Rose, H. (1967–1968). *Optik* **26**, 289.

Rose, H. (1968). *Optik* **27**, 466, 497.

Rose, H. (1968–1969). *Optik* **28**, 462.

Rose, H. (1970). *Optik* **32**, 144.

Rose, H. (1971a). *Optik* **33**, 1.

Rose, H. (1971b). *Optik* **34**, 285.

Rose, H. (1978). *Optik* **51**, 15.

Rose, H., and Moses, R. W. (1973). *Optik* **37**, 316.

Rose, H., and Pejas, W. (1979). *Optik* **54**, 235.

Rose, H., and Petri, U. (1971). *Optik* **33**, 151.

Rose, H., and Plies, E. (1973). In "Image Processing and Computer-Aided Design in Electron Optics" (P. W. Hawkes, ed.), p. 344. Academic Press, London and New York.

Rose, H., and Plies, E. (1974). *Optik* **40**, 336.

Rus, P. J. (1965). Correctie van sferische aberratie met behulp van een gaaslens. Afstudeerverslag, Technische Hogeschool, Delft.

Rust, H.-P., Krahl, D., and Herrmann, K.-H. (1978). *Proc. Int. Cong. Electron Microscopy, 9th, Toronto* **1**, 90.

Saxton, W. O. (1978). *Adv. Electron. Electron Phys. Suppl. 10.*

Scherzer, O. (1936). *Z. Physik* **101**, 593.

Scherzer, O. (1946). *Phys. Blätter* **2**, 110.

Scherzer, O. (1947). *Optik* **2**, 114.

Scherzer, O. (1948). *Z. Naturforsch.* **3a**, 544.

Scherzer, O. (1949). *Optik* **5**, 497.

Scherzer, O. (1950). *Proc. Int. Cong. Electron Microscopy, 1st, Paris* p. 191 [published 1953].

Scherzer, O. (1978). *Proc. Int. Cong. Electron Microscopy, 9th, Toronto* **3**, 123.

Schiske, P. (1957). *Optik* **14**, 34.

Schiske, P. (1970). *Proc. Int. Cong. Electron Microscopy, 7th, Grenoble* **2**, 43.

Sekunova, L. M. (1977). *Zh. Tekh. Fiz.* **47**, 2030; *Sov. Phys. Tech. Phys.* **22**, 1181.

Sekunova, L. M., and Yakushev, E. M. (1975). *Zh. Tekh. Fiz.* **45**, 723, 732; *Sov. Phys. Tech. Phys.* **20**, 458, 463.

Seman, O. I. (1951). *Dokl. Akad. Nauk SSSR* **81**, 775.

Seman, O. I. (1952). *Zh. Tekh. Fiz.* **22**, 1581.

Seman, O. I. (1953a). *Dokl. Akad. Nauk SSSR* **93**, 443.

Seman, O. I. (1953b). *Zh. Eksp. Teoret. Fiz.* **24**, 581.

Seman, O. I. (1954). *Dokl. Akad. Nauk SSSR* **96**, 1151.

Seman, O. I. (1955). *Trudy Inst. Fiz. Astron. Akad. Nauk Eston. SSR* No. 2, 3 and 30.

Seman, O. I. (1958). *Uch. Zap. Rostov. na Donu Gos. Univ.* **68**, 77.

Senoussi, S. (1971). Étude d'un dispositif de filtrage des vitesses purement magnétique adaptable à un microscope électronique à très haute tension. Thèse de 3e Cycle, Paris-Sud, 59 pp.

Senoussi, S., Henry, L. and Castaing, R. (1971). *J. Microsc.* **11**, 19.

Septier, A. (1954). *Ann. Radioél.* **9**, 374.

Septier, A. (1966). *Adv. Opt. Electron Microsc.* **1**, 204.

Septier, A., ed. (1967). "Focusing of Charged Particles," two volumes. Academic Press, New York.

Shpak, E. V. (1978). *Zh. Tekh. Fiz.* **48**, 823; *Sov. Phys. Tech. Phys.* **23**, 484.

Siegbahn, K. (1942). *Ark. Mat. Astron. Fys.* **28A** (17), 27 pp.

Smith, D. L. (1970). *Nucl. Instr. Methods* **79**, 144.
Smith, T. (1921–1922). *Trans. Opt. Soc.* **23**, 311.
Smith, T. (1923–1924). *Trans. Opt. Soc.* **25**, 177.
Smith, D. J., and Gaskell, P. H. (1980). In "Electron Microscopy and Analysis 1979" (T. Mulvey, ed.), p. 441. Institute of Physics, Bristol.
Soa, E.-A. (1959). *Jenaer Jahrbuch* Pt. I, 115.
Soma, T. (1977). *Optik* **49**, 255.
Speidel, R., and Vorster, F. (1975). *Optik* **42**, 383.
Speidel, R., Kurz, D., and Gaukler, K. H. (1979). *Optik* **54**, 257.
Speidel, R., Kilger, G., and Kasper, E. (1979–1980). *Optik* **54**, 433.
Steffen, K. G. (1965). "High Energy Beam Optics." Wiley-Interscience, New York and London.
Strashkevich, A. M. (1962). *Zh. Tekh. Fiz.* **32**, 1142; *Sov. Phys. Tech. Phys.* **7**, 841.
Strojnik, A., and Passow, C. (1978a). *Optik* **50**, 169.
Strojnik, A., and Passow, C. (1978b). *Scanning Electron Microsc. 1978* I, 319.
Sturrock, P. A. (1951). *C. R. Acad. Sci. Paris* **233**, 146, 243.
Sturrock, P. A. (1955). "Static and Dynamic Electron Optics." Cambridge University Press, Cambridge, England.
Szilágyi, M. (1969). *Periodica Polytechnica (Electrical Engineering)* **13**, 221.
Szilágyi, M. (1977a). *Optik* **48**, 215.
Szilágyi, M. (1977b). *Optik* **49**, 223.
Szilágyi, M. (1978a). *Optik* **40**, 35.
Szilágyi, M. (1978b). *Optik* **50**, 121.
Szilágyi, M. (1978c). *Proc. Int. Cong. Electron Microscopy, 9th, Toronto* **1**, 30.
Szilágyi, M., Blaschta, F., Kando, K., Ovsyannikova, L. P., and Yavor, S. Ya. (1973). *Optik* **38**, 416.
Szilágyi, M., Blaschta, F., Ovsyannikova, L. P., and Yavor, S. Ya. (1974). *Optik* **39**, 351.
Tamura, N. (1979). *Scanning Electron Microsc. 1979* I, 31.
Tanguy, P., and Durand, A. (1978). *Nucl. Instr. Methods* **148**, 149.
Taya, S. (1978). *Nucl. Instr. Methods* **152**, 399.
Taya, S., Hirose, H. Tsuyama, H., and Matsuda, H. (1978). *Nucl. Instr. Methods* **152**, 407.
Thomson, M. G. R. (1972). *Optik* **34**, 528.
Thomson, M. G. R. (1973). *Proc. Annual Meeting EMSA, 31st (New Orleans)* p. 262.
Thomson, M. G. R. (1975). *J. Vac. Sci. Technol.* **12**, 1156.
Thomson, M. G. R., and Jacobsen, E. H. (1971). *Proc. Annual Meeting EMSA, 29th (Boston)* p. 16.
Tovey, N. K., and Wong, K. Y. (1978). *Scanning Electron Microsc. 1978* I, 381.
Tretner, W. (1950). *Optik* **7**, 242.
Tretner, W. (1954). *Optik* **11**, 312.
Tretner, W. (1955). *Optik* **12**, 293.
Tretner, W. (1956). *Optik* **13**, 516.
Tretner, W. (1959). *Optik* **16**, 155.
Typke, D. (1968–1969). *Optik* **28**, 488.
Typke, D. (1972a). *Optik* **34**, 573.
Typke, D. (1972b). *Optik* **36**, 124.
Typke, D. (1976). *Optik* **44**, 509.
Typke, D., and Hoppe, W. (1972). *Proc. Eur. Cong. Electron Microscopy, 5th, Manchester* p. 72.
Typke, D., Hoppe, W., Sessler, W., and Burger, M. (1976). *Proc. Eur. Cong. Electron Microscopy, 6th, Jerusalem* **1**, 334.

Ueda, M., and Nagami, K. (1975). *Optik* **43**, 319.

Ueda, M., Nagami, K., and Kuroda, H. (1969). *Oyo Butsuri* **38**, 1037.

Ueda, M. Nagami, K., and Kuroda, H. (1970). *Oyo Butsuri* **39**, 320.

Ueda, M. Nagami, K. and Kuroda, H. (1971). *Oyo Butsuri* **40**, 33.

Ueda, M., Nagami, K., and Kuroda, H. (1973). *Optik* **37**, 528.

Underwood, M. (1978). A magnetic lens coincidence spectrometer with reduced spherical aberration, dissertation, London.

Ura, K., and Morimura, N. (1973). *J. Vac. Sci. Technol.* **10**, 948.

Ura, K., Fujioka, H., and Hosokawa, T. (1978). *Scanning Electron Microsc. 1978* **I**, 747.

Uyeda, N., Kobayashi, T., Ishizuka, K., and Fujiyoshi, Y. (1978–1979). *Chem. Scr.* **14**, 47.

Vaidya, N. C. (1972). *Proc. Inst. Electr. Electron. Eng.* **60**, 245.

Vaidya, N. C. (1975a). *J. Phys. D: Appl. Phys.* **8**, 368.

Vaidya, N. C. (1975b). *Optik* **42**, 129.

Vaidya, N. C., and Garg, R. K. (1974). *Proc. Int. Cong. Electron Microscopy, 8th, Canberra* **1**, 150.

Vaidya, N. C., and Hawkes, P. W. (1970). *Proc. Int. Cong. Electron Microscopy, 7th, Grenoble* **2**, 19.

van der Merwe, J. P. (1978a). *Univ. Zululand Publ. Ser 3* No. 23.

van der Merwe, J. P. (1978b). *Univ. Zululand Publ. Ser. 3* No. 24.

van der Merwe, J. P. (1978c). *Univ. Zululand Publ. Ser. 3* No. 25.

van der Merwe, J. P. (1979). *S. Afr. J. Phys.* **2**, No. 4, 117.

van Heel, A. C. S. (1953). "Inleiding in de Optica." Martinus Nijhoff, The Hague; 5th ed. (1964).

Veneklasen, L. H. (1972). *Optik* **36**, 410.

Veneklasen, L. H., and Siegel, B. M. (1972). *J. Appl. Phys.* **43**, 4989.

Verster, J. L. (1963). *Philips Res. Rept.* **18**, 465.

Walsh, J. (1977). In "The State of the Art in Numerical Analysis" (D. Jacobs, ed.), p. 501. Academic Press, London and New York.

Watanabe, M., Taoka, T., Ohta, S., Anazawa, N., and Kato, S. (1974). *J. Phys. E: Sci. Instr.* **7**, 412.

Wiesner, J. C. (1973). *Scanning Electron Microsc. 1973*, 33.

Wiesner, J. C., and Everhart, T. E. (1969). *Proc. Annual Meeting EMSA, 27th (St. Paul)* p. 174.

Wiesner, J. E., and Everhart, T. E. (1973). *J. Appl. Phys.* **44**, 2140.

Wiesner, J. C., and Everhart, T. E. (1974). *J. Appl. Phys.* **45**, 2797.

Wollnik, H. (1967a). *Nucl. Instr. Methods* **52**, 250.

Wollnik, H. (1967b). *In* "Focusing of Charged Particles" (A. Septier, ed.), Vol. 2, p. 163. Academic Press, New York.

Wollnik, H. (1971). *Nucl. Instr. Methods* **95**, 453.

Wollnik, H. (1972). *Nucl. Instr. Methods* **103**, 479.

Wollnik, H., Matsuo, T., and Kasseckert, E. (1976). *Optik* **46**, 255.

Worster, J. (1969a). *Int. J. Electron.* **27**, 49.

Worster, J. (1969b). *Optik* **29**, 498.

Worster, J. (1970). *Int. J. Electron.* **28**, 117.

Yavor, S. Ya. (1968). "Fokusirovka Zaryazhennykh Chastits Kvadrupol'nymi Linzami" [Focusing of Charged Particles by means of Quadrupole Lenses]. Atomizdat, Moscow.

Yavor, S. Ya. (1971). *Radiotekh. Elektron.* **16**, 2008; *Radio Eng. Electron. Phys.* **16**, 1797.

Yavor, S. Ya., Ovsyannikova, L. P., and Baranova, L. A. (1972). *Nucl. Instr. Methods* **99**, 103.

Zanchi, G., Perez, J. Ph., and Sevely, J. (1975). *Optik* **43**, 495.
Zanchi, G., Sevely, J., and Jouffrey, B. (1977a). *J. Microsc. Spectr. Electron.* **2**, 95.
Zanchi, G., Sevely, J., and Jouffrey, B. (1977b). *Optik* **48**, 173.
Zworykin, V. K., Morton, G. A., Ramberg, E. G., Hillier, J., and Vance, A. W. (1945). "Electron Optics and the Electron Microscope." Wiley, New York, and Chapman and Hall, London.

Emittance and Brightness:
Definitions and Measurements*

CLAUDE LEJEUNE AND JEAN AUBERT

*Institut d'Electronique Fondamentale
Université Paris
Orsay, France*

I. Introduction

The use of a beam of charged particles of a given energy requires the presence of a series of optical elements between the particle emitter and the target. These elements play various roles: formation of the beam, its acceleration and transport, selection of particles of interest, and very often, focusing of the beam into a spot. This set of elements constitutes the "particle gun" and the "beam transport system."

In order to describe the performance of a beam or a gun, we must first consider the energy distribution of the beam—the kinetic energy of the

* Translated from the French by Dr. P. W. Hawkes of the C.N.R.S. Laboratory of Electron Optics in Toulouse.

particles and any possible energy spread—and the total beam intensity, together with any time structure. Next, we must examine the optical properties of the beam, which should accurately describe its behavior in a beam transport system. In particular, we are interested in its suitability for forming high-quality images (in microscopes and spectrometers, for example); the possibility of focusing it into a very small spot without excessive angular spread of the trajectories (for interaction experiments involving targets); and its capacity for being transported over long distances satisfactorily, in other words, without losses and with inexpensive and compact equipment (microwave tubes, particle accelerators). These optical qualities are, of course, dependent on the intensity and energy distribution of the beam; quantitative characterization of these various aspects of the optical properties must therefore be based on an analysis of the behavior of an ensemble of charged particles traveling in an electromagnetic field, and from a formal viewpoint this will represent the combination of beam formation unit and beam transport system. If these characteristic quantities are to give meaningful information about the performance of the beam in its transport system, they must be based on the invariants of motion. These must be determined, even at the cost of restrictive conditions, as being imposed on either the beam or the transport system. With these invariance conditions satisfied, the performance of the beam will be equally characteristic of that of the gun itself. If, however, invariance is not maintained, whatever beam cross section we consider, there must be a deterioration in the optical properties, and it should be possible to analyze the origin of this in terms of the corresponding experimental information.

There are two main analytical approaches to the dynamics of beams of charged particles, one based on the "paraxial ray formalism," the other on the "Hamiltonian formalism." The former is developed in terms of particle trajectories in real space as calculated from the second-order equations of motion of a single particle. In the context of the linear approximation—or Gaussian optics approximation—the particles are assumed to travel near some optic axis and only linear transverse variations of the electric and magnetic fields are considered. This approach then leads to the "paraxial ray equation," which involves the fields and their derivatives calculated on the optical axis (Lawson, 1977). This equation is the basis for corpuscular optics and is very suitable for studying laminar beams, for which all the trajectories are related. It enables us to explore focusing and image-forming properties and to study the position and size of the image by considering a few particular rays (Grivet, 1965, 1972) and, if necessary, the self-fields due to space charge (Pierce, 1959; Kirstein *et al.,* 1967; Nagy and Szilágyi, 1974). The operating principles of each type of component found in transport systems have thus been examined in detail (see Septier, 1967, and Lawson, 1977, for general accounts and Steffen, 1965, for the particular case of high energies). Nevertheless, to be strictly satisfied, laminarity requires both a point emitter and optical elements free of aberrations—that is, perfectly linear and nondispersive. These conditions clearly cannot be satisfied exactly in practice: real sources are extended and have thermal velocity spread, geometric aberrations and aberrations due to space charge are not always negligible, and alignment is never perfect . . . !

In order to include these reasons for beam nonlaminarity, the concepts of "emittance" and especially of "brightness" have been introduced, by analogy with the concepts of "geometrical etendue" and "luminance," commonly used in optics. These quantities are defined for beams of relatively small cross section and small inclination relative to the optic axis. Their invariance is then a consequence of the Helmholtz–Lagrange theorem, which in turn imposes certain restrictive conditions (Davey, 1971). With the aid of these concepts, the paraxial formalism has been improved to explain the influence of thermal effects on the focal properties of the narrow beams used in microscopy and in microwave tubes (Kirstein *et al.,* 1967; Levi-Setti, this volume, p. 261). Furthermore, a "paraxial envelope equation" has been associated with the paraxial ray equation for a particle; provided that the emittance is invariant, and hence that the transport optics has no aberrations, this envelope equation describes the behavior of a "perfect beam." The latter is a nonlaminar beam, the particular phase space distribution function of which is specially chosen to enable the envelope equation to be derived (Lawson, 1975).

This preliminary extension to real beams proves to be inadequate, however, when we wish to follow the evolution of an intense beam with appreciable spatial dimensions in a complicated transport system, such as those encountered in large accelerators. During the 1950s, when these machines were being developed, progressively more refined theoretical and experimental procedures for studying the variation of the beam density distribution function in phase space became necessary, for various reasons. First, by means of such methods, the design and operating parameters of a beam transport system for a given beam could be determined a priori: this is the problem of "beam line design" (Banford, 1966; Wilson and Brewer, 1973). Second, the parameters of the beam transport system could subsequently be optimized to prevent deterioration of the injected beam: this is the problem of "beam line control and optimization." The solution of these problems is considerably simplified by the use of the "Hamiltonian formalism," which governs the trajectories of points representing particles in phase space. The collective or statistical aspect of this formalism can be exploited by studying the trajectories in phase space and the associated invariants, which may involve the trajectories themselves or the entire distribution of trajectories. The concept of phase space conservation, which results from Liouville's theorem, as well as that of the adiabatic variation of the Hamiltonian during the motion, have been extensively used in the accelerator literature. The problem of phase space dynamics has been exhaustively examined by Lichtenberg (1969). The concepts of brightness and emittance were introduced in terms of the invariants that result from Liouville's theorem and subsuquently refined, in order to obtain a description of the particle distribution function in phase space that is both realistic and well suited to the practical problems in question.

A considerable amount of work has been devoted to these problems, but all too often the results have remained in the form of unclassified internal reports, circulated between the various high-energy physics laboratories but otherwise little known. As a result, many of these findings are no longer accessible. Moreover, very few papers have been devoted to the sophisticated concepts of brightness and emittance: their definitions, the invariance conditions, and the methods of measurement. The invariance of the emittance, regarded as a consequence of Liouville's theorem, and the apparent violations of this, were however discussed by Banford (1966). Lapostolle (1969) drew attention to the distinction that need to be drawn between "section emittance" and "projection emittance," and also introduced the notion of root-mean-square (rms) emittance (Lapostolle, 1972), later discussed more exactly by Lawson et al. (1973). The relation between these various emittances and the brightness, has, conversely, always been treated in a very summary fashion (Van Steenbergen, 1965; Septier, 1967; Walcher, 1972; Lawson, 1977). As far as the interpretation of the results obtained by the various methods developed in the main accelerator centers is concerned, and the comparison of the information obtained, the only authoritative reference is the article by Van Steenbergen (1967)b, which antedates the distinctions emphasized by Lapostolle (1969). Even today, these distinctions are rarely mentioned when results are quoted, with the result that comparisons are all too often made between quantities that are not comparable, or comparable only in very special conditions. In addition to this source of confusion, we must mention the misunderstanding that can arise from the lack of standardization in terminology, notation, definitions, and units. Ingrained habit has meant that different conventions have become traditional among each of the main group of users. Confronted with this situation, we felt that it was desirable to begin by imposing some unity on all these problems. After a brief recapitulation of the Hamiltonian formalism, therefore, we summarize the conditions in which Liouville's theorem can be used legitimately in phase space of six, four, and two dimensions. It is then possible to develop procedures for applying Liouville's theorem to the ensemble of particles, the variation of the distribution function of which illustrates the behavior of the beam as it propagates (Section II,A).

The basic quantities used to characterize the domain occupied by the points representing the beam are then introduced, in a transverse four-dimensional space; this is the space that is explored experimentally and is referred to as trace space. The invariance of the characteristic quantities—brightness, hyperemittance, emittance, and section emittance—in this domain is then discussed, as are the relations between emittance and brightness and between the brightness of a beam and the luminance of a radiative surface (Section II,B).

After a brief examination of the special features of distribution functions of real beams, we describe the improvements that have been made to these basic definitions, to take account of these special features. These improvements enable us to make valid comparisons between the performances of beams and to reveal any deterioration of the optical properties during propagation, using the "intensity–emittance curve" and the "rms emittance"; they also simplify the task of analyzing beam dynamics (using the envelope equation or matrix transformations) by an idealization of the real domain and the introduce of an "equivalent perfect beam," the variation of which is a useful approximation to that of the real beam associated with it (Section II,C).

Section III is devoted to methods of measuring emittance and brightness. A classification of the various devices in use is suggested, based on the principle they use and on the type of information they are capable of giving. The ways of interpreting the information and their validity are examined, with reference to the characteristic quantities mentioned earlier. We emphasize the advantages and drawbacks of the different methods and arrangements (the nature of the information, sensitivity, resolution, ease of use, and possibility of automation, for example) so that the potential user can choose the technique that best suits the beam in question and the information required.

In a forthcoming review, we plan to examine the problems associated with beam transport and with the deterioration of beam emittance and brightness between source and zone of application, whether an image or a target spot.

II. Definitions and Basic Properties

A. Hamiltonian Formalism and Liouville's Theorem

1. Hamiltonian Formalism

a. *The Hamiltonian.*   The Newtonian equations of motion are identical, after suitable transformation, with the Euler–Lagrange equations corresponding to the Lagrangian

$$L(q_i, \dot{q}_i, t) \tag{1}$$

which is a function of a set of generalized coordinates q_i (positions) and their total-time derivatives $\dot{q}_i = dq_i/dt$ (velocities). A system with k degrees of freedom depends on $2k$ dynamical variables and time t. The conjugate or canonical momentum corresponding to a position coordinate, q_i, is defined with the aid of the Lagrangian thus:

$$p_i = \partial L/\partial \dot{q}_i \tag{2}$$

The Hamiltonian is then given by

$$H(p_i, q_i, t) = \sum_1^k p_i q_i - L \tag{3}$$

The Hamiltonian—or canonical—equations of motion consist of a set of $2k$ first-order differential equations

$$\begin{aligned} \dot{q}_i &= dq_i/dt = \partial H/\partial p_i \\ \dot{p}_i &= dp_i/dt = -\partial H/\partial q_i \end{aligned} \tag{4}$$

one pair for each degree of freedom. Conversely, the system consisting of the particles and the external forces is said to be Hamiltonian if there exists a function $H(q_1, \ldots, q_i, \ldots, q_k; p_1, \ldots, p_i, \ldots, p_k, t)$, depending on the coordinates, the conjugate momenta, and possibly the time, such that the equations of motion are of the form of Eqs. (4), from which it can be shown that

$$\dot{H} \equiv dH/dt = \partial H/\partial t \tag{5}$$

The Hamiltonian is a "total energy" function, which constitutes one of the advantages of this formalism, energy being a familiar concept to physicists and engineers. From Eqs. (4), one may anticipate that H will include a potential energy term ($\dot{p}_i$ is the force in the i direction) and a kinetic energy term ($\dot{q}_i$ is the velocity). If time does not appear explicity in H, the latter is an invariant of motion (see Eq. 5) and is the sum of the potential and kinetic energy; the latter property remains approximately valid for nonrelativistic motion subject to time-varying forces.

b. *Phase Space Representation.* The motion of a particle having k degrees of freedom may be represented as the position of a point with coordinates $(q_1, \ldots, q_k, p_1, \ldots, p_k)$ in a $2k$-dimensional space, known as "phase space."

For a gas consisting of N particles each having three degrees of freedom, the state of the system at time t may be represented by a point in $6N$-dimensional phase space, referred to as "Γ_{6N} space." In order to characterize the dynamics of the system a probability function f_{6N} $(p_1, \ldots, p_{3N}, q_1, \ldots, q_{3N}, t)$ is associated with every point in Γ_{6N} space. This function is known as the density distribution in phase space; the more probable configurations of the ensemble of particles are represented by higher values of the phase space density.

For the particular but common case of N *identical and noninteracting particles*, the Hamiltonian of a particle depends only on its six coordinates, $H(q_1, q_2, q_3, p_1, p_2, p_3, t)$, and the motion of each particle is described by six equations of the form given in Eqs. (4). The motion will then be represented in a six-dimensional phase space (Γ_6 space). The state of the whole system at an instant of time is characterized by a set of points in Γ_6 space, with which is associated a real *density in phase space* and a corresponding *distribution function of density*

$$f_6(p_1, p_2, p_3, q_1, q_2, q_3, t) = f_6(\mathbf{p}, \mathbf{q}, t) \tag{6}$$

The number of particles in an element of volume of phase space, $d\mathcal{V}_6 = dp_1\, dp_2\, dp_3\, dq_1\, dq_2\, dq_3$, in the vicinity of the point in phase space defined by the vectors $\mathbf{p}$ and $\mathbf{q}$ is therefore

$$d^6N = f_6(\mathbf{p}, \mathbf{q}, t)\, d\mathcal{V}_6 \tag{7}$$

The extension in phase space is the volume of the domain occupied by the representative points of the N particles, that is,

$$\mathcal{V}_6 = \int_{\text{all points}} d\mathcal{V}_6 \tag{8}$$

a quantity that can be defined precisely only if the domain has well-defined boundaries. For a system evolving toward equilibrium, f may be an explicit function of time. Conversely, when the system has attained a steady state, f does not depend explicitly on time although for individual particles, $\mathbf{p}$ and $\mathbf{q}$ do depend on time.

Further simplification arises if the motion associated with each degree of freedom is independent of the other two. The Hamiltonian then separates into a sum of terms, each involving only one p_i, q_i pair, and each pair of Eqs. (4) is then independent of the other two pairs:

$$H(\mathbf{p}, \mathbf{q}, t) = H_1(p_1, q_1, t) + H_2(p_2, q_2, t) + H_3(p_3, q_3, t) \qquad (9a)$$

$$\dot{p}_i = -\partial H_i(p_i, q_i, t)/\partial q_i, \qquad \dot{q}_i = \partial H_i/\partial p_i, \qquad i = 1, 2, 3 \qquad (9b)$$

In these conditions, the motion of a particle can be represented by a trajectory in each of the three two-dimensional-phase planes associated with each degree of freedom (Γ_2^i phase plane). It is then easy to visualize the motion of a particle in phase space as well as the density of the points in the phase plane, which may be shown along a third axis. As far as the motion of a group of particles is concerned, the Hamiltonian formalism provides a great deal of information without requiring any knowledge of the individual paths either in phase space or in real or "configuration" space. This information can be extracted by considering both the particular properties of trajectories in phase space and the invariants of motion. We summarize without proof (see Lichtenberg, 1969, Chapter 1) the main properties of the trajectories associated with the coordinates (p, q) and independent of the two other, that is, satisfying Eqs. (9b).

    i. The trajectories in phase plane depend uniquely on the initial values (p_0, q_0) and the time. Thus, at a given instant of time the trajectories corresponding to different initial pairs nowhere intersect. As a consequence, if the Hamiltonian is time independent—so that H is an invariant of motion—the trajectories in the phase plane Γ_2 are independent of time and cannot intersect. In the case of an oscillatory system, the curves of constant H are closed and do not intersect.

    ii. A boundary in the phase plane, C_1, that encloses a group of particles at time t_1 will transform into a boundary C_2 at time t_2 enclosing the same group of particles. The limits to the domain within which a large group of particles are enclosed at time t can therefore be traced by following the motion of a much smaller number of boundary particles.

    iii. Phase space domains bounded by straight lines or by ellipses are very convenient when working with linear systems of forces. A linear transformation that maps the initial coordinates in phase space into their final values can then be defined. It can be shown straightforwardly that straight lines transform into straight lines, parallel lines remaining parallel, and that ellipses transform into ellipses. For Hamiltonian systems, the area of the ellipse is conserved, although the eccentricity changes, since the determinant of the transfer matrix is equal to unity for nondissipative equations of motion.

    For discussion of the invariants of motion, and in particular those related to integral invariants, the reader is referred to Lichtenberg (1969) or texts on classical mechanics (e.g., Goldstein, 1950). The present account is restricted to the invariants associated with Liouville's theorem.

2. Liouville's Theorem

a. *Statement and Validity.*   Liouville invariance corresponds to the condition of continuity of the density f of phase points, treated as a gas without sources and sinks (Judd, 1958; Pierce, 1954). Taking into account the canonical Eqs. (4), the continuity equation in phase space leads to

$$\frac{df}{dt} = 0 \tag{10}$$

That is, the total time derivative of the density distribution function must vanish. Condition (10) may be written in the form

$$\frac{df}{dt} = \frac{\partial f}{\partial t} + \sum_{1}^{k} \left(\frac{\partial f}{\partial q_i} \, \dot{q}_i + \frac{\partial f}{\partial p_i} \, \dot{p}_i \right) = 0 \tag{11}$$

which emphasizes the rate of change of the density at a point corresponding to a given particle as it moves in phase space, the $\dot{q}_i$ and $\dot{p}_i$ being the $2k$ components of the "velocity" of a point in phase space. Liouville's theorem then states that:

> For Hamiltonian systems, the density of the representative points — or particles — in the appropriate phase space is invariant along the trajectory of any given point.

The theorem can also be expressed in terms of the invariance of the phase space hypervolume enclosing a chosen group of points as they move in phase space: the fictitious gas of phase points thus behaves as an incompressible fluid:

$$\frac{d\mathcal{V}}{dt} = 0 \qquad \text{or} \qquad \mathcal{V} = \int_{N \text{ points}} d\mathcal{V} = \text{const} \tag{12}$$

The shape of the domain boundary in phase space may be considerably deformed, for example, under the effect of nonlinear forces (filamentation phenomenon, see Lichtenberg 1969), but the volume enclosed remains constant. Liouville's theorem applies to Hamiltonian systems, that is, conservative systems in which the forces can be derived from a potential $\phi(\mathbf{q}, t)$, which may be time dependent but must not depend on the momentum of the particles. Any system of external macroscopic electric and magnetic fields acting on charged particles is therefore Hamiltonian if the following conditions are satisfied:

1. Wave mechanical effects can be ignored.
2. Electromagnetic radiation can be neglected.
3. There are no close-range interactions between particles or with targets (collisions).
4. There are no long-range interactions depending on particle velocity such as those that may be caused by collective space charge fields.

Provided that these conditions are all satisfied, Liouville's theorem applies in the phase space in which the Hamiltonian is evaluated, and subject to any special features of the system such as symmetry and any possible interdependence between the degrees of freedom. It is not, however, necessary actually to calculate the Hamiltonian but only to establish that it exists; for this a set of coordinates satisfying Eqs. (4) or a more restrictive form, such as Eqs. (9), must be found, which are hence canonically conjugate. In particular cases, it can be convenient to use some independent variable other than the time t, and the position coordinates need not describe spatial position (see following section). Liouville invariance may thus be applied to each of the following:

1. f_{6N} in Γ_{6N} phase space for nonidentical or long-range interacting particles each with three degrees of freedom (to include rotational degrees of freedom, higher dimensional phase spaces are required);
2. f_6 in Γ_6 phase space for identical noninteracting particles;
3. f_4 in Γ_4 phase space if two degrees of freedom are coupled but independent of the third;
4. f_2 in Γ_2 phase plane if the degree of freedom is independent.

One point must be emphasized when applying Liouville invariance: it is essential to specify precisely which assembly of particles is being analyzed. For each phase plane (or Γ_4 phase space) one may, for example, consider the motion of the N particles of the whole system (or of a fraction of it) whatever the coordinates associated with the two other components. The domain in the Γ_2 phase plane then appears as the *projection* of the hypervolume occupied in Γ_6 onto the particular Γ_2 phase plane, and the density f_2 satisfies the relations

$$f_2(p_1, q_1) = \int\int\int\int f_6(p_1, p_2, p_3, q_1, q_2, q_3) \, dp_2 \, dp_3 \, dq_2 \, dq_3 \quad (13)$$

$$N = \int\int f_2(p_1, q_1) \, dp_1 \, dq_1 \quad (14)$$

where as the projected phase plane area is

$$\mathscr{A}^{q_1} = \iint_{\text{all } N \text{ points}} dp_1 \, dq_1 \tag{15}$$

Alternatively, one may consider the behavior of a limited fraction of the particle cloud—for example, particles satisfying conditions imposed on the coordinates of the other two degrees of freedom. Particular "*sections*" through Γ_6 phase space are then obtained. If we assume that $p_2 = p_3 = q_2 = q_3 = 0$, and hence follow only particles that move in the vicinity of the $p_1 - q_1$ phase plane, the density distribution function $d_2(p_1, q_1)$ will be proportional to

$$d_2(p_1, q_1) \sim f_6(p_1, q_1, 0, 0, 0, 0) \tag{16}$$

the proportionality factor depending on the "width" of the allowed region in the neighborhood of the $p_1 - q_1$ plane (Section III).

From the properties previously described it may be shown that if the degrees of freedom are not coupled, Liouville invariance applies both to "projection" and to "section" phase space domains. These domains do not, however, refer to the same number of particles, and, in general, their extent and density in phase space are different. These considerations must be kept in mind for a proper analysis of beam emittance measurements (Section III).

b. *Extension of Liouville's Theorem.* (1) *Influence of non-Hamiltonian forces.* If the non-Hamiltonian forces are denoted by Q_i, generalized momenta may be defined thus:

$$\dot{p}_i = -\partial H/\partial q_i + Q_i \tag{17}$$

In the associated generalized phase space the Liouville invariance condition, Eq. (10), becomes

$$\frac{df}{dt} = -f \sum_1^k \frac{\partial Q_i}{\partial p_i} \tag{18}$$

This is the Boltzmann equation, which gives the rate of change of phase space density under the action of non-Hamiltonian forces. It transpires that, (1) the phase space density and extension may be preserved, provided that the non-Hamiltonian forces are not dependent on the momenta, and (2) the sign of the derivative $\partial Q_i/\partial p_i$, rather than the sign of Q_i determines whether the phase space volume increases or decreases ($Q_i < 0$ for a lossy system). For radiating systems, the volume usually decreases whereas collisional effects increase the volume and decrease the density (Lichtenberg, 1969). Lawson (1977) has devoted a chapter of his book to an analysis of the behavior of beams with energy loss and particle scattering.

(2) *Influence of space charge forces.*   The Γ_{6N} phase space is of little use in comparison with the more physical Γ_6 phase space. It is therefore of interest to investigate the conditions in which Liouville invariance is valid in Γ_6 when interparticle coulomb forces are present. Various approaches to the problem have been developed, either directly (Mills and Sessler, 1958) or from the "B B G K Y hierarchy" (Rostoker and Rosenbluth, 1960). A synthesis has been proposed by Lichtenberg (1969), which leads to the conclusion that Liouville's theorem applies approximately in Γ_6 phase space in the limit of very small correlation between particles, so that the behavior of each particle can be considered identical with that of all the others, each particle thus moving in the collective field of all the others. Quantitatively, this situation is satisfied if the number of particles in the Debye sphere surrounding any particle is large, that is,

$$\lambda_D \gg n^{-1/3} \tag{19}$$

where n is the density of charged particles in real space and λ_D is the Debye length, the ratio of the thermal velocity, $(kT/M)^{1/2}$, to the plasma frequency $\omega_p = (q^2 n/M\epsilon_0)^{1/2}$, q and M being the particle charge and mass. For a more detailed definition of the Debye length applied to a beam, see Lawson (1977). In the limit of the inequality (19), the individual fluctuations of potential relative to the motion of a given particle are outweighted by the effect of the surrounding cloud. A smoothed out potential due to all particles may then be calculated from the density distribution in real space and its contribution included in the Hamiltonian system of forces appearing in Liouville's equation (11). This procedure leads on to the derivation of the Maxwell–Vlasov equation, which describes the self-consistent behavior of an assembly of charged particles (see standard textbooks on plasma).

3. Phase Space Representation of Beams

a. *Independent Variable and Representative Assembly.*   The notion of a beam is associated with the existence of a privileged direction, such that the velocity component of interest in this so-called "direction of propagation" is much greater than those describing transverse displacements. The axis of propagation need not be straight; it may be defined by some particular trajectory, selected as reference curve in view of the symmetry of the system and referred to as the optic axis. The position of a particle P in the vicinity of this axis is characterized by a set of three orthogonal curvilinear coordinates: z, x, y, where z is the distance along the optic axis measured from some fixed initial point to the point on the axis closest to P, and x and y are the transverse displacements from the optic axis, measured along the normal and binormal, respectively (that is, along the Frenet unit vectors). If the optic axis is a straight line, these two directions remain parallel. The beams and the force fields that we shall be considering are assumed to exhibit either rotational symmetry or two planes of symmetry, which contain the x and y axes. These two geometries correspond to those encountered with real beams, always supposing that the problems of aligning the various optical components of the beam transport system have been solved.

Under the action of an electromagnetic field, the motion of identical, nonradiating, and noninteracting particles forming a beam may be represented in a Γ_6 phase space of position and canonical momentum: x, y, z, p_x, p_y, p_z, with time as independent variable. We recall that the electrodynamic momentum vector is given by

$$\mathbf{p} = m\mathbf{v} + q\mathbf{A} \tag{20}$$

which degenerates to the mechanical momentum only if the magnetic vector potential ($\mathbf{A}$) vanishes. It is now necessary to choose the assembly of particles, the evolution of which along the optic axis will characterize the behavior of the beam through its transport system; the result will correspond to any "probe" plane $z = z_p$ in which the beam structure is to be investigated and may vary with time if the beam possesses a time structure. With a view to numerical simulation of the beam dynamics, this representative assembly may conveniently be defined as the group of N particles injected into (or emitted from) a particular cross section (z_{in}) during a short period of time (δt) about the time of injection (t_{in}). If I is the beam current and q the particle charge, we have $qN = I \, \delta t$. For a continuous beam, δt can be set equal to the unit of time; we shall return to this special case below.* In the most general case, in which the axial and transverse motions are coupled, this assembly occupies a six-dimensional hypervolume in Γ_6, to which Liouville's theorem can be applied. The evolution of this hypervolume is characterized by that of the corresponding distribution function

$$f_6(x, y, z, p_x, p_y, p_z; t) \tag{21}$$

This in turn may be characterized at every time t by its projections on each of the three Γ_2 phase planes, with

$$I = \int_{\mathcal{V}_6} f_6 \, d\mathcal{V}_6 = \iint_{\mathcal{A}_2^x} f_2^x(x, p_x) \, dx \, dp_x = \cdots \tag{22}$$

---

* For a bunched beam, it is often convenient to consider the density distribution of all the particles of a bunch at time t_{in}.

The variation of these different density distributions with the position of the assembly along the optic axis can be obtained via the equation of motion of a reference test particle, the center of gravity of the original distribution for preference. If the solution of this equation is denoted by $z_g(t)$ and the coordinates of any other particle relative to those of the test particle by Δz, Δp_z, the density distribution may be obtained from Eq. (21) as a function of the independent variable z_g in the form

$$f_6(x, y, \Delta_z, p_x, p_y, \Delta p_z; z_g) \tag{23}$$

The distribution is now centrosymmetric as far as the spread of axial positions and momenta is concerned. It must, however, be emphasized that the projections of such a distribution cannot be rigorously determined experimentally because the experimental devices are situated in various transverse cross sections of the beam (z_p). They thus give information about the particles as they flow across these sections, which imposes the condition: $\Delta z = 0$, whatever the further purpose of the device (see below and Section III). This condition defines a "section" through the region occupied in Γ_6 phase space, and the measurements will therefore not characterize the evolution of the assembly considered initially.

The curvilinear abscissa z can also be introduced as independent variable, instead of time, directly into the equations of motion of a particle (Courant and Snyder, 1958; Montague, 1977). The Hamiltonian form is again obtained with a new Hamiltonian, $G = -p_z$, which no longer has the dimensions of energy; the pairs of canonically conjugate variables are now

$$x, p_x; \quad y, p_y; \quad t, -H \tag{24}$$

This set of variables is very convenient because the external forces are usually given in terms of axial position. It is particularly useful for analysing the beam dynamics in radiofrequency (rf) accelerators. Again choosing a reference particle, the density distribution in Γ_6 phase space can be obtained in a form similar to Eq. (23):

$$f_6(x, p_x, y, p_y, \Delta t, -\Delta H; z) \tag{25}$$

This function satisfies Liouville's theorem. The spread in axial position and momentum is now expressed in terms of phase shift and energy difference relative to the reference particle; these parameters form the set of coordinates defining "synchrotron phase space" (Hereward, 1970; Lichtenberg, 1969).

b. *Transverse Phase Space.*   If the axial and transverse motions of the particles are not coupled, then Liouville invariance can be applied to the projection of the hypervolume occupied by the particles in Γ_6 phase space onto the Γ_4 transverse phase space (x, p_x, y, p_y) and also to its projection onto the Γ_2 axial phase plane $(\Delta z, \Delta p_z)$ [or $(\Delta t, \Delta H)$]. As we have seen, these invariances can be legitimately exploited only in a numerical approach, however, and not in an experimental study of the behavior of the beam. This result is more readily appreciated when we realize that a natural dispersion in the axial velocities is visible as a spread of positions about the reference particle. The particles analyzed at z_p, which cross this section within time δt of the moment when the reference particle crosses, do not belong to the same assembly of N particles as those initially injected. Liouville's theorem does not strictly apply to them, therefore. This problem is a consequence of the difference between geometric space—in which the measuring equipment is located—and phase space, in which Liouville's theorem applies and which we should like to explore.

This restriction vanishes if we assume that the position of any particle along the optic axis is the same for all the particles or, in other words one drift velocity along the axis is common to all the particles of the assembly. The relationship $z_g(t)$ is then also common to all particles. The dispersion in momentum and position then disappears whichever beam cross section we consider: $\Delta z = 0$ and $\Delta p_z = 0$ (or $\Delta t = 0$, $\Delta H = 0$). From Eq. (23) for the density, we see that the ensemble of points representing the assembly occupies a purely transverse four-dimensional domain while the projection on the Γ_2 axial phase plane collapses to a singular point. This degenerate domain of $\mathscr{V}_6$ in $\mathscr{V}_4$ is then accessible to experiment, in principle at least, since $\Delta z = 0$ (or $\Delta t = 0$). It can, furthermore, be related to the representative distribution in the Γ_6 phase space of the ensemble N_T of beam particles, which in steady state conditions occupy all the space available between the injection and exit planes. The section through this domain by the hyperplane $z = z_p$ and $p_z = p_z(z_p)$ gives a distribution in four transverse dimensions characterizing the ensemble of $N(z_p, t)$ particles within unit length of the beam around the section with abscissa z_p (and at time t, if the beam is not continuous). If the distribution over the axial phase plane is singular (with the above approximations), the density distribution of the particles present in a section of the beam at a given instant and the flux distribution of transverse phase space per unit time through this section will be identical apart from a multiplicative factor. The latter can be obtained from the relation between N and $N(z_p)$, namely,

$$N = N(z_p)v(z_p) \tag{26}$$

The above assumptions are important for not only do they enable us to interpret the experimental measurements correctly, but they are also the basis upon which the matrix formalism is constructed; the latter gives a compact description of the transformation of the transverse phase space and is used in the design and optimization of beam transport systems (Banford, 1966; Lichtenberg, 1969) for both static beam optics and dynamical accelerator problems. From the practical standpoint, the assumptions are justified in the following conditions:

1. Effects due to space charge fields are negligible; for quantitative criteria, see, for example, Lawson (1977) or Osher (1977).
2. The trajectories remain close to the axis and are never steeply inclined to it, so that the transverse equations of motion are linear while the axial motion is unaffected by small transverse displacements and velocities. This is the paraxial (or gaussian) optics approximation.
3. The initial axial velocity spread is sufficiently small for there to be no significant separation between the trajectories of particles with different initial energies after a certain amount of acceleration.

Fortunately, these requirements are very often satisfied by the higher-energy particles of beams produced by electron or ion guns, which have little initial energy spread. All three assumptions can, however, break down in the zone in which beams from an emitter are formed and accelerated. Similarly, interactions due to the space charge and axial energy spread of the particles may become important in the intense bunched beams of large accelerators (Gluckstern, 1970).

c. *Transverse "Trace Space."*   Various arrangements can be used to determine the slopes of the trajectories at different points in a beam cross section relative to the optic axis (Section III). In analyzing the transverse momenta, the axial velocity spread is not measured and is assumed to be negligible. The measurement may be made during a suitably chosen period δt when the beam possesses a time structure that we wish to establish. In the continuous case, of course, the measurement is independent of time. The experimental results are usually expressed as a density distribution function, per unit time, plotted in the two planes with coordinates x, x' and y, y', respectively, where x' and y' denote the gradients of the trajectories in the $x–z$ and $y–z$ planes (Fig. 1):

$$x' = dx/dz, \qquad y' = dy/dz \qquad (27)$$

In the paraxial approximation, $x' = \tan \alpha_x \approx \alpha_x$ and $y' \approx \alpha_y$; x' and y' are therefore direct measures of the angle between the particle trajectory projections and the optic axis. Each trajectory then correspond to a point (x, y, x', y') in a T_4 coordinate space, which Fronteau (1967) has named T_4 *"trace space,"* and with which two projected T_2 trace planes are associated, T_2^x and T_2^y.

This distinction between trace space and transverse phase space is not commonly used. However, it is of interest because it draws attention to

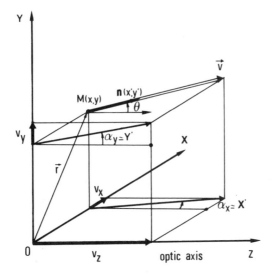

FIG. 1. Geometric space Cartesian coordinates, x, y, z, and T_4 trace space coordinates relative to transverse motions about the optic axis: x, y, x', y'. Here x, y define the particle position r in the beam cross section; x', y' define the direction (n) of the particle velocity.

the fact that (x, x') and (y, y') are not pairs of conjugate coordinates and that, in the more general case, Liouville invariance does not apply rigorously to the trace space. From Eq. (20) we obtain

$$p_x = mv_x + qA_x = m_0 c \beta \gamma x' + qA_x \tag{28}$$

where β and γ are the usual relativistic parameters for the axial motion, namely,

$$\beta = v_z/c, \qquad \gamma = 1/(1 - \beta^2)^{1/2} \tag{29}$$

Only if three conditions are satisfied, therefore—one restricting the magnetic field ($A_x = A_y = 0$) and the other the axial motion (p_z invariant along the beam and independent of the particle considered)—will (x, x') and (y, y') form pairs of conjugate variables and Liouville's theorem be applicable in trace space (T_4). As discussed above, this last condition implies that the domain $\mathcal{V}_6$ degenerates into a domain $\mathcal{V}_4$ in Γ_4 transverse phase space. The distribution function then becomes identical, apart from a constant factor, with that obtained experimentally and plotted in T_4 trace space. If the volume occupied by the N representative points and their density in T_4 are denoted by V_4 and ρ_4, respectively, we obtain

$$\mathcal{V}_4 = (m_0 c \beta \gamma)^2 V_4 \tag{30}$$

$$f_4(x, p_x, y, p_y) = \rho_4(x, x', y, y')/(m_0 c \beta \gamma)^2 \tag{31}$$

The areas $\mathcal{A}_2$ and A_2 of the projected domains in two dimensions are related by

$$\mathcal{A}_2^x = m_0 c \beta \gamma A_2^x = p_z A_2^x \qquad (32)$$

B. Emittance and Brightness: Basic Definitions

1. Brightness and Hyperemittance

a. *Definitions and Invariance Conditions.*   In each transverse cross section z_p, a beam may be characterized by the experimentally determined density distribution $\rho_4(x, y, x', y', z_p)$ of the representative points in the T_4 trace space *per unit time*, namely,

$$\rho_4 = d^4 I / dV_4 = \rho_4(\mathbf{r}, \mathbf{n},) \quad (\text{A rad}^{-2}\,\text{m}^{-2}) \qquad (33)$$

This density in trace space, sometimes called the *microscopic brightness,* is thus the number of charged particles passing through a given point of the cross section $\mathbf{r}(x, y)$, in a given direction $\mathbf{n}(x', y')$ per unit time and per unit of trace space volume $dV_4 = dx\,dx'\,dy\,dy'$ (Fig. 2). Two parameters may be defined as a first step toward characterizing the distribution function, which is assumed to possess a sharp boundary:

1. *The hyperemittance,* ϵ_4, which is related to the hypervolume V_4 enclosing all particle points in the T_4 trace space:

$$\epsilon_4 = V_4 / \pi^2 \quad (\pi^2\,\text{rad}^2\,\text{m}^2) \qquad (34)$$

The origin of the factor π^2 and its effect on numerical results will be discussed below, in connection with the emittance (Section II,B,2).

2. *The brightness, B,* which is the average value of the density in trace space (Van Steenbergen, 1965; Walcher, 1972):

$$B = \bar{\rho}_4 = I/V_4 = I/\pi^2 \epsilon_4 \quad (\text{A rad}^{-2}\,\text{m}^{-2}) \qquad (35)$$

With this definition, brightness is not conserved as the beam propagates through the system, that is, it does not take the same value for all values of the coordinate z_p along the optic axis, unless certain conditions are satisfied. These may be derived from the discussion in the previous section:

  i. the force field must be Hamiltonian;
 ii. particles must not be lost or created;
iii. the axial and transverse motion must be independent;
 iv. the axial velocity must be constant over any cross section;
  v. the axial velocity must be constant along the optic axis;
 vi. the magnetic field must be entirely transverse ($A_x = A_y = 0$).

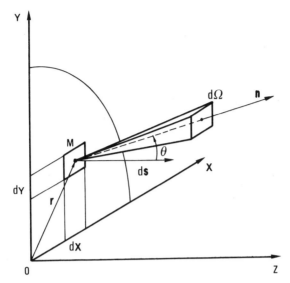

FIG. 2.   Definition of the microscopic brightness $\rho_4(\mathbf{r}, \mathbf{n})$ and luminance $L(\mathbf{r}, \mathbf{n})$ of a beam cross section or a radiating surface (Eqs. 33 and 46).

If Condition v is not satisfied, invariants of the motion can be established by considering the domain occupied in Γ_4 transverse phase space. This leads us to define "normalized" or "physical" quantities instead of those given by Eqs. (34) and (35), which are sometimes known as the "geometric" values (Amman, 1970). From Eqs. (30) and (31), we see that the invariants are

$$\mathcal{V}_4 = p_z^2 V_4 = \text{const}, \qquad \bar{f}_4 = B/p_z^2 = \text{const} \qquad (36)$$

3. *The normalized hyperemittance* is then defined as the hypervolume in transverse phase space in units of $(m_0 c \cdot m)^2$, thus:

$$\epsilon_{4n} = \mathcal{V}_4/\pi^2 m_0^2 c^2 = (p_z/m_0 c)^2 V_4/\pi^2 \qquad (37)$$

Recalling that $p_z = m_0 c \beta \gamma$, we obtain

$$\epsilon_{4n} = \beta^2 \gamma^2 V_4/\pi^2 = \beta^2 \gamma^2 \epsilon_4 \qquad (38)$$

4. *The normalized brightness* is defined by

$$B_n = I m_0^2 c^2/\mathcal{V}_4 = B/\beta^2 \gamma^2 \qquad (39)$$

or

$$B_n = I/\pi^2 \epsilon_{4n} \qquad (40)$$

This normalization procedure not only brings out the invariants of beam propagation but also measures them relative to the rest mass. The product $\beta\gamma$—the normalized axial momentum in units of m_0c or particle rest mass momentum—is dimensionless. ϵ_{4n} and B_n can therefore be expressed in the same units as ϵ_4 and B. In order to emphasize that the result is referred to the rest mass, we may also give numerical results in the form $\epsilon_{4n} = X (\pi^2 \cdot m_0^2 c^2 \cdot m^2)$; this is commonly employed by users of electron (Miller, 1970) or positron (Amman, 1970) accelerators. This form is equivalent to $\epsilon_{4n} = X (\pi^2 \cdot rad^2 \cdot m^2)$, usual for ion beams. The first form shows unambiguously that the result is a normalized one, as does the appearance of π^2 in the definition of ϵ_{4n} (Eqs. 37–38). A normalized brightness could equally well be written in the form

$$B_n = Y \quad (A \ m_0^2 c^2 \ m^{-2}) \equiv Y \quad (A \ rad^{-2} \ m^{-2})$$

With these normalized quantities, a valid comparison can be made between different beams, whatever their current, particle mass, and charge and energy. Nevertheless, beams with the same value of ϵ_{4n} and the same energy but consisting of particles of different masses do not have the same geometrical hyperemittances in the area examined experimentally. For nonrelativistic beams, the values vary as the mass. It is for this reason that users of low-energy ion beams usually prefer to use the "momentum-normalized invariants" (Banford, 1966); these seem more realistic in some applications (Billen, 1975; Doucas et al., 1976). In the nonrelativistic case, the momentum is proportional to the square root of the kinetic energy (W) for each mass m, $p_z = (2m_0W)^{1/2}$. From Eqs. (36), therefore, we can define a "physical hyperemittance" (ϵ_{4p}) and a "physical brightness" (B_p) thus:

$$\epsilon_{4p} = W\epsilon_4 \quad (\pi^2 \ m^2 \ rad^2 \ eV) \tag{41}$$

$$B_p = B/W \quad (A \ m^{-2} \ rad^{-2} \ eV^{-1}) \tag{42}$$

Other units, better adapted to the phase extension of the beam, are also in use: $(\pi^2 \cdot cm^2 \cdot mrad^2 \ MeV)$ or $(\pi^2 \cdot cm^2 \cdot mrad^2 \ keV)$. In order to transfer from one normalization to another, we have merely to evaluate the conversion factor relating the systems of units (Rose, 1974). We note that $\epsilon_{4n} = \epsilon_{4p}(2/\mathcal{U}_0)$ and $B_n = B_p\mathcal{U}_0/2$, where $\mathcal{U}_0$ is the rest energy of the particles (989.1 MeV for protons).

If in addition Condition iv is not satisfied, the invariants of propagation can again be determined by calculation, at a thermal emitter, for example, in the form

$$B_n = I(m_0c)^2/\mathcal{V}_4^* \tag{43}$$

$$\epsilon_{4n} = \mathcal{V}_4^*/\pi^2(m_0c)^2 \tag{44}$$

$\mathcal{V}_4^*$ is the volume of Γ_4 transverse phase space occupied by the projection of the domain $\mathcal{V}_6$ that is occupied by the representative points in Γ_6 phase space; in these conditions, this domain is not degenerate. Liouville's theorem tells us that $\mathcal{V}_4^* = \mathcal{V}_4$. The value of ϵ_{4n} calculated in this way can therefore be compared with the experimental value obtained after the particles have been accelerated sufficiently for Condition iv to be satisfied.

These quantities provide a valid description of a beam of charged particles; the hyperemittance represents it capacity to be transported without losses and with least expense from the emitter to the zone of application. The brightness, which introduces the beam intensity, indicates the maximum performance that one can hope to attain at the target plane. The invariance of the normalized values, subject to certain conditions, means that we can meaningfully characterize a particle emitter or a gun in terms of its hyperemittance and its brightness.

b. *Brightness Invariance and the Optical Theorems.* With this definition of brightness, beams having an appreciable extent in phase space can also be accommodated. It is more general than that employed in electron microscopy to characterize the fine beams of interest there. In the latter case, the brightness is a measure of the current per unit area per unit solid angle (Glaser, 1952; Simpson, 1967) so that for a beam centered on the optic axis,

$$B = I/S\,\Omega_{(\theta=0)} \qquad (45)$$

S denotes the area of cross section of the beam, which is assumed to be small and is taken normal to the axis of propagation ($\theta = 0$) and Ω is the solid angle enclosing all the rays emerging from a point on the axis (Fig. 3). The notion of hyperemittance is now replaced by that of "geometrical etendue,"—the product of emissive surface area and solid angle into which particles are emitted—which is commonly used to characterize radiating surfaces. It is interesting to relate the microscopic brightness, defined in terms of the domain occupied in phase space (ρ_4 or f_4) to the luminance of a radiator defined by (Fig. 2)

$$L(\mathbf{r},\,\mathbf{n}) = \frac{d^4 I}{\mathbf{n} \cdot dS\,d\Omega} = \frac{d^4 I}{dS\,d\Omega\cos\theta} \qquad (46)$$

A more general definition, involving the modulus of the momentum and hence associated with a Γ_6 phase space, has been suggested by Arakengy (1957), who examined its invariance properties and its connection with the density in phase space. For a surface isotropically emitting particles with the same momentum (a heated cathode, for example), Walcher

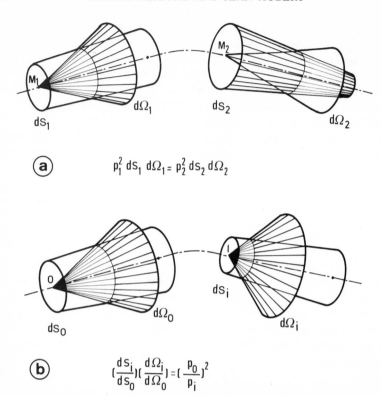

$$p_1^2 \, dS_1 \, d\Omega_1 = p_2^2 \, dS_2 \, d\Omega_2$$

(a)

$$\left(\frac{dS_i}{dS_0}\right)\left(\frac{d\Omega_i}{d\Omega_0}\right) = \left(\frac{p_0}{p_i}\right)^2$$

(b)

FIG. 3. Diagram illustrating the invariance of hyperemittance. (a) Arbitrary pairs of points M_1 and M_2 on the optic axis. $d\Omega_1$ is the solid angle subtended at M_1 by the bundle of rays passing through both M_1 and the area dS_2 around M_2. $d\Omega_2$ is the corresponding solid angle subtended at M_2 by the rays passing through the area dS_1 around M_1. (b) Optically conjugate image and object (I and O): dS_i/dS_0 and $d\Omega_i/d\Omega_0$ are the linear and angular magnification, respectively, between object (o) and image (i).

(1972) has shown that

$$d\mathcal{V}_4^* = d\mathcal{V}_4 = p^2 \, dS \, d\Omega \cos \theta \qquad (47)$$

even for a beam with a wide aperture. The density in the domain projected onto Γ_4 transverse phase space is then

$$d^4I/d\mathcal{V}_4^* = f_4(\mathbf{r}, \mathbf{n}) = L(\mathbf{r}, \mathbf{n})/p^2 \qquad (48)$$

so that

$$B_n = \bar{f}_4(m_0 c)^2 = \bar{L}/\beta^2\gamma^2 = \bar{L}_n \qquad (49)$$

in which β and γ correspond to the total velocity of the particle. The normalized brightness is the same as the normalized luminance averaged over the whole range of radiating surface elements and over the solid angle occupied by the particle paths. Conversely, dV_4 is not equal to $dS \, d\Omega \cos \theta$ and $\rho_4(\mathbf{r}, \mathbf{n})$ is not the same as the local geometrical luminance of the emitter. We have already mentioned that, in those conditions where there is a spread of axial velocities, B is not conserved. If we now consider a section of the beam for which $p_z = \text{const}$—this occurs for ion emission from the edge of a plasma (Self, 1963, 1965)—we find that $dV_4 = dS \, d\Omega/(\cos^2 \theta)$. The microscopic brightness defined by Eq. (33) is not the same as the luminance unless the beam divergence is small ($\theta \approx 0$):

$$\rho_4(\mathbf{r}, \mathbf{n}) = \frac{d^4 I}{dS \cdot d\Omega \, (\theta \approx 0)} = L(\mathbf{r}, \mathbf{n}) \qquad (50)$$

$$B = \overline{L}(\mathbf{r}, \mathbf{n}) = I \Big/ \int_S \int_\Omega dS \cdot d\Omega \, (\theta \approx 0) \qquad (51)$$

In a real extended beam, each surface element dS has a different solid angle of emission, Ω. If B is to be calculated from Eq. (51), therefore, these solid angles must be known, either by measuring or calculating the emittance. For beams consisting of a narrow range of pencils of rays, however, this variation may be neglected, and Eq. (51) reduces to Eq. (45). For each of these extreme cases, which are encountered as the beam progresses, the normalized brightness is equal to the mean normalized luminance; the invariance of the latter, which is related to that of $p^2 \, dS \, d\Omega \cos \theta$ and known as the Lagrange–Helmhotz theorem, can be demonstrated directly without involving Liouville's theorem by applying Maupertuis' principle of least action to the trajectories in real space (Sturrock, 1955; Pierce, 1959; Davey, 1971). The last of these authors has discussed the physical assumptions made in deriving the invariance law and the consequences of their failure. An extension of the brightness invariance to the case of a beam with energy spread is proposed and applied to the problem of calculating the brightness of a thermal emitter. This method of deriving the law resembles that in which Fermat's principle of least time is used to establish the invariance of the physical etendue of a light beam, in the form $n^2 \, dS \, d\Omega \cos \theta = \text{const}$; this is known as Clausius' theorem. The light optical refractive index, n, replaces the electrodynamic momentum (Eq. 20), which may be closely identified with the particle refractive index (Ehrenberg and Siday, 1951; Glaser, 1952, 1956; Grivet, 1965). The meaning of these various kinds of invariance is illustrated in Fig. 3a and b, for a narrow beam centered on the optic axis, for an arbitrary pair of points on the axis and for a pair of optically conjugate points (image and object). In the latter case, the invariance expression takes the familiar form of the Helmhotz–Lagrange relation, allowing for the linear and angular magnification between object (o) and image (i):

$$\left(\frac{dS_i}{dS_o}\right)\left(\frac{d\Omega_i}{d\Omega_o}\right) = \left(\frac{p_0}{p_i}\right)^2 = \left(\frac{n_0}{n_i}\right)^2 = \left(\frac{f_0}{f_i}\right)^2 \tag{52}$$

Here, f_0 and f_i denote the object and image focal lengths of the system that focuses the object onto the image plane (Grivet, 1965; Lawson, 1977). Walcher (1972) discusses these analogies among the various invariants in the case of wide-angle beams.

c. *Richtstrahlwert.* The brightness is an average over the whole trace space of the beam. Another important figure of merit is the maximum value of the microscopic beam brightness, ρ_4^M. Normally, this maximum is attained on the optic axis (in real space), which corresponds to the origin of coordinates in trace space irrespective of the beam section considered. In a drift space, ρ_4^M is invariant; in an accelerating region, it is $\rho_4^M/\beta^2\gamma^2$ that is invariant. These invariants are of considerable practical importance and deserve to have special names. The use of the German term *"Richtstrahlwert"* together with "normalized *Richtstrahlwert*" is recommended by Fink and Schumacher (1974), and these are certainly very suitable, although they are frequently used among electron microscopists to denote the brightness as defined by Eq. (45) [see von Ardenne (1956) and Simpson (1967), for example, and the numerous papers by Lauer and Hanszen, which contain extensive measurements of electron microscope gun brightness and much careful analysis of the information provided by these measurements]. An account of this and related work will be found in a forthcoming review by Lauer. We therefore adopt the following definitions:

$$R = \rho_4^M = (d^4I/dV_4)_{x=y=x'=y'=0} \tag{53}$$

$$R_n = \rho_4^M/\beta^2\gamma^2 \tag{54}$$

$$R_p = R/W \tag{55}$$

Light has recently been shed on the importance of this quantity for electron beams produced by homogeneous thermal emitters by Fink and Schumacher (1974, 1975). In this case, it can be expressed in simple terms as a function of the system parameters in certain sections of the beam: a focal plane, an image plane, or the plane of emission. If the emitter is uniform, R is the same as the brightness, B. The *Richtstrahlwert* R can also be obtained straightforwardly at a crossover ("focal point") by determining the maximum current density and the solid angle Ω, within which all rays that intersect the axis are included (Fig. 4); R is then given by

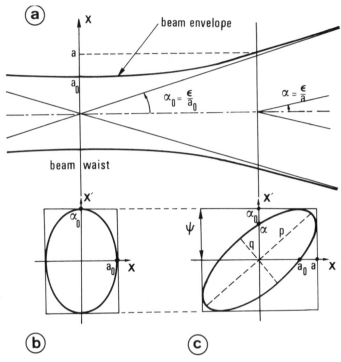

FIG. 4.   Emittance ellipse of a normal beam in terms of beam envelope. (a) Beam envelope in a drift space under the actions of emittance only: $\epsilon = a_0\alpha_0 = a\alpha$. (b) Upright emittance ellipse at the beam waist. (c) Oblique emittance ellipse downstream from the beam waist (diverging beam): $\epsilon = a\alpha = pq$. a is the beam half-width and ψ the semiangular spread.

$$R = j_{max}/\Omega_o \tag{56}$$

provided that Ω_o is so small that R does not vary with the slope of the trajectories. For a rotationally symmetric beam, for which the angle at the tip of the cone of emission is α_0, we have

$$R = j_{max}/\pi\alpha_0^2 \tag{57}$$

and for a beam with two planes of symmetry,

$$R = j_{max}/4\alpha_o\beta_o \tag{58}$$

The practical importance of this quantity is due to the fact that $B \ll R$, but a beam that is not very bright can be transformed into a much brighter beam of lower current. This can be achieved simply by excluding all but the central region of the beam at a crossover with the aid of a small aperture. Grivet (1965) remarks that for electron beams, values of the brightness equal to 80–90% of R can be obtained, although the value of R at the crossover may be of the order of ten times the brightness of the entire beam.

2. Emittance

a. *Definitions and Invariance Conditions.*   Full characterization of an extended beam requires a knowledge of its hyperemittance. Some devices provide information from which V_4 can be extracted directly (Section III). In the most usual procedure, however, the density distribution functions are determined experimentally in the trace planes T_2, corresponding to either projections or sections of T_4, after which V_4 is calculated from the areas A_2 of the domains occupied by the representative points in T_2. Whatever the shape of these domains may be, the *emittance* is defined by

$$\epsilon^x = A_2^x/\pi = (1/\pi) \int\int dx \cdot dx' \quad \text{(rad m)} \tag{59}$$

If the system is rotationally symmetric, a single emittance ϵ completely characterizes the beam. If it has two planes of symmetry, two emittances, ϵ^x and ϵ^y, are necessary. If the beam possesses a time structure, ϵ may be an instantaneous value, $\epsilon(z_p, t)$, but the average value over time is more usual. The most common measuring procedure yields projections of the distribution; we have seen that these are more truly representative (Eqs. 13–14) than sections, since they correspond to the ensemble of I particles of the assembly, the propagation of which is being investigated. It is for this reason also that the parameters associated with the projections of the distribution appear in the envelope equations, which define the behavior of the beam in a given transport system (Sacherer, 1971; Lapostolle, 1971a; Lee and Cooper, 1976). In order to prevent any misunderstanding, we shall use the term *emittance* (ϵ) exclusively to describe *projections* of distributions; in cases where the measurements yield *sections* of distributions, we shall speak of the *section emittance* (ϵ_s).

For these emittances (ϵ and ϵ_s) to be conserved, not only must the conditions in which brightness is invariant be satisfied but also that permitting Liouville's theorem to be applied in two-dimensional phase space must fulfilled: this implies independence of the motion corresponding to this particular degree of freedom. If Condition v is not satisfied, two types of invariant can be obtained, just as those for the brightness and the hyperemittance:

(1) A *"normalized emittance"* (ϵ_n) *and its section counterpart* ($\epsilon_{s,n}$):

$$\epsilon_n^x = \mathscr{A}_2^x/\pi m_0 c = p_z A_2^x/\pi m_0 c \tag{60}$$

$$\epsilon_n^x = \beta\gamma A_2^x/\pi = \beta\gamma\epsilon = (\pi \text{ rad m}) \quad \text{or} \quad (\pi m_0 c \text{ m}) \tag{61}$$

(2) A *"physical emittance"* (ϵ_p, $\epsilon_{s,p}$):

$$\epsilon_p = W^{1/2}\epsilon \quad [\pi \text{ m rad (eV)}^{1/2}] \tag{62}$$

Here again, various submultiples of these quantities that are more convenient in practice are in use, in particular (π mrad cm) and (π mrad cm $(\text{MeV})^{1/2}$). If in addition there is an appreciable spread of axial velocity (Condition iv), the invariant of motion can be calculated from the area $\mathscr{A}_2^*$ of the domain corresponding to the projection of the points in Γ_6 phase space:

$$\epsilon_n^* = \mathscr{A}_2^*/\pi m_0 c \tag{63}$$

even though Eq. (32) is no longer valid and the distribution obtained in T_2 trace space no longer corresponds to an invariant of the motion.

The inclusion of the factor π in the definition of the emittance dates from early work on relatively narrow beams (Eq. 45), since the Lagrange–Helmholtz invariance for a rotationally symmetric beam may be written in the form $p^2 R^2 \alpha^2 = \text{const}$ or $pR\alpha = \text{const}$. The emittance then denoted this product of beam radius (R) and semiangle (α) of the rays at the beam axis (Fig. 4a). With the definition of ϵ given by Eq. (59), however, this earlier connotation only applies in the limiting case in which the domain is bounded by an ellipse, the area of which is given by $A_2 = \pi R \alpha = \pi\epsilon$ whether or not the axes of the ellipse coincide with the coordinate axes. When they do coincide, R and α are the semiaxes; this situation occurs at the extreme of the beam envelope, a waist corresponding to a minimum of R. Definition (59) has therefore survived, and been generalized to include boundary curves of arbitrary shape, however illogical it may then be (Lapostolle, 1969; Walcher, 1972). It continues to be used because of the importance of elliptical contours in phase space dynamics and in establishing the envelope equations. Defined in this way, ϵ appears directly in these equations and in the cartesian or matrix equations for an elliptical boundary. Some authors do not include the factor π in their definitions, however (Larson and Jones, 1977). It is therefore essential to state which convention is being used when giving results or comparing the performances of different sources. We recommend that in giving results in numerical form, one of the following two types of expression should be used, depending on individual preference:

$$\epsilon = A_2/\pi \leftrightarrow \epsilon = X \quad (\pi \text{ rad m}) \tag{64}$$

or

$$\epsilon = A_2 \leftrightarrow \epsilon = \pi X \quad \text{(rad m)} \tag{65}$$

The definition adopted is thus clear and unambiguous, and whichever is chosen, it is easy to compare results; the quantity X is the product of the semiaxes of the "ellipse."

   b. *The Relation between the Various Emittance and the Brightness; the Notions of "Normal Beam" and "Perfect Beam."* The relation connecting the brightness B and the emittances ϵ^x and ϵ^y in the two symmetry planes of a beam depend on the relation between the hypervolume V_4 and its projections A_2^x and A_2^y on the T_2 trace planes (or between V_4 and ϵ_s^x, ϵ_s^y if the section emittances are employed). This is a complex problem (Miller, 1966) to which we shall return in connection with the interpretation of measurements made using a variety of methods (Section III). The relation between V_4 and A_2^x, A_2^y can be calculated straightforwardly only it the curve enclosing the distribution has a simple geometrical shape. Furthermore, different types of hypervolume can be considered a priori, given the curves for A_2^x, A_2^y. Fortunately, if we examine a range of simple boundary curves (Van Steenbergen, 1965; Becherer and Prévot, 1972) or several choices of hypervolume (Ames, 1978), the relations are similar and have the general form

$$V_4 = A_2^x A_2^y / \chi \rightarrow B = \chi I / A_2^x A_2^y \tag{66}$$

in which χ is a form factor, approximately equal to 2. This value corresponds to a hyperellipsoid in T_4 trace space, the projections of which have elliptical boundaries (Walsh, 1963). Such curves arise naturally in the T_2 trace plane (or the Γ_2 phase plane). In particular the trajectory of a harmonic oscillator is an ellipse in this plane, and elliptic domains will therefore occur if (1) the particles move in a field that attract them linearly toward the axis (paraxial approximation, no optical aberrations or nonlinear space-charge fields) and (2) the motion is unbounded in configuration space. The latter condition is necessary since collimation by a pair of slits, for example, would give parallelogram boundary contours (Banford, 1966). Following Banford's terminology we shall say that a beam with elliptical boundaries in both Γ_2 phase space planes is a *"normal beam."* We note, however, that this term is used by Walsh (1962, 1963) to describe more restrictive conditions, namely, the case in which the projection domains on each of the planes (x, y), (x, x'), (y, y'), and (y', x') of trace (or phase) space have a uniform density within elliptical boundaries. It seems preferable to use the term *"perfect beam"* to describe this latter case however, by analogy with the "perfect gas." This concept of a "perfect beam" proves to be most fruitful, despite the lack of physical reality of the distribution function that would yield such projections. This function in T_4 in fact corresponds to a surface density uniformly distributed over a hyperellipsoid, and is known *as the $K-V$ distribution* (after Kapchinsky and Vladimirsky, 1959) *or the microcanonical distribution* (Lawson, 1975, 1977). It gives rise to linear space charge fields so that the propagation of such beams can be studied analytically, even when the current is high, for it represents a self-consistent solution of the problem (Gluckstern, 1970; Sessler, 1972). Unfortunately, practical distributions are not uniform in T_2, and the K-V distribution is therefore far from "normal," however "perfect" it may be!

Given the importance of elliptic boundaries in beam dynamics and the smallness of the variation of form factor χ (Eq. 66) for other simple curves, it seems justifiable to ascribe more general validity to the relations applicable to normal beams; in order to unify the calculations of B and of V_4, therefore, we define

$$V_4 = A_2^x A_2^y/2 \rightarrow \epsilon_4 = \epsilon^x \epsilon^y/2 \tag{67}$$

$$B = 2I/A_2^x A_2^y = 2I/\pi^2 \epsilon^x \epsilon^y \tag{68}$$

whatever shape the boundary curves in the projection domains may be, with analogous expressions for the normalized and physical quantities. For a rotationally symmetric beam, we have $A^x = A^y = A^r$, together with the various relations corresponding to this case. These conventions for V_4 and B have been widely adopted by many authors, although relations corresponding to rectangular distributions are also to be found in the literature (Van Steenbergen, 1965; Wroe, 1968).

If the shape of the boundary enclosing the representative points of the beam is very different from an ellipse, as a result of filamentation, for example, the notions of an "effective emittance" and an "effective brightness" may be introduced, in order to characterize the optical properties more realistically and to show more clearly how the beam is matched to the transport system (Section II,C). *The quantities defined in this section, which are related to the domain actually occupied in trace space, are then regarded as "theoretical" emittances and brightnesses, which are conserved even if the abberrations of the optical system are not negligible and space charge causes nonlinearities.*

c. *Coupling Due to the Magnetic Field.* Optical elements that produce magnetic fields may cause coupling between the transverse components of the motion. The field of an infinite magnetic quadrupole with hyperbolic pole pieces is truly transverse ($A_x = A_y = 0$) and gives rise to linear forces. Quadrupoles (and also gradient magnets) do not introduce any coupling between the x and y motions, provided that they are carefully aligned relative to the beam symmetry planes. On the other hand, a small rotation about the z axis does introduce linear coupling between the transverse motions, terms proportional to y now appearing in the x equation and conversely (Steffen, 1965). An axial component of magnetic field likewise causes coupling between the transverse motions, introducing a force proportional to the velocity $\dot{y}$ in the x motion and vice versa. Linear coupling can thus arise as a result of imperfections in the magnetic system: constructural errors, lateral displacements, tilts, and stray fields. The orbital motion in the presence of a weak linear coupling has been analyzed by Courant and Snyder (1958) and Laslett (1967). We stress that the effect of weak linear coupling on the beam emittance must be distinguished from that of nonlinear coupling, which may be due to space charge effects or nonlinear magnetic fields (Lapostolle et al., 1968).

If the beam has axial symmetry and the focusing is achieved with solenoids, the equations of motion can be decoupled by transforming into the Larmor frame of reference, which rotates around the optic axis at the Larmor frequency, $\Omega_L = \omega_c/2 = qB/2m$; Ω_L is thus half the cyclotron frequency, ω_c. In this frame, the axial and radial components of electric and magnetic fields are transformed in such a way that, in a uniform axial magnetic field B_{z_0}, the charged particles appear to move under the action of a radial force corresponding to an equivalent electric field:

$$E_{r_L} = -\tfrac{1}{2}r\Omega_L B_{z_0} = -\gamma m_0 \Omega_L^2 r/q \tag{69}$$

while the axial field B_{z_L} is removed ($B_{z_L} = 0 \leftrightarrow A_{\theta_L} = 0$). In the Larmor frame the canonical angular momentum therefore reduces to the mechanical momentum, p_θ, and since the force is toward the axis, the projections of all trajectories on two orthogonal surfaces through the axis are sinusoidal and described in terms of x_L, x'_L, y_L, and y'_L by independent linear equations, exactly as for uncoupled motion. The behavior of beams in the Larmor and laboratory frames has been discussed in detail by Lawson (1975, 1977), who derived paraxial ray equations and envelope equations. From this, it emerges that the departures from nonlaminarity of a cylindrical beam, transported by an axial magnetic field, and various associated effects, can be understood more easily when analyzed in the Larmor frame. Thus, in the laboratory frame, a rotating laminar beam consisting of helical trajectories winding round the optic axis with constant angular velocity has an emittance of

$$\epsilon = (p_\theta)_R/\beta\gamma m_0 c = Rv_\theta/v_z \tag{70}$$

where $(p_\theta)_R$ denotes the angular momentum at the beam edge ($r = R$). In a frame rotating at the same angular velocity, however, the beam emittance is zero: the beam is laminar. It is important to realize that such de-coupling is impossible for nonrotationally symmetric systems, for which 4 × 4 matrices are required to describe the motion even in the paraxial approximation. Liouville's theorem then applies only in the four-dimensional transverse phase space.

3. The Acceptance of a Beam Transport System; Matching

Charged-particle beams propagate through evacuated regions under the action of electromagnetic forces; this combination constitutes the "beam transport system," more often referred to as the "beam line." This system is designed both to transport the injected beam and also to opti-mize it in some way, relative to the exact criteria to be satisfied in the zone of application of the beam. The beam line thus imposes both geomet-rical constraints (walls and diaphragms) and physical constraints (fields of force) on the particles. The problem is usually to design a transport system capable of guiding a given beam, of known current and emittance, generated by a commercial type of gun, in such a way that the loss of par-ticles and deterioration of the original optical properties are kept as low as possible. The problem is thus one of optimization, with the cost of con-struction as an additional constraint. The solution requires an analysis of the beam dynamics and is considerably facilitated by the use of the phase space representation.

For any given optical element of a transport system, or for the entire system consisting of several elements, we define the *acceptance domain* to be the region of phase space within which the motion of all particles in-jected at the entrance to the system will be stable through the whole system; by this, we mean that the particles do not strike the walls and are hence transmitted. Depending on the coupling between the degrees of freedom of the motion within the system, the acceptance domain has to be defined in Γ_6 phase space, in Γ_4 transverse phase space, or in the Γ_2 phase planes. The acceptance domain is equivalent to the maximum hyperemit-tance domain that a beam may occupy if it is to pass through the system without loss of particles. As far as the transverse motion is concerned, ideas similar to those introduced to describe the phase extension of the beam can be used to characterize the transport system at the plane of in-jection. Thus, for decoupled transverse components of motion, we define an *"acceptance area"* in each T_2 trace plane, together with a *(geometric-al) acceptance*, a *normalized acceptance*, and a *physical acceptance*:

$$Y^x = A_{\frac{x}{2}}/\pi, \qquad Y^x_n = \beta\gamma A_{\frac{x}{2}}/\pi, \qquad Y^x_p = W^{1/2}Y^x \qquad (71)$$

Section acceptances (Y^x_s, . . .) can likewise be introduced as required.

From this definition of the acceptance, it is clear that a beam injected into the system will be wholly transmitted if its emittance diagram is completely contained within that of the system. The shape of the emittance contour may well alter during propagation, but in every section it will lie within the acceptance contour of the system corresponding to the same section. If this is not the case at injection, some of the particles will be lost, intercepted by the walls while being transported through the system (Fig. 5). Provided that the beam emittance is less than the acceptance of the system, optical elements can be inserted into the system, the main purpose of which will be to transform the emittance diagram of the beam in such a way that in the injection plane, it lies within the acceptance diagram of the system.

This first condition is necessary to ensure that particles are not lost during transport, but may not be sufficient to prevent deterioration of the

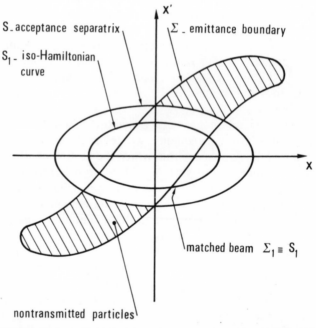

FIG. 5.   Beam and optical element matching. The acceptance separatrix (S) is assumed to be a particular iso-Hamiltonian curve of a piecewise constant focusing element. The particles of the emittance domain Σ which lie on the outside of S will be lost; the particles of Σ on the inside of S will be transmitted but may be scattered all over S because the emittance contour is not matched to the optical element, that is, it does not coincide with one of its iso-Hamiltonian curves. Conversely Σ_1 is a matched emittance domain, its boundary contour being identical with an iso-Hamiltonian curve S_1 of the optical element.

optical properties of the injected beam. For this, precautions must be taken to avoid the phenomenon of "filamentation" of the emittance domain, the mechanism of which is now well understood (Hereward, 1954). This is possible if the emittance curve for each optical element of the system, which is assumed to provide constant focusing everywhere, can be brought into coincidence with a curve along which the Hamiltonian is constant for that element; this curve will correspond to a particular trajectory of representative points of the beam in phase space. In these conditions, the emittance domain is unaltered during transport through the element. The beam is then said to be *matched* to the optical element. The matching of the beam to each element is achieved in *"matching sections,"* which must simultaneously match all the different degrees of freedom of the particle motion (Banford, 1966; Steffen, 1965; Lawson, 1977). If the matching is not performed correctly, the emittance domain rotates during propagation; it does, however, remain within an iso-Hamilton curve (S) corresponding to the particle farthest from the axis (Fig. 6). If the forces are not linear, the angular velocities of rotation of

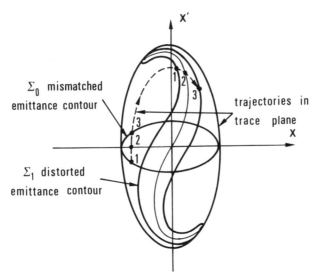

FIG. 6. Mechanism of filamentation of the emittance domain. In a nonlinear piecewise constant focusing system, the iso-Hamiltonian curves (S, S_1), which are the trajectories of particles in phase plane, cease to be elliptical and the angular velocity of rotation of phase points (1, 2, 3, for example) depends on their initial position. As a consequence the mismatched emittance contour Σ_0 (see Fig. 5) becomes deformed as the beam propagates along the optic axis, that is, particles oscillate in real space or rotate in the phase plane; Σ_1 is obtained after a quater-wavelength propagation. After a large number of wavelengths a strong filamentation of the emittance domain will occur.

the representative points in the phase plane vary with their radial distance, with the result that the emittance diagram becomes deformed and filamentation occurs. Even though the Liouville invariance is unaffected (in the absence of coupling), the representative points become scattered over a much larger region of phase space, corresponding to the curve S.

This brief account gives an idea of the importance of "beam phase space transformations" in solving the problem of optimizing the design and operating parameters of a beam line. The reader interested in pursuing this further will find a quantitative discussion in the work of Lichtenberg (1969).

C. Improvement of the Concept of Emittance

1. Experimental Observations

Emittance diagrams obtained experimentally or by numerical simulation do not correspond to that of a "perfect beam." The form of real diagrams is governed by various factors, of which the following are the most important.

a. *Absence of Sharp Boundaries.* Beams are normally surrounded by some kind of halo, due essentially to scattering processes. This particle cloud may well extend quite far, but indeed it has been reported by various authors that typically 90% of the total beam intensity falls within 50% of the total measured trace space area. Transport of such a cloud would therefore be quite an expensive item in terms of optical system construction; the contribution of the cloud is, moreover, very often neglected in beam dynamic problems.

b. *Nonuniformity of the Density Distribution in Both Real Space and Trace Space.* The distribution may be represented by plotting equidensity contours, corresponding to particular fractions of the maximum density, in the T_2 trace planes; this gives an "emittance plot" or "emittance diagram" (Fig. 7a). An alternative representation of the domain in trace space is obtained by plotting the equidensity curve either enclosing 90% of the beam or relative to a threshold density, and the density profile $\rho_2(x', x_i)$ for various positions x_i along the transverse axis (Fig. 7b). These different sets of curves, which are nowadays in common use, can be obtained straightforwardly with the automated systems that are in use for measuring emittance (see Section III, Fig. 20). It is important to realize that the area within any isodensity curve and the number of representative points enclosed are invariants of motion, provided that Liouville's

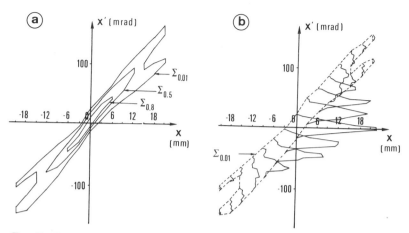

Fig. 7. Representations of the distribution function of projected density in T_2-trace plane; argon beam (1.55 mA, 10 keV) from a duoplasmatron with expansion cup operating in the starvation mode of the discharge (Aubert *et al.*, 1978). (a) "Emittance plot": equidensity contours Σ_f, corresponding to discrete fractions (f) of the maximum density. (b) Density profiles for various positions x_i along the x axis and equidensity contour $\Sigma_{0.01}$ corresponding to $f = 0.01$.

theorem applies to the two-dimensional space. This is easily understood since the theorem implies that particles that are initially neighbors, either on adjacent equidensity curves or along the same curve, will always be neighbors on the same isodensity curves, defined in terms of their fraction of the maximum density. Property ii of the trajectories in phase space (Section II,A) implies these invariances.

c. *Departure from Ellipticity of the Equidensity Curves.* In the most favorable situation, the equidensity curves resemble slightly distorted concentric ellipses. The distortion may be the result of beam collimation or caused by nonlinear forces, due to optical aberrations or space charge forces for "nonperfect beams." Coupling between the transverse components of motion may also contribute to the deformation. If effects due to nonlinear forces are important, either because of marked nonlinearity (Walcher, 1972) or because the action occurs over a considerable distance (Lawson, 1977), several ellipses may appear in the diagram. These correspond to "translaminar beams," propagating simultaneously within the main beam (Fig. 8). In the extreme situation, this leads to "filamentation" of the emittance diagram. It is clear that for a detailed analysis of the behavior of a beam in a transport system, the equidensity curves of the two (x and y) emittance diagrams provide the most helpful description. This representation is not, however, much use for comparing the perform-

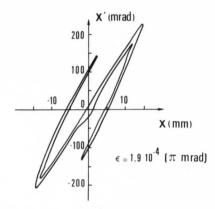

FIG. 8. "Translaminar beams," taken from the emittance domain of a beam extracted from a duoplasmatron source, the expansion cup of which is not optimized (H$^+$; 420 mA; 55 keV). (Courtesy of Kobayashi *et al.*, 1972.)

ances of different beams, for describing the change in the structure of a beam as it travels through the transport system, or as an aid to comprehension of analytical treatments of beam dynamics.

The concepts that we now discuss enable us to satisfy these various requirements. They came into being during the 1960s, in the course of efforts to increase the currents that could be injected into big accelerators, with the consequent study of the influence of space charge phenomena.

2. The Intensity–Emittance Characteristic Curve

The fractional intensity I that flows inside an equidensity contour (Σ) of the emittance diagram may be plotted as a function of the enclosed emittance:

$$I = \int\int_\Sigma \rho_2(x, x') \, dx \, dx' \tag{72}$$

$$\epsilon = (1/\pi) \oint_\Sigma x' \, dx \tag{73}$$

These quantities remain invariant during propagation, as stated earlier, and the curve $I = I(\epsilon)$ [or $I = I(\epsilon_n)$] gives a good idea of the beam quality (Taylor, 1963; Taylor *et al.*, 1966); it gives a direct measure of the current that can be transmitted through a given acceptance. A complete representation of a nonaxially symmetric beam requires two "current emittance" characteristics. These are now routinely used to describe accelerators and are coming into use to characterize the performance of ion sources, following the recommendations of Lapostolle (1969).

Similarly, we may consider an "intensity–hyperemittance" curve, $I = I(\epsilon_4)$, and an "intensity brightness" curve, $I = I(B_0/B)$, as defined from the isodensity surfaces of the distribution of microscopic brightness in the four-dimensional trace space. They are very convenient to characterize the performance of a particle beam or a particle gun. Unfortunately, for the most general distribution, these curves cannot be derived from the knowledge of the two distribution functions of projected density into T_2^x and T_2^y trace planes. This impossibility results form the fact that the fractional intensity I associated to the two emittances, $\epsilon^x(I)$ and $\epsilon^y(I)$, differs—because of the projection—from the fractional intensity, which has to be associated to the hyperemittance, the projection of which are $\epsilon^x(I)$ and $\epsilon^y(I)$ (see Ames, 1978). This hyperemittance is calculated approximately from Eq. (67)—thus, $\epsilon_4(I) = \epsilon^x(I)\epsilon^y(I)/2$—but the enclosed fractional intensity cannot be calculated unless I is very close to the total beam intensity. In the latter condition the difference between the two fractional intensities vanishes. Conversely some measurement procedures do in fact give directly the curves $I(\epsilon_4)$ and $I(B)$ (Section III).

The $I-\epsilon$ characteristics corresponding to the more familar theoretical density distributions are plotted in Fig. 9: these consist of the family of hyperellipsoidal distributions. For hyperellipsoidal distribution in an n-dimensional space, $x_1, x_2, \ldots, x_n$, the density of representative points can be written as a function of a single variable r_n, where

$$r_n = (x_1^2/a_1^2 + \cdots + x_n^2/a_n^2)^{1/2} \tag{74}$$

The function $\rho_n = f(r_n)$ distinguishes the different distributions of this family, the equidensity surfaces of which are homothetic hyperellipsoids. If the hyperellipsoids are oblique, a change of axes enable us to express the equidensity surfaces by means of similar equations. The relations connecting the distributions in two-, three-, four-, or six-dimensional spaces have been analyzed by Lapostolle (1966) and Van Steenbergen (1967a). Other families of distributions can likewise be considered, to give an optimal representation of the experimental distributions (Tanguy and Durand, 1978). If I_T and ϵ_T are the total intensity and total emittance of the beam, it can be seen that (1) a "perfect" beam corresponds to a straight line, as far as ϵ_T; (2) uniform density in the T_4 hyperellipsoid gives a parabola up to ϵ_T (Lapostolle et al., 1968):

$$I/I_T = a[\epsilon/b - c(\epsilon/d)^2] \tag{75}$$

while (3) a Gaussian distribution in either T_4 trace space or the T_2 trace

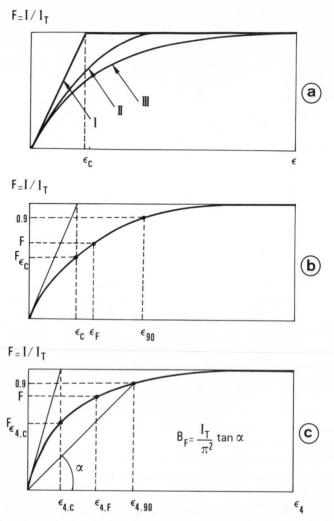

Fig. 9. (a) "Intensity–emittance characteristics" for various hyperellipsoidal distributions: (I) Kapchinsky–Vladimirsky distribution of a "perfect beam"; (II) uniform density in T_4 four-dimensional trace space; (III) Gaussian distribution. (b) The meaningful parameters of an "intensity–emittance curve": ϵ_{90}, enclosing 90% of the total beam intensity, and ϵ_c, the "emittance constant" with its appropriate percentage of I_T, $F_{(\epsilon_c)}$; for a Gaussian distribution, this is 63%. (c) The meaningful parameters of an "intensity-hyperemittance curve": $\epsilon_{4,90}$ and ϵ_{4c}, the "hyperemittance constant," with its appropriate percentage of I_T, $F_{(\epsilon_{4,c})}$. ϵ_F and $\epsilon_{4,F}$ are the emittance and hyperemittance enclosing the factor F of the total beam intensity.

plane gives

$$I/I_T = 1 - \exp(-\epsilon/\epsilon_c) \tag{76}$$

In this figure, the three distributions are assumed to have the same central density in the T_2 trace plane; the curves therefore have the same tangent at the origin, since

$$\rho_2(0, 0) = (I/\pi\epsilon)_{\epsilon \to 0} = (1/\pi)(dI/d\epsilon)_{\epsilon=0} \tag{77}$$

Comparison of experimental results with these theoretical curves shows that the last two distributions give an accurate representation of the behavior of beams in linear accelerators (Taylor *et al.*, 1966; Lapostolle *et al.*, 1968; Evans and Warner, 1972). A few comparisons for ion beams just after formation (Kuznetzov *et al.*, 1970) indicate that the beam extracted from a duoplasmatron can be represented by a Gaussian, whereas the work of Doucas *et al.* (1976) suggests that there is an appreciable difference between ion beams extracted from a plasma (which are quasi-Gaussian) and those obtained by sputtering (which are not). The curves $I = I(\epsilon)$ characterizing real beams are typified by two particular emittances, ϵ_{90} and ϵ_c. ϵ_{90} encloses 90% of the total intensity of the beam and hence characterizes the significant fraction of the beam. ϵ_c is the "*emittance constant*" (Lapostolle *et al.*, 1968; Lapostolle, 1969), defined as the value of the abscissa at the point of intersection of the tangent at the origin and the horizontal line corresponding to the total intensity (Fig. 9b). This constant is characteristic of the central part of the beam.

For a Gaussian beam (Eq. 76), 63% of the total intensity corresponds to ϵ_c and 86.5% to $2\epsilon_c$; the corresponding isodensity contours represent $\sqrt{2}$ and 2 times the standard deviation of the Gaussian function (Taylor, 1970). For a perfect beam, however, ϵ_c corresponds to the entire beam. The fractions of the intensity corresponding to ϵ_c and $2\epsilon_c$ can be used to measure the difference between a real beam and a Gaussian beam in the central region and over its entire extent.

It is convenient to associate the brightness of the significant part of the beam—that is, 90%—with the two pairs of emittances characterizing a real beam: ϵ_c^x; ϵ_c^y (with the appropriate percentage of the total intensity); and ϵ_{90}^x, ϵ_{90}^y. As mentioned above the brightness B_{90} corresponding to 90% of the total beam intensity may be calculated with a good approximation from the relation:

$$B_{90} = 2 \times 0.9 I_T / \pi^2 \epsilon_{90}^x \epsilon_{90}^y \tag{78}$$

In the case where the curve $I = I(\epsilon_4)$ is obtained directly from the data reduction, the beam quality can be conveniently described in terms of the "hyperemittance constant" ($\epsilon_{4,c}$)—defined as above from the tangent at the origin of the curve $I(\epsilon_4)$—and of the hyperemittance which encloses 90% of the total beam intensity ($\epsilon_{4,90}$) as shown in Fig. 9c. The slope of the curve $I(\epsilon_4)$ is related to the microscopic brightness value corresponding to isodensity surface enclosing the hyperemittance ϵ_4:

$$\rho_4(\epsilon_4) = (1/\pi^2)(dI/d\epsilon_4)\epsilon_4 \tag{79}$$

The maximum of the microscopic brightness ($R = B_0$), which is assumed to be obtained on the optic axis, that is, $\epsilon_4 \rightarrow 0$, is then given by the relation

$$R = B_0 = I_T/\pi^2\epsilon_{4,c} \tag{80}$$

Here again to complete the beam quality description, B_{90} will be associated to B_0. The determination of B_{90} is straightforward from the graph $I(\epsilon_4)$ (Eq. 35).

3. Root-Mean-Square Emittance; "Equivalent Perfect Beam"

The variation of the envelope of a perfect beam in a transport system may be obtained by solving the system of equations known as the Kapchinsky–Vladimirsky (K–V) equations, since they were originally introduced by these authors in 1959. The notion of root-mean-square (rms) emittance was introduced by Chasman et al. (1969) and subsequently defined more exactly by Lapostolle (1970), in an attempt to extend the range of application of the K–V equations to include the behavior of any beam, given its emittance diagram in the two orthogonal transverse directions corresponding to the symmetry of the system. This notion is therefore closely related to that of the "equivalent perfect beam," for any real beam. The idea here is that it is possible to define a perfect beam, the behavior of which indicates that of the real beam (Sacherer, 1971; Lapostolle, 1970, 1971b, 1972). This concept proved to be invaluable, both for solving problems of beam dynamics (concerning the envelope equations and the matrix formalism) and for its intrinsic value as a figure of merit, measuring the order or disorder in the domain occupied by the beam in trace space.

In order to explain this, we consider a real beam, the projection of which in T_2 trace space is a density distribution of $\rho_2(x, x')$. The second moments of this distribution, $\overline{x^2}$, $\overline{x'^2}$ and $\overline{xx'}$, are related to the beam width, the velocity spread, and the beam divergence, respectively, and therefore offer an alternative mean of describing the emittance plot and the beam behavior (Hereward, 1969). The "equivalent perfect beam," equivalent to this real beam, is then defined to be the *perfect beam having the same intensity and the same second moments of the trace plane projected distribution.* Note that

$$\overline{x^2} = \frac{\displaystyle\int\int x^2 \rho_2(x, x') \, dx \, dx'}{\displaystyle\int\int \rho_2(x, x') \, dx \, dx'} \tag{81}$$

For a "perfect beam"—corresponding to a uniformly filled ellipse—the beam half-width (a) in the x direction is the maximum value for x (Fig. 4); this can be shown to be given by

$$a \equiv x_{\max} = 2\left(\overline{x^2}\right)^{1/2} \tag{82}$$

The half-angular velocity spread, Ψ, defined to be $x'_{\max}$, is then

$$\Psi \equiv x'_{\max} = 2\left(\overline{x'^2}\right)^{1/2} \tag{83}$$

whereas the emittance, ϵ, is

$$\epsilon = pq = 4\left[\overline{x^2}\,\overline{x'^2} - \left(\overline{xx'}\right)^2\right]^{1/2} \tag{84}$$

irrespective of the orientation of the ellipse relative to the axis (Lapostolle, 1970). For an upright ellipse, $\overline{xx'} = 0$. Alternatively, we can regard these relations as the convention adopted for characterizing the emittance plot of a real continuous beam unambiguously; we thus specify the beam dimensions and its emittance, which we denote $\bar{\epsilon}$ to distinguish it from the area ϵ actually occupied by the domain in T_2:

$$\bar{\epsilon} = 4\left[\overline{x^2}\,\overline{x'^2} - \left(\overline{xx'}\right)^2\right]^{1/2} \tag{85}$$

These quantities can then be characterized by the elliptical curve of the equivalent perfect beam, the equation of which is derived from $\bar{\epsilon}$ and the second-order moments of the distribution. Similar definitions apply to the y direction of course, where the beam width is denoted by b. These definitions may even be extended to include the longitudinal direction, in order to describe the behavior of bunched beams; we then have $a = \sqrt{5}\,(\overline{x^2})^{1/2}$ and $\bar{\epsilon} = 5[\overline{x^2}\,\overline{x'^2} - (\overline{xx'})^2]^{1/2}$ (Weiss, 1973; Warner and Weiss, 1976).

This rms emittance is useful for characterizing the optical properties of a beam for the following reasons.

1. The mean-square values are bounded for all distributions of practical interest and in particular, for Gaussian hyperellipsoidal distributions, for which

$$\bar{\epsilon} = 2\epsilon_c \tag{86}$$

(Warner, 1972), where ϵ_c is the emittance constant. From this, we conclude that 86% of the total beam intensity will flow within an elliptical curve, the area of which is equal to $\bar{\epsilon}$. The quantity $\bar{\epsilon}$ is therefore a highly indicative measure of the fraction of interest for the most real beams. It is very close to the 90% value of the beam emittance and can legitimately replace it in comparing the performances of different beams (Curtis, 1976).

2. The rms emittance of the beam is an *invariant of the motion* if and only if the focusing effect of the transport system is linear (Teng, 1971). It is important to realize that this invariance is a consequence of the transformations imposed, on an ellipse by a linear system and not of Liouville's theorem, which is only applicable to a surface enclosing an ensemble of effective representative points. As a particular application of this theorem, we note that the area within an isodensity curve is conserved as the particles move through any system that may be nonlinear but is Hamiltonian (ϵ = const); $\bar{\epsilon}$, on the other hand, will increase as a result of distortion or even filamentation of the emittance diagram (Lawson, 1976, 1977). The variation of $\bar{\epsilon}$ is not governed by Liouville's theorem but is related to any departures from linearity of the transport system. The usefulness of this definition and the associated notion of an equivalent perfect beam is due to these two properties; they are convenient for establishing the envelope equation or matching a beam to a linear beam transport system and describing the deterioration of an emittance diagram, under the action of nonlinear forces.

3. The rms emittance is a figure of merit for the beam quality. We illustrate this with the aid of the following example; $\bar{\epsilon} = 0$ for a straight line through the origin, which corresponds to the transport of a laminar beam in a linear system. Conversely, even if $\epsilon = 0$, $\bar{\epsilon} \neq 0$ for a curve, which corresponds to the distortion of a laminar beam traveling through a nonlinear system. Thus, $\bar{\epsilon}$ provides a well-defined quantitative measure of the *effective emittance* of a beam. For this reason, it has now supplanted the earlier notion of the "circumscribing ellipse," which was somewhat unsatisfactory, owing to the need to choose the shape and position of the curve. Furthermore, the choice of $\bar{\epsilon}$ can be justified on theoretical grounds, for Lawson *et al.* (1973) have established a close connection between the entropy of a beam and its rms emittance; in addition, the optical quality of a beam can be conveniently described by its entropy. The latter quantity (S) is defined either by thermodynamic considerations or by means of the real distribution in phase space. A relation of the form

$$S_0 = S/kN = 2 \log \bar{\epsilon} + C \qquad (87)$$

is obtained, where N is the number of points in phase space and the constant C is related to the area of the cell in phase space.

III. Measurement of Emittance and Brightness

A. General Comments on Particle-Beam Diagnostics

As applications of particle beams have been increasingly widely developed in various fields of pure and applied physics and in technology, the experimental approach has become highly sophisticated, with a threefold goal: (1) to inform potential users about the performance to be expected from commercially available sources of particle beams, at a given period; (2) to facilitate the calculation of transport optics matched to existing beams (beam line design), followed by monitoring and optimization of the beam in this system (beam line control and optimization); (3) to enable the phenomena (emission, space charge, aberrations) that determine the brightness and emittance of the main types of gun to be analyzed, with a view to improving these properties. The latter govern both the ultimate performance available to the user and the cost of the installation, a particularly crucial parameter in the case of large accelerators.

The conventional methods of measuring the current transported by the beam and the current density distribution in various cross sections rely on scanners (Section III,D,2) or calorimetric devices (Cooper et al., 1972; Coupland et al., 1973), which give information about the dimensions of the beam and its divergence on the axis. It is then possible to calculate the emittance and the brightness (Eqs. 45 and 56) corresponding either to the entire beam or to a part of it in the vicinity of the optic axis. This procedure is commonly used to characterize relatively narrow beams, in particular, those used in electron or ion microscopy or as beam probes (cf. Section III,B,2). It is also used to describe the very large, intense beams employed to heat plasmas in fusion experiments (Green, 1974). Although this method reaches the first of the three objectives listed above, it is almost always incapable of attaining the other two, for which an exact knowledge of the distribution function $\rho_4(x, y, x', y')$ is required in four-dimensional trace space, T_4, or else, the projections (or particular cross sections) on the two two-dimensional trace spaces, T_2^x and T_2^y (see Section II,B). Special devices known as emittance-meters, designed to provide these quantities, appeared during the 1960s. They operate on a principle that may be regarded as an extension of the pinhole camera developed by Cutler and Hines (1955) for studying thermal velocity effects in electron guns. The beam is intercepted by a screen, normal to the optic axis, in which a mobile aperture (a hole or a slit) or several fixed apertures have been drilled. These define position variables (x, y) in the plane of measurement (abscissa z_p) or spatial defining plane. One or several sample beamlets are thus selected, and their transverse velocity spread or the gradients (x', y') of their various trajectories are then determined in another cross-section plane (the angular analysis plane), a suitable distance downstream (Fig. 10a). The particles are detected either by means of a photosensitive receiver (quartz, film, etc.) or by measuring the current incident on a mobile probe, or passing through a mobile aperture (hole or slit) and collected by a Faraday cup, or falling on a fixed array of collectors. Numerous arrangements based on this principle have been designed and tested. They differ only in the shape of the diaphragms, the system adopted for detecting the beamlets, and the relative motions of these various components. References to the earlier versions, with a commentary, are to be found in the book by Banford (1966) and in the review by Van Steenbergen (1970). Although the underlying principle has altered little since 1966, designers have made appreciable efforts to improve their properties, particularly in the following respects: accuracy and fidelity of measurements of position; spatial and angular resolution (dimensions of the diaphragms); sensitivity of the detectors; speed of measurement; ease of use; technological features, particularly in the analysis of high-energy beams (slit design and material). It is obvious that a compromise must be struck among these frequently conflicting desiderata, and that the various methods do not all lend themselves to simultaneous improvement of emittance-meter performance. The user must make a choice, and we now attempt to provide some guidance for this.

Considerable progress has been made by interfacing these measuring systems to minicomputers. The latter simplify the tasks of systematic displacement (or deflection of the beamlets) and of data collection and handling, with the result that emittance diagrams, graphs and the related characteristic parameters defined in Section II,C,2–3. can be displayed on a screen and recorded on the line printer immediately. Their ease of application and the speed of execution are such that methods for analyzing the density distribution in phase space in great detail have been developed and tested quantitatively; the time resolution of discontinuous beams has likewise been studied. This progress in emittance-meters using computer-aided methods was reflected in a large number of the papers presented at the Proton Linear Accelerator Conference at Batavia (1970). These aspects of emittance measurement are discussed in Section III,E, as are the effects that may arise from the introduction of the measuring device into the beam. Almost all of the beam is intercepted in the defining plane in all the various methods based on this principle, which are hence known as destructive or direct methods. Nondestructive but indirect methods can be used instead of these, either because the direct methods are unsuited to the dimensions and energy of the beam, or to monitor the

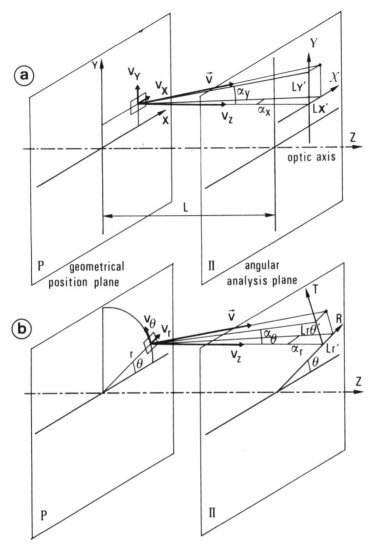

Fig. 10. Trace space coordinates and conventions adopted for labeling points in an emittance measurement reduction process. (a) Cartesian coordinates: x, y in "geometrical position plane," P; angular divergences $\alpha_x \approx x'$ and $\alpha_y \approx y'$ are obtained from the point of arrival X, Y in the "angular analysis plane," Π, located at a distance L downstream from the first plane. Choosing the origin of the X–Y axes appropriately, one obtains $x' \approx X/L$; $y' \approx Y/L$. (b) Cylindrical polar coordinates: position r, θ; angular divergences, referred to rectangular axis R–T: $\alpha_r \approx r' \approx R/L$, $\alpha_\theta \approx r\theta' \approx T/L$.

beam quality and matching to the transport system actually during an experiment. The principle of these indirect methods is based on the assumption that the beam is "normal"—that is, its equidensity contours are elliptical—and involves using the geometrical properties of ellipses to which linear transformations have been applied to calculate the parameters of the boundary curve. We discuss these methods in Section III,D.

When confronted with the choice of various types of emittance-meters, the user must first find an acceptable compromise between the resolution desired in the description of the distribution function in T_4 and the complexity of the resulting design and the quantitative analysis of the results. The points that must be borne in mind are then the purpose of the measurement and any special features of the beam affecting its distribution function—symmetry elements, for example, or the separability of the variables relative to the degrees of freedom. Thus, in the design of a beam line and optimization of its parameters by analytic methods (matrix formalism or envelope equation), a knowledge of the projections of the distribution function on the two trace planes T_2^x and T_2^y is sufficient, provided that these two degrees of freedom are uncoupled. If, on the contrary, effects due to aberrations of the optical elements or to space charge are important, the variation of the function $\rho_4(x, x', y, y', z_p)$ is more informative (Solnyshkov *et al.*, 1972). Whatever the beam may be, this function can only be determined experimentally by examining every point in trace space, a task that was inconceivable before devices interfaced to computers were available. If, however, the distribution function possesses special features—either proved, in which case the problem is already solved, qualitatively at least, or, as is more usual, hypothesized—the measurement procedure can be simplified; it is reduced to a study of the density distribution in particular sections of trace space defined by the coordinate planes [trace planes (x, x') and (y, y') or gradient plane (x', y')]. The measurements can now be used to obtain quantitative information, which characterizes the whole ensemble of particles in the beam.

For these reasons, in order to guide the would be user among the various possibilities, we have classified emittance-meters into three groups: those with which the emittance boundary ellipse can be measured (nondestructive methods, Section III,D); those giving the projected density distribution on the two-dimensional trace planes (Section III,B); those yielding the four-dimensional density distribution, although special features may be required (Section III,C). For each of these categories, we present first the principle of a widely used and satisfactory arrangement; next, we explain how it is employed to obtain quantitative information and in particular, the emittance plot and characteristic quantities,* to which we devote considerable attention. We then examine the main variants of the device (modes of displacement, deflection, and detection), and, finally, we discuss briefly the advantages and disadvantages of the main method and the various alternatives, from the viewpoint of the other criteria that may determine the user's choice (accuracy, practical difficulty, automation, etc.). For practical information about the design and construction, we indicate various articles that seem the most relevant. We conclude with a table, in which the various methods are recapitulated, with their practical requirements and some aspects of their quantitative exploitation. A comparison of their advantages and drawbacks is thus clearly shown.

B. Integrated Trace-Space Density Distribution

In this subsection, we consider two methods, which yield not the "microscopic brightness" of the beam, $\rho_4(x, y, x', y')$ (see Eq. 33) but quantities corresponding to integration of this distribution function with respect to certain variables and, where appropriate, between certain limits. Integration over all positions and slopes corresponding to a degree of freedom is obtained by using two parallel slits, effectively infinitely long in the direction of the slits; this is the "two-slit method," with which we can measure the distribution function of the density of the projection of the four-dimensional domain onto the two-dimensional trace plane, thus:

$$\rho_2(x, x') = \int\int_{-\infty}^{\infty} \rho_4(x, x', y, y') \, dy \, dy' \quad \text{(A m}^{-1}\text{ rad}^{-1}) \qquad (88)$$

Alternatively, the integration may be performed over all four variables, within the limits defined by two openings, circular or rectangular, depending on the symmetry of the beam. This is the "two-aperture method," with which we measure the fractional intensity of the beam accepted in the hypervolume defined by these two apertures; the brightness corresponding to this fraction of the beam can then be calculated, using

$$B = I/V_4 = I \Big/ \int\int\int\int dx \, dy \, dx' \, dy' \qquad (89)$$

1. Two-Dimensional Projected-Density Distribution: The "Two-Slit Method"

a. *Principle of the Method* (Fig. 11a).   As described above, a beamlet is selected and its angular distribution is then analyzed by means of two parallel slits of infinite extent in one direction (y, say), which can be moved independently in the other direction (x), at least in the most usual

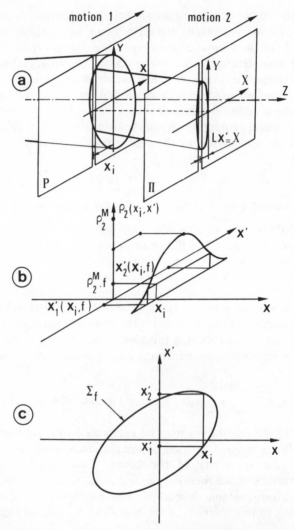

FIG. 11. The "two-slit method." (a) Schemãtic representation of the principle. (b) Profile of projected density for a chosen position x_i of the selection slit and determination of the parameters of a particular equidensity contour Σ_f corresponding to the fraction f of the maximum density ρ_2^M [Σ_f is drawn in (c)].

version of this arrangement. The abscissa X of the analyzer slit, which is followed by a beam intensity monitor, is measured relative to an origin that is defined, for each position x_i of the selection slit, by the trajectory parallel to the optic axis. For any pair of values x_i, X_j, particles that pass through both slits have the following coordinates in trace space:

$$x_i, \; x'_j = X_j/L,$$

y and y' are arbitrary, between $-\infty$ and ∞; L denotes the distance between the position defining plane and the angular analysis plane. If we introduce the width of the selection slit, δx, which characterizes the spatial resolution (cf. Section III,E), and that of the analysis slit, δX, which determines the angular aperture $(\delta x' = \delta X/L)$ of the pencil beam "accepted" for each point in the selection slit, the element of current at the detector will be given by

$$\delta^2 I(x_i, x'_j) = \int_{x_i}^{x_i+\delta x} \int_{x_j}^{x'_j+\delta x'} \int_{-\infty}^{\infty} \int_{-\infty}^{\infty} \rho_4(x, x', y, y') \, dx \, dx' \, dy \, dy' \quad (90)$$

With the aid of Eq. (88), this becomes

$$\delta^2 I(x_i, x'_j) = \rho_2(x_i, x'_j) \, \delta x \, \delta x' = \rho_2(x_i, x'_j) \pi \, \delta Y^x \quad (91)$$

in which

$$\delta Y^x = \delta x \, \delta x'/\pi = \delta x \, \delta X/\pi L \quad (92)$$

and is now seen to be the acceptance of the collimation system formed by the two slits (Banford, 1966; Larson and Jones, 1977); it therefore characterizes the emittance-meter. The element of current $\delta^2 I(x, x')$ passing through the two slits is therefore proportional to the two-dimensional projected density:

$$\delta^2 I(x, x') \propto \rho_2(x, x') = \frac{\partial^2 I}{\partial x \, \partial x'} \quad (93)$$

The distribution function, $\rho_2(x, x')$, is obtained by shifting the analysis slit continuously and simultaneously recording the current $\delta^2 I(x_i, x') = \rho_2(x_i, x') \pi \, \delta Y^x$ for a range of discrete values of the selection slit (x_i) (Fig. 11b).

b. *Presentation and Reduction of the Results.* This distribution function may be represented as a surface in a coordinate system (ρ_2, x, x'), which may be shown in perspective (Fig. 11b) or plotted in a plane (Fig. 7). Alternatively to obtain the "emittance plot," equidensity contours may be drawn relative discrete chosen values of the fraction f of the maximum density ρ_2^M occuring in the trace plane; this maximum is usually encountered on the optic axis $(x = x' = 0)$. For each position x_i of the selection slit, the intersection of the density distribution with the fractional density $\rho_2^* = f\rho_2^M$ $(x = 0, x' = 0)$, $0 \leqslant f \leqslant 1$, provides a set of two values, $x'_1(x_i, f)$ and $x'_2(x_i, f)$, which define the angular dispersion to be considered in order to obtain the desired equidensity contour Σ_f (Fig. 11b and c). For $f = 0$, we obtain the zeros of the density distribution, which define the domain boundary in the trace plane, Σ_0. This boundary curve encloses the total beam emittance ϵ_T and all the representative points, that is, the total beam current I_T. The fractional current $I(f)$ and emittance $\epsilon(f)$ within a particular equidensity contour Σ_f are then evaluated from the relations

$$\epsilon^x(f) = (1/\pi) \oint_{\Sigma_f} x' \, dx = (1/\pi) \int_{-\infty}^{\infty} dx \int_{x_1'(x_i,f)}^{x_2'(x_i,f)} dx' \tag{94}$$

$$I(f) = \int\int_{\Sigma_f} \rho_2(x, x') \, dx \, dx'$$

$$= (1/\pi \, \delta Y^x) \int_{-\infty}^{\infty} dx \int_{x_1'(x_i,f)}^{x_2'(x_i,f)} \delta^2 I(x_i, x') \, dx' \tag{95}$$

This double integral can equally well be calculated from the function $\epsilon^x = \epsilon^x(f)$ given by Eq. (94), and from its representative curve $f(\epsilon^x)$ by integrating the latter from zero to the emittance corresponding to the contour Σ_f, thus:

$$I(f) = \pi \rho_2^M \int_0^{\epsilon^x(f)} f(\epsilon^x) \, d\epsilon^x$$

or directly:

$$I(\epsilon^x) = \pi \rho_2^M \int_0^{\epsilon^x} f \, d\epsilon^x \tag{96}$$

There is no particular reason why a graph of the function $I(f)$ against f, where $f = \rho_2/\rho_2^M$, should be a straight line and the 10% isodensity contour does not in general correspond to 90% of the total beam intensity, therefore (Billen, 1975; Ames, 1978). The contour Σ_f that does correspond to ϵ_{90} and enclose 90% of the beam must hence be determined from the $I = I(f)$ curve, which will give the appropriate value of f for this purpose. From the above equations, the current-emittance characteristic relative to the transverse direction x can be plotted, and this in turn provides the characteristic quantities ϵ_c^x and ϵ_{90}^x (Fig. 10b). The quantities defining the "equivalent perfect beam" (Eqs. 82–84) may be obtained straightforwardly from $\rho_2(x, x')$. As an example of this, the second moment $\overline{x^2}$ (see Eq. 81) becomes

$$\overline{x^2} = \frac{\displaystyle\sum_i x_i^2 \int_{x_1'(x_i,0)}^{x_2'(x_i,0)} \rho_2(x_i, x') \, dx'}{\displaystyle\sum_i \int_{x_1'}^{x_2'} \rho_2(x_i, x') \, dx'} \tag{97}$$

as a result of the sampling in the x direction.

It is worth emphasizing that this quantitative exploitation of the results in terms of the emittance or the "equivalent perfect beam" characterizing all or a well-defined fraction of the beam relies on no particular assumptions concerning the beam symmetry, the shape of the emittance boundary or the density distribution function. This is a consequence of the fact that all particles crossing the section of the beam under study are taken into account, in a full exploration over x and x'. If the beam line has two symmetry planes, however, a similar analysis must be performed on the transverse motion in the y direction, the measurements being repeated after rotation of the device through $\pi/2$. The method is therefore well suited to problems concerning beam transport and is widely used today for this reason. Conversely, as has been already mentioned (Section II,C,2), this method is not convenient to characterize the optical quality of a beam in terms of its hyperemittance and brightness. If we wish to determine the curves $I = I(\epsilon_4)$ and $I = I(B)$, some assumptions must be made both about the geometry of the hypervolume occupied in T_4 trace space and about the distribution function of microscopic brightness in this space. This problem has been recently discussed by Ames (1978). He demonstrates that to a first approximation these curves may be derived from the two curves —$I(\epsilon^x)$ and $I(\epsilon^y)$—if one assumes (1) the separability of the distribution function of microscopic brightness, relative to the x and y degrees of freedom, and (2) a hyperellipsoid domain in T_4. With these assumptions, in order to calculate $\epsilon_{4,F}$ or B_F, relative to percentage F of the total beam current, one has to consider the two emittances $\epsilon^x_{\sqrt{F}}$ and $\epsilon^y_{\sqrt{F}}$ which in the T_2 trace planes correspond to the percentage $\sqrt{F}$ of the total beam current. This results from the fact that to these projected areas corresponds a hyperellipsoid which encloses a fractional current

$$I = I_{(\epsilon^x)}I_{(\epsilon^y)}/I_T = FI_T \tag{98}$$

and which hyperemittance is, from Eq. (67),

$$\epsilon_{4,F} = \epsilon^x_{\sqrt{F}} C^y_{\sqrt{F}}/2 \tag{99}$$

The brightness associated to this fractional current is then

$$B_F = 2FI_T/\pi^2 \epsilon^x_{\sqrt{F}} C^y_{\sqrt{F}} \tag{100}$$

The variation of F from 0 to 1, in the three above relations, gives the parametric equations of the curves $I(\epsilon_4)$ and $I(B)$. As a particular value, the brightness on the optic axis $(\epsilon_4 \to 0)$ is obtained from

$$B_0 = R = 2I_T/\pi^2 \epsilon^x_c \epsilon^y_c \tag{101}$$

These two curves—as far as their conditions of validity are satisfied—and the particular values B_0, B_{63}, and B_{90}; $\epsilon_{4,c}$ and $\epsilon_{4,90}$ which can be read off them complete the presentation of the results of a measurement of emittance by the two-slit method. The data reduction process in recapitulated in Table I.

c. *Principal Arrangements in Use.* Designing a device on the slit–slit principle is not straightforward (Kuhlmann *et al.*, 1970): two screen displacements driven by independent motors are necessary, and the position of each slit must be accurate and reproducible. Such a device is nonetheless of considerable interest, since it provides a continuous trace of the angular distribution, and the step length of the spatial definition slit can be chosen arbitrarily. This flexibility makes it a very suitable instrument for

TABLE I

THE "TWO-SLIT METHOD": DATA REDUCTION PROCESS

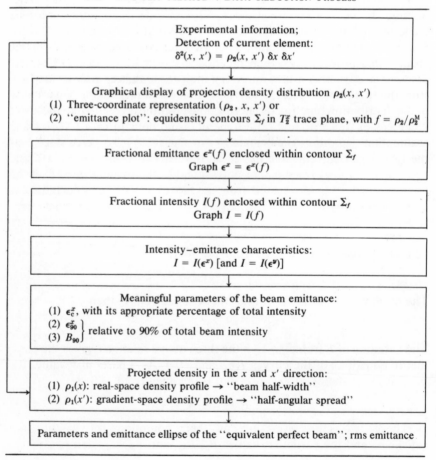

measuring the emittance of beams, the dimensions of which may change considerably from one experiment to the next; its parameters thus can be chosen to optimize the accuracy of measurement (cf. Section III,E,2). Some simplification of the design can be achieved by replacing the unit consisting of mobile analysis slit and beam monitor by a simple moving wire (Lord *et al.*, 1967); elimination of effects due to secondary electrons is then more difficult, however (Gautherin, 1967).

One displacement can be avoided by replacing the moving screen containing one of the slits by a fixed screen containing an array of regularly space slits (Rose *et al.*, 1964; Bauman *et al.*, 1976). The spacing between these slits must be matched to the geometrical dimensions of the beam, and overlapping of the sample beamlets must be avoided, which renders the device less versatile. The other displacement can likewise be avoided by using photographic recording or a quartz plate; with the latter, the luminescence can be observed directly for qualitative analysis or photographed for quantitative work (Wroe, 1967, 1968; Kobayashi *et al.*, 1972, 1974). The latter involves the use of a microdensitometer, and only the first stages of the analysis are different from those discussed above (see Van Steenbergen, 1967b). It must, however, be mentioned that these indirect methods of detecting particle fluxes (quartz plates, photographic films, nuclear emulsions—or in earlier times, filter paper or vacuum grease!) cause problems in quantitative work. A careful study of the detector response curve (particle energy and dose) is essential if serious errors are to be avoided. Fukomoto *et al.* (1971) have proposed an elegant solution to this problem. Nevertheless, the quantitative aspects of these devices must be treated with caution, although their advantages for a qualitative approach are obvious. Even so, they have now been supplanted by instruments in which the beam and sample beamlets are deflected—by an electric or magnetic field—with fixed slits. The data collection rate is high, and a continuous trace of the emittance plot can be displayed on an oscilloscope. We return to these devices in Section III,E,1, where we also discuss automation of the measurements, which can easily be incorporated if we use a mobile probe in the form of a parallelepiped (Fig. 12); the entry face of this contains a slit, and the inside surface of the opposite face is covered with a series of collectors parallel to the entry slit. The angular distribution can thus be sampled for each position of the probe in the beam.

2. Intensity-Brightness Curve: "Two-Aperture Methods"

a. *Principle of the Method.* An original method was developed by Miller (1966) for studying highly relativistic electron beams. This yields

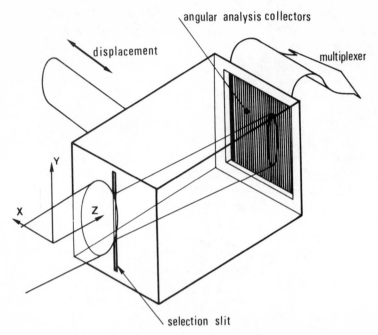

FIG. 12.   The "two-slit method": probe for automated destructive emittance measurements.

the current–hyperemittance curve, $I = I(\epsilon_4)$ or the current–brightness curve $I = I(B/B_0)$ directly, without measuring the microscopic brightness distribution function. This method is therefore suitable for measuring overall beam performance, which explains why it has been little used to date for analyzing extended beams. It is essentially an extension of the "two-aperture" method, used by microscopists to determine the brightness of their beams, which are kept narrow by passing them through small apertures. This method is often assumed to give a direct measurement of the beam brightness, but it should be stressed that it in fact gives the brightness of that part of the beam that is accepted by the hypervolume defined by the two apertures, centered on the optic axis, distance L apart (Fig. 13a), and not the brightness of the entire beam (Hoffmann, 1972). Thus, from Eq. (89), we have

$$B(I) = I/\pi^2 \cdot Y_4 \qquad (102)$$

where Y_4 is the hyperacceptance of the set of two apertures and I is the beam current passing through them. The value thus obtained is the mean value of the microscopic brightness in the domain Y_4 of T_4 trace space. If

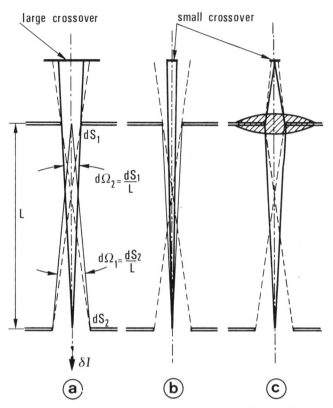

FIG. 13. The "two-aperture method": principle and limitations. (a) Homogeneous illumination of the two-aperture arrangement is achieved with a large enough source or beam crossover. (b) The crossover is too small and the solid angle $\delta\Omega_2$ is not completely illuminated. The brightness of point sources cannot be measured with this arrangement. (c) Addition of a lens to the previous arrangement provides homogeneous illumination.

the two apertures are circular, we have

$$Y_4 = \delta S \; \delta\Omega/\pi^2 = (r_1 r_2/L)^2 \tag{103}$$

for nonrelativistic beams. The value given by Eq. (102) for B will be correct only if the second aperture is fully illuminated by the beamlet defined by the first, that is, if the angular spread of the trajectories in the beam ($\Delta\Omega$) is greater than the angular definition $\delta\Omega$ of the arrangement (Fig. 13a). If this condition is not satisfied, the resulting measurement is a default value of the effective brightness of the apertured beam (Fig. 13b). If both apertures are very small ($\delta S \to 0$, $\delta\Omega \to 0$), the method yields the *Richtstrahlwert* ($R = B_0$), as defined above (Eq. 53); this is assumed to be

the maximum value of the microscopic brightness. If the radii of the apertures are variable, the whole $I = f(B/R)$ curve, which characterizes the
entire beam completely, can be obtained.

b. *Practical Use of the Method.*   In order to ensure that the second
diaphragm is illuminated correctly, von Borries (1948) recommands
placing a lens between the apertures: this is the "two-aperture with lens"
method (Fig. 13c). Lauer and Hanszen (1975; Lauer, 1975) have examined
the limitation of this method, resulting from the spherical aberrations of
the lens. They describe an experimental arrangement with which this difficulty can be surmounted. A modification of the two aperture with lens
method, suitable for obtaining the brightness of electron microscope
beams, was suggested by von Ardenne (1956); this exploits the lenses of
the microscope itself. For very small particle sources, such as those using
field emission from a pointed tip—which are used in high-resolution electron microscopy and to obtain very small probes—the two-aperture
method is no longer reliable: the second aperture cannot be uniformly illuminated since the virtual emitter is so small (2–10 Å). For such sources,
the brightness can only be estimated; we then speak of the "intrinsic
brightness," as opposed to the "extrinsic brightness" obtained when the
beam is apertured. This "intrinsic brightness" is obtained, using Eq. (45),
by calculating the radius of the virtual emitter and measuring the emission
angle with a mobile slit or wire system. The reader interested in this topic
will find further details on p. 261 of this volume, where Levi-Setti de-
votes Section III to "sources of high specific brightness."

Miller (1966) replaces the second aperture by a photographic emul-
sion, analyzing the images obtained for various values of the radius of the
first aperture with the aid of a microphotometer. It is then easy to establish whether the conditions in which Eq. (102) is valid are satisfied. Miller
also compares the results obtained by the two-aperture method with those
of a two-slit measurement in the special case of a Gaussian distribution in
T_4 trace space.

C. Four-Dimensional Trace-Space Density Distribution

1. Beams without Symmetry: "Pepper-Pot Method"

a. *Principle of the Method* (Fig. 14a).   The selection screen, or
"pepper-pot plate," contains a regular array of identical holes over its
whole surface (positioned at x_i, y_k). The sample beamlets thus defined fall
on a photographic plate (or a quartz plate) situated in the angular analysis
plane: the two plates form a "multipinhole camera." If the beamlets do

not overlap, the flux incident per unit area of the plate at a point (X_j, Y_l) of the spot corresponding to the beamlet from (x_i, y_k) is given by

$$\frac{\partial^4 I}{\partial X \, \partial Y} = \rho_4(x_i, y_k, x'_j, y'_l) \, \delta S / L^2 \tag{104}$$

in which δS denotes the area of the openings and $x'_j = X_j/L$, $y'_l = Y_l/L$. The same convention as before is used to label points in the analysis plane. Provided that the receiver has been suitably chosen for the particle energy and illumination in question, in the sense that its response is linear for the flux incident, the image obtained in the plane of analysis—known as the "pepper-pot emittance pattern" (Fig. 14b)—will represent the distribution function in T_4 trace space, sampled at the points defined by the holes in the pepper-pot plate. Thus, the pepper-pot pattern is in fact a "hyperemittance pattern."

   b. *Presentation and Reduction of the Results.* This method is therefore capable of providing an exhaustive analysis of the domain occupied in trace space T_4, but two obstacles can limit its usefulness for quantitative measurements. First, a photographic plate must be used, or a quartz receiver, which must in turn be photographed, and the response curves of these media can cause problems (see above). Second, full exploitation of the experimental results is a long and thankless task unless the recorded image is treated digitally by a data analysis program. Given that the first difficulty has been surmounted, the complete data reduction process is essentially an extension of that employed in the "two-slit method," now extended to include several diagrams rather than just one. For each beamlet spot (position x_i, y_k in the beam cross section), the angular density distribution $\rho_4(x_i, y_k, x', y')$ is extracted from the photograph with the aid of a "pinhole" densitometer, the response of which is a function n:

$$n = n(x', y')_{x_i, y_k} = C\rho_4(x_i, y_k, x', y') \tag{105}$$

This represents the density distribution in gradient space and can be represented either as a surface in a three-dimensional cartesian coordinate system (n, x', y') or by isodensity curves $n = $ constant in the gradient plane (x', y') (see Fig. 14c). The experimental data are therefore represented by as many "density diagrams" as there are holes in the "pepper-pot plate"; they may be gathered in a single "hyperemittance plot" as shown in Fig. 14d. These results are then exploited quantitatively as follows:

   1. The highest density maximum is found, n^M; this is usually situated on the optic axis, at $x = y = x' = y' = 0$.
   2. A factor, between 0 and 1, is chosen, which defines a threshold

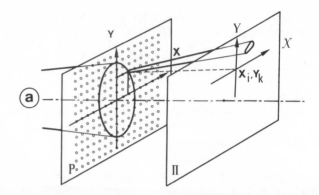

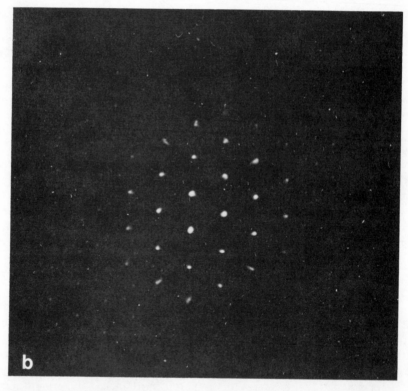

FIG. 14.   The "pepper-pot method." (a) Schematic representation of the principle. (b) Pepper-pot hyperemittance pattern for a hydrogen beam extracted from a duoplasmatron (40 mA; 200 keV) (courtesy of Emigh *et al.*, 1972). (c) Distribution function of microscopic brightness in a gradient plane (x', y') for a selected beamlet (x_i, y_k). (d) Hyperemittance plot: meaningful equidensity contours of microscopic brightness for all sample beamlets; one may choose those enclosing 90 and 63% of the total beam current and corresponding respectively to $\epsilon_{4,90}$ and $\epsilon_{4,c}$; the correlated fraction f_1 and f_2 of the maximum of density has to be determined from the data reduction process.

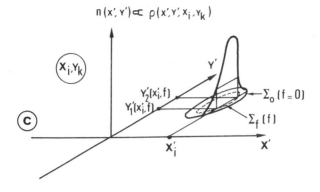

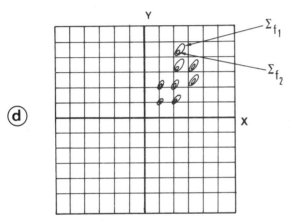

FIG. 14. *Continued.*

density, $n^* = fn^M$, for which the corresponding isodensity curve is found in each diagram and the area enclosed within each contour $\{\Sigma_f\}$ is obtained:

$$S(f, x_i, y_k) = \int\int_{\Sigma_f} dx' \, dy' \qquad (106)$$

3. The fractional hyperemittance $\epsilon_4(f)$ corresponding, for the beam ensemble, to the hypervolume enclosed by the equidensity contour $n^* = fn^M$ is calculated; this is also a contour of equal microscopic brightness:

$$\epsilon_4(f) = (1/\pi^2) \int_{-\infty}^{\infty} dx \int_{-\infty}^{\infty} dy \int\int_{\Sigma_f} dx' \, dy'$$

$$= (1/\pi^2) \int_{-\infty}^{\infty} \int_{-\infty}^{\infty} S(f, x, y) \, dx \, dy \qquad (107)$$

4. The fractional current $I(f)$ corresponding to the ensemble of representative points contained in this hyperemittance is evaluated

$$I(f) = C \int_{-\infty}^{\infty} dx \int_{-\infty}^{\infty} dy \int \int_{n \geq n \!\! / \!\! k}^{n^{max}(x_i, y_k)} n(x', y')_{x_i, y_k} dx' dy' \qquad (108)$$

where $n_{max}(x_i, y_k)$ is the maximum possible density for the points x_i, y_k in question. Here too, the double integral can be calculated from the function $f(S, x_i, y_k)$, obtained above (Eq. 106), which then has to be integrated from the value of f selected and the maximum possible value of f, for the point x_i, y_k, that is, a surface S equal to zero. Thus,

$$I(f) = Cn^{M} \int_{-\infty}^{\infty} dx \int_{-\infty}^{\infty} dy \int_{0}^{S(f, x_i, y_k)} f(S, x_i, y_k) \, dS \qquad (109)$$

Alternatively, the fractional intensity can be calculated from the function $f(\epsilon_4)$, which has already been determined (Eq. 107). Recalling the definition of $\rho_4 = \partial^4 I / \partial V_4$, we have

$$I(\epsilon_4) = \pi^2 Cn^{M} \int_{0}^{\epsilon_4} f \, d\epsilon_4 \qquad (110)$$

which is an extension of Eq. (96), used in the two-slit method. The constant Cn^{M}, which depends on the receiver and on the analyzer arrangement, is obtained by measuring the total current, which also occurs in Eq. (110) for $f = 0$.

5. Finally, the curves $I = I(\epsilon_4)$ and $I = I(B)$ are plotted.

The complexity of this process and the practical difficulty of representing the results graphically are obvious. Nevertheless, complete information about the density distribution in trace space can be obtained and exploited for studying both the transport of the beam and the forces exerted on the particles. Symmetry properties, nonlinearity, or coupling effects can thus be displayed. It is possible to calculate the densities projected on the trace planes $T\frac{x}{z}$ and $T\frac{y}{z}$, after which the characteristics of the ellipses for the "equivalent perfect beam" corresponding to the two principal directions can be determined.

When we realize that this very precise method could be interfaced to an automated image-processing system, several variations of which are already operating satisfactorily and becoming less and less costly, it seems reasonable to expect that with full automation this method will be generalized to cover numerous applications of particle beams. It has the immense advantage that no mechanical movements are required. A first attempt to automate the method has been made by the Los Alamos group, using a Vidicon recorder (Emigh et al., 1971). We must, however, point out that hitherto the "pepper-pot hyperemittance pattern" has been mainly used for qualitative analysis of the beam symmetry and aberrations (to show the presence of translaminar beams, for example: Mueller *et al.*, 1972; Allison *et al.*, 1971). Quantitative analyses have mostly been of a simplified kind, in which only the density distribution in the sections of T_4 by the trace planes ($y = 0$, $y' = 0$, for example) have been determined; we return to this below.

c. *Practical Application.* The problem of putting this method into practice arises from the need to photograph the luminescent quartz. For a transport line, the solution is to switch the beam by means of a magnetic deflector, at the end of which it falls on the measuring system (Schubaly *et al.*, 1976). There are variants of the "pepper-pot method," with which trace space can be explored without using a quartz plate or photographic film. These, however, require mobile elements, for defining each point in the position defining and angular analysis planes. In the "two-hole method," two plates each containing one hole and movable in both directions are employed. Alternatively, two pairs of crossed slits may be used, which can again be shifted independently in the two directions.

The first of these has been abandoned in practice, and the second is mainly used for exploring the density distributions in sections of T_4 by the coordinate planes. The advantage of these devices with mobile openings is that the entire volume of trace space can be examined without sampling in position, whereas the latter can lead to considerable uncertainly when used to determine the beam characteristics (see Section III,E). When using a pepper-pot plate care must therefore be taken to ensure that it is matched to the dimensions of the beam being investigated.

2. Beams with Axial Symmetry

The process of interpreting the emittance pattern obtained by the pepper-pot method is simpler if the density distribution function in trace space exhibits some special features, at the point where the measurements are made. For each type of special features, measuring devices or more suitable methods of exploiting the results can be devised.

The domain occupied in trace space by the particles representative of the beam in a given cross section can be described in cartesian coordinates or in cylindrical polar coordinates (Fig. 10a and b). The geometrical position is defined by (r, θ) while a trajectory is identified by two angles measured relative to the optic axis: the radial deviation $\alpha_r \simeq r' = v_r/v_z$ and the azimuthal deviation $\alpha_\theta \simeq r\theta' = v_\theta/v_z$. The equations relating the two systems are as follows:

$$x = r \cos \theta, \qquad x' = \alpha_r \cos \theta - \alpha_\theta \sin \theta$$
$$y = r \sin \theta, \qquad y' = \alpha_r \sin \theta + \alpha_\theta \cos \theta \tag{111}$$

and the corresponding Jacobian, $J = \partial(x, y, x', y')/\partial(r, \theta, \alpha_r, \alpha_\theta) = r$. The hypervolume occupied in trace space can therefore be calculated from the integrals,

$$V_4 = \iiiint dx \, dy \, dx' \, dy' = \iiiint r \, dr \, d\theta \, d\alpha_r \, d\alpha_\theta \tag{112}$$

while the intensity corresponding to the points within this hypervolume is given by

$$I = \iiiint \rho_4(x, y, x', y') \, dx \, dy \, dx' \, dy'$$
$$= \iiiint \rho_4(r, \theta, \alpha_r, \alpha_\theta) r \, dr \, d\theta \, d\alpha_r \, d\alpha_\theta \tag{113}$$

For an axially symmetric beam, integration over θ from 0 to 2π yields

$$I = 2\pi \int_0^R \int_{-\pi/2}^{\pi/2} \int_{-\pi/2}^{\pi/2} \rho_4(r, \alpha_r, \alpha_\theta) r \, dr \, d\alpha_r \, d\alpha_\theta \tag{114}$$

and

$$V_4 = 2\pi \int_0^R \int_{-\pi/2}^{\pi/2} \int_{-\pi/2}^{\pi/2} r \, dr \, d\alpha_r \, d\alpha_\theta \tag{115}$$

where R is the radius of the beam, which may alternatively be defined by some requirements on the density $\rho_4(r, \alpha_r, \alpha_\theta)$.

a. *Beams with Azimuthal Dispersion: The "Hole–Screen Method."* If the beam is axially symmetric but the individual trajectories are spread out azimuthally, the diagrams in gradient space $(\alpha_\theta, \alpha_r)$ corresponding to different points along a ray characterize it completely. The measuring device then can be simplified, as far as the method of selecting beamlets is concerned: the pepper-pot plate need be pierced with holes along a diameter only; plates with a single hole need be moved only in one direction; of the two-crossed slits, one can be fixed. The last two methods have the advantage that the number of points sampled and their position can be chosen at will. The angular spread is still commonly analyzed with the aid of a quartz or photographic plate, hence the name "hole–screen method" (Collins and Stroud, 1964; Ivanov *et al.*, 1965; Abroyan *et al.*, 1969).

The procedure developed for exploiting pepper-pot emittance patterns, originally suggested by Ivanov *et al.* (1965), can be applied to this special case. For each point, the quantity

$$S(f, r) = \int\int_{\Sigma_f} d\alpha_r \, d\alpha_\theta \tag{116}$$

is calculated, where $f = n^*/n^M$. This gives the fractional hyperemittance

$$\epsilon_4(f) = (2/\pi) \int_0^R S(f, r) r \, dr \tag{117}$$

and the current corresponding to this hyperemittance

$$I(f) = 2\pi C \int_0^R r \, dr \int_0^{S(f,r)} f(S, r) \, dS \tag{118}$$

which may also be calculated directly using Eq. (110).

It is clear that this procedure is not suitable for determining the projections of the density distribution on the T_2^x and T_2^y trace planes. These can, however, be calculated from the experimental results but the principal attraction of the method is that it reveals any differences between the radial and azimuthal angular distributions, even for a rotationally symmetric beam, as proved experimentally by Ivanov *et al.* (1965). This method is therefore very suitable for studying ion sources for which the emitter and extraction optics are rotationally symmetric, an extremely common situation. In order to obtain the curves $I = I(\epsilon)$, in which ϵ is the emittance projection, Ivanov *et al.* (1965) assume that V_4 is a hyperellipsoid and that $\epsilon(f) = \sqrt{2\epsilon_4(f)}$, whereas $I(f)$ is still given by Eq. (118). But owing to the projection, this assumption is not satisfied and Eq. (99) must be used, as has been discussed in the case of the two-slit method.

With regard to the "hole–screen method," it is appropriate to mention the arrangement known as the "shadow method" for emittance diagram display; it is used by microscopists to study the aberrations of electron guns (Lauer and Hanszen, 1975). Measurement of the area of the diagram is not the main object; its shape, however, is important since the aberration coefficients of the optical system can be determined from it (Wilson and Brewer, 1973), and a method giving a direct photographic record of this emittance diagram is therefore of interest. In the solution adopted, the defining plate containing a single hole and the photographic plates are coupled in such a way that they move simultaneously in perpendicular directions (Fig. 15).

b. *Beams without Azimuthal Dispersion: "Method of Two Pairs of Crossed Slits."* If we assume that the spread of gradients in the azimuthal direction is negligible ($\Delta\alpha_\theta \ll \Delta\alpha_r$), so that the trajectories are vir-

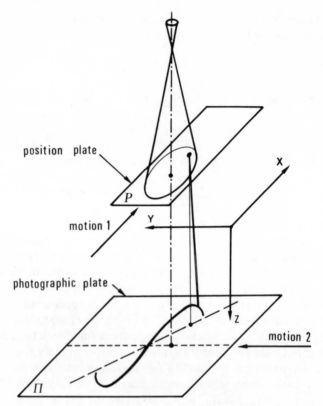

FIG. 15.   Principle of the shadow method for photographic recording of the emittance domain.

tually planes and lie in planes containing the optic axis, the quantities characterizing the ensemble of the beam can be established by studying the trajectory distribution in one of these planes, $x-z$ for example. Whether this approximation is legitimate must, however, be checked experimentally: the hyperemittance pattern given by the pepper-pot method or the hole–screen method shows this immediately. The arrangement consisting of two pairs of crossed slits can also be used to test the assumption, each pair selecting a point in the position defining plane and the analysis plane, respectively (Fig. 16). Each slit must, however, be mobile in the direction normal to its length. The use of this method for studying beams with axial symmetry has been discussed by Van Steenbergen (1967b). The device allows through an element of current that is proportional to the microscopic brightness of the beam:

$$\delta^4 I = \rho_4(x, x', y, y') \, \delta x \, \delta y \, \delta x' \, \delta y' \tag{119}$$

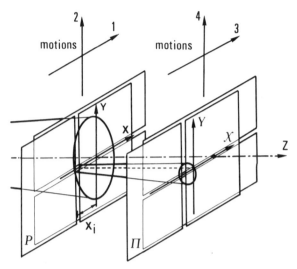

FIG. 16. Principle of the "two pairs of crossed-slits method."

where $\delta x' = \delta X/L$, $\delta y' = \delta Y/L$, and δx, δy, δX, and δY denote the dimensions of the two slits. Here it is assumed that the variations of ρ_4 over the width of the various slits can be neglected. Investigation of the trajectories in the neighborhood of the plane x–z [$y = y' = 0$ or $\theta = \alpha_\theta = 0$] gives a function

$$\delta^4 I(x, x') = \rho_4(x, x', y = y' = 0) \; \delta x \; \delta y \; \delta x' \; \delta y' \qquad (120)$$

This can be represented in the trace plane $T_2^x(x, x')$ or $T_2^r(r, \alpha_r)$ by a specific density $d_2(x, x') = d_2(r, \alpha_r)$ such that

$$\delta^4 I(x, x') = d_2(x, x') \; \delta x \; \delta x' \qquad (121)$$

$$d_2(x, x') = \rho_4(x, x', y = y' = 0) \; \delta y \; \delta y'$$
$$d_2(r, \alpha_r) = \rho_4(r, \alpha_r, \theta = \alpha_\theta = 0) \; \delta y \; \delta y' \qquad (122)$$

The "section-emittance plot" of the beam then may be obtained from the isodensity curves of this distribution, defined by the normalized microscopic brightness $f = \rho_4/\rho_4^M = d_2(r, \alpha_r)/d_2(0, 0)$. Then this enables us to calculate the fractional section emittances as a function of f; thus, $\epsilon_s = \epsilon_s(f)$. With rotational symmetry, the corresponding fractional currents, $i(f)$, can be calculated as follows:

$$i(f) = 2\pi \int_0^R \int_{\alpha_{r_1}(r,f)}^{\alpha_{r_2}(r,f)} \int_{-\delta y'/2}^{\delta y'/2} \rho_4(r, \alpha_r, 0, 0) r \; dr \; d\alpha_r \; d\alpha_\theta \qquad (123)$$

$$i(f) = 2\pi \, \delta y' \int_0^R \int_{\alpha_{r_1}}^{\alpha_{r_2}} \rho_4(r, \alpha_r, 0, 0) r \, dr \, d\alpha_r \tag{124}$$

These integrals can be evaluated, recalling the relation between ρ_4 and $\delta^4 I$ (Eq. 120). The current $i(0)$, obtained by setting f equal to zero does not, however, correspond to the total intensity in the beam unless all the particles selected by the first hole are analyzed as the second hole is moved along a diameter. For this to be the case, the azimuthal spread of these particles ($\Delta\alpha_\theta$ or $\Delta y'$) must be smaller than the angular aperture defined by the width and position of the analyser slit, namely, $\delta y' = \delta Y/L$; this quantity has been used to determine the limits of integration in Eq. (123). We thus require

$$\Delta y' = \Delta\alpha_\theta \leqslant \delta y' = \delta Y/L \tag{125}$$

With this condition, the device provides direct integration of the density distribution, ρ_4, over the angular divergence $\delta y'$. Thus, the density, which is experimentally determined from the detected current (Eq. 120) and which then appears in Eq. (124), is in fact a fictitious value corresponding to the average of the density function over $\delta y'$ because the function itself cannot be resolved. But only if the condition (125) is satisfied will $i(f)$ be the same as $I(f)$, the fraction of the beam ensemble of which the representative points in T_4 trace space lie within the domain bounded by the contour of equal microscopic brightness, $\rho_4 = f\rho_4^M$. The curve $I = I(\epsilon_s)$ obtained by combining $I(f)$ and $\epsilon_s(f)$ then indicates an interesting feature of the total beam: it can be used to analyze the transport of the beam along an optical channel of known section admittance Y_s. From the curve $I(f)$, the particular value of f, corresponding to given percentage of the total beam intensity can be determined. The brightness for $63\%, \ldots, 90\%, \ldots$ of the beam then can be calculated easily, as the mean of the microscopic brightness between the origin (ρ_4^M) and the iso-density contour ρ_4 thus, for example:

$$B_{90} = (\rho_4^M/0.9I_T) \int_0^{0.9I_T} f(I) \, dI \tag{126}$$

It is not possible to calculate the hypervolume $\epsilon_4(f)$ directly and exactly from the "section-emittance plot." This quantity can be obtained from the function $I(f)$, by transposing expression (126), used above:

$$\epsilon_4(I) = (1/\pi^2\rho_4^M) \int_0^I dI/f(I) \tag{127}$$

Van Steenbergen (1967b) states that Condition (125) can be satisfied for a beam in a big accelerator by a suitable choice of the analyzer slit, since

$\Delta\alpha_\theta \ll \Delta\alpha_r$ because of effects associated with the geometrical aberrations of the optical elements. This condition is not, however, satisfied close to the zone of formation of the beam, since the particle emission processes are quasi-isotropic.

c. *Beams with Azimuthal Dispersion: The "Hole–Slit Method."*
(1) *Principle of the method.* In order to avoid the laborious complexity of the "hole–screen method" and the incertainly that may attend a study restricted to trajectories lying in a plane by means of the "method of two pairs of crossed slits," the Orsay group (Septier *et al.*, 1966) investigated the "hole–slit method," subsequently reexamined by various authors. Here a sample beamlet is selected by a hole (or two crossed slits), which can be moved along a radius (abscissa x or r), while the analysis is performed by means of a slit, infinite in the Y direction and movable in the X direction (Fig. 17). With such an arrangement, therefore, all particles with trajectories that depart from the x–z plane are collected, with the result that as the angular analysis slit is moved in the X direction, all the particles selected by the hole are investigated. The element of current passing through the system and subsequently collected by a Faraday cage is hence given by the following expression (with the same type of notation as used earlier):

$$\delta^3 I(x_i, x_j') = \delta x \; \delta y \; \delta x' \int_{-\infty}^{\infty} \rho_4(x_i, x_j', y = 0, y') \, dy' \qquad (128)$$

In the T_2^x trace plane, this current corresponds to a density $D_2(x_i, x_j')$ of representative points

$$\delta^3 I = D_2(x_i, x_j') \, \delta x \, \delta x' \qquad (129)$$

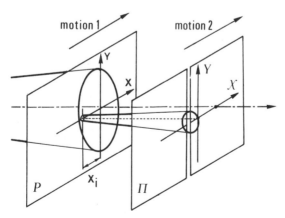

FIG. 17. Principle of the hole–slit method.

which gives, on comparison with Eq. (128),

$$D_2(x_i, x_j') = \delta y \int_{-\infty}^{\infty} \rho_4(x_i, x_j', y = 0, y') \, dy' \qquad (130)$$

The distribution function $D_2(x, x')$ corresponds to the density of points obtained by taking a cross section, defined by the plane x–z ($y = 0$), through the domain occupied in T_4, followed by a projection in the y' direction. This density is therefore not proportional to the microscopic brightness ρ_4 of the beam, unlike that given by the other methods described in this section. Here, we obtain a particular cross section ($y = 0$) through the occupied domain in a three-dimensional space (x, y, x'), characterized by a density $\rho_3(x, y, x')$:

$$\frac{\partial^3 I}{\partial x \, \partial y \, \partial x'} = \rho_3(x, y, x') = \int_{-\infty}^{+\infty} \rho_4(x, y, x', y') \, dy' \qquad (131)$$

This results from projection of T_4 in the y' direction. We therefore have

$$D_2(x, x') = \rho_3(x, x', y = 0) \, \delta y \qquad (132)$$

which in cylindrical polar coordinates becomes

$$D_2(r, \alpha_r) = \rho_3(r, \alpha_r, \theta = 0) \, \delta y \qquad (133)$$

(2) *Exploitation of the results.*   Here again, the distribution function is displayed as isodensity contours in a T_2 trace plane: a "section–projection emittance plot" is obtained. For each of these, a fractional emittance, $\epsilon_{sp}(f)$, can be defined, the suffix sp (section–projection) recalling the relation between $D_2(x, x')$ and the domain occupied in T_4 trace space. If the beam is axially symmetric, this emittance is a suitable quantity for characterizing it. It is even possible to associate with each isodensity curve the fraction $I(f)$ of the total current enclosed; with the aid of eqs. (114) and (133), we obtain

$$I(f) = 2\pi \int_0^R \int_{\alpha_{r_1}}^{\alpha_{r_2}} \rho_3(r, \alpha_r) r \, dr \, d\alpha_r \qquad (134)$$

or

$$I(f) = (2\pi/\delta y) \int_0^R \int_{\alpha_{r_1}(r,f)}^{\alpha_{r_2}(r,f)} D_2(r, \alpha_r) r \, dr \, d\alpha_r \qquad (135)$$

and these expressions can be evaluated from the isodensity curves, by numerical or graphical methods.

It is thus possible to determine the current–emittance curve, $I = I(\epsilon_{sp})$, which gives a suitable representation of a rotationally symmetric beam. It must, however, be emphasized that this curve is different, in the general case at least, from the one that would be obtained with the two-slit method, $I = I(\epsilon)$. Care must be taken, therefore, when using this curve to define the quality of a beam or the fraction transmitted by a system of given acceptance. The way in which this acceptance has been defined and calculated or measured must be borne in mind; a section–projection acceptance can, however, certainly be adopted to characterize an axially symmetric beam transport system. We note too that the volume $V_4(f)$ occupied by the particles enclosed in the isodensity contour Σ_f in T_4 space cannot be calculated here: the limits on α_θ, which appear in Eq. (115), are not determined in this experimental procedure and an equation analogous to Eq. (127), cannot be found since $\rho_3 \neq \rho_4$. Strictly speaking, therefore, the brightness cannot be measured by this method. However, an approximate value for 90% of the beam can be obtained by adapting the expression connecting B and ϵ (Eqs. 68 and 78), namely (Gautherin, 1967),

$$B_{90} = 2 \times 0.9\, I_T / \pi^2 (\epsilon_{\mathrm{sp},90})^2 \qquad (136)$$

(3) *Practical exploitation.* Despite this ambiguity, this is a very suitable method for studies concerning the aberrations of rotationally symmetric ion sources. The information provided is less coarse than that obtained with the two-slit method and the practical aspects are easier to implement than in the case of the hole–screen method. The method is particularly convenient for exploring beams with large geometrical dimensions (very intense beams, for example), for which the two-slit method can pose technological problems. In the normal arrangement, the moving hole is replaced by a fixed screen, which is thoroughly cooled, in which a line of holes has been drilled; these must be arranged along a diameter of the beam. The angular spread of the sample beamlets is analyzed by means of a wire perpendicular to the direction of the holes, capable of being moved past them (Gautherin, 1967, 1968; Rhee *et al.*, 1971; Bex *et al.*, 1976). The system can be straightforwardly interfaced to a minicomputer if the mobile probe has the form of a box with a hole in the entry face, the rear wall being covered with an array of collection segment targets as in Fig. 12 (Aubert *et al.*, 1976). Rotation of this box through $\pi/2$ enables us also to analyze the azimuthal spread of the trajectories as a function of r.

3. *Beams with Density Distribution of the Form* $\rho_4 = \rho_4^M F(x, x')G(y, y')$: *The "Two Pairs of Crossed-Slits Method"*

a. *Principle of the Method.* Doucas and Hyder (1974) have shown that if the distribution function in T_4 trace space is separable with respect to the variables corresponding to each degree of freedom, and is hence of the form $\rho_4 = \rho_4^M F(x, x')G(y, y')$, it is possible to determine ρ_4 and then derive all the quantities characterizing the beam very simply; it is only necessary to measure the density distribution in the T_2^x and T_2^y trace planes for trajectories lying in the $x-z$ and $y-z$ planes, respectively. If we consider the trajectories in the plane $x-z$ ($y = y' = 0$), we see that their distribution in the T_2^x trace plane corresponds to a section through the four-dimensional domain, the density being proportional to $\rho_4(x, x', 0, 0) = \rho_4^M F(x, x')G(0, 0)$. The "two pairs of crossed-slits method," which we have already discussed, is therefore perfectly suited for studying such beams, giving ρ_4, that is, the microscopic brightness; exploration of trace space merely involves shifting holes along the coordinate axes. This method was adopted by Doucas and Hyder (1974) for a high-resolution study of the optical properties of ion sources (see also Doucas *et al.*, 1975, 1976). For the particular distribution studied, however, the densities obtained in the T_2^x trace plane are identical, apart from a constant factor, whatever method is used—emittance (two slits), section projection emittance (hole–slit), or section emittance (two pairs of crossed slits). The projection density (cf. Eq. 88) is given by

$$\rho_2(x, x') = \rho_4^M F(x, x') \left\{ \int\int G(y, y') \, dy \, dy' \right\} \tag{137}$$

The section projection density (cf. Eq. 130) is given by

$$D_2(x, x') = \rho_4^M F(x, x') \left\{ \int G(y_i, y') \, dy' \right\} \delta y \tag{138}$$

The section density (Eq. 122) is given by

$$d_2(x, x') = \rho_4^M F(x, x')G(y_i, y_i') \, \delta y \, \delta y' \tag{139}$$

Each of these methods may be used to determine first $F(x, x')$ and then $G(y, y')$. The method involving two pairs of crossed slits that can be moved separately has the advantage that the assumption that the variables are separable can be verified, since the distribution obtained is independent of the values of y_i, y_i' chosen apart from a constant factor (Eq. 139). The other methods are easier to implement and require distinctly less intense a beam to give the same current at the detector; the values of these currents may be compared using Eqs. (137)–(139). Theoretical justification for the assumption that ρ_4 can be factorized requires examination of the symmetry and properties of the particle emitter, the symmetry of the beam line and the independence of the motion corresponding to the two transverse degrees of freedom.

b. *Exploitation of the Results.* If we assume that the maximum density is encountered on the optic axis $\rho_4^M = \rho_4(0, 0, 0, 0)$ the dimensionless functions $F(x, x')$ and $G(y, y')$ will be such that $F(0, 0) = G(0, 0) = 1$.

The densities of points in the trace planes corresponding to trajectories in the planes x–z and y–z are given by (cf. Eq. 122)

$$d_2^x(x, x')_{y=y'=0} = \rho_4^M F(x, x') \, \delta y \, \delta y' \quad \text{in} \quad T_2^x \tag{140}$$

and

$$d_2^y(y, y')_{x=x'=0} = \rho_4^M G(y, y') \, \delta x \, \delta x' \quad \text{in} \quad T_2^y \tag{141}$$

The fractional section emittances in each trace plane can then be calculated: $\epsilon_s^x(f)$ and $\epsilon_s^y(f)$. If the initial assumption is valid, the curves representing these functions will be identical with those for $\epsilon^x(f)$ and $\epsilon^y(f)$, respectively. The fractional currents $I(f)$ are calculated using

$$I(f) = \rho_4^M \iint F(x, x') \, dx \, dx' \iint G(y, y') \, dy \, dy' \tag{142}$$

Each double integral is calculated from the corresponding diagram, by one or other of the two possible routes that are now in common use (Eqs. 95 and 96); the simpler gives

$$I(f) = \pi^2 \rho_4^M \int_0^{\epsilon_s^x(f)} f(\epsilon_s^x) \, d\epsilon_s^x \int_0^{\epsilon_s^y(f)} f(\epsilon_s^y) \, d\epsilon_s^y \tag{143}$$

since $F(x, x') = d_2(x, x')/d_2(0, 0) = f$.

From this graph of $I(f)$, we derive the curves showing current against section emittance, for the two directions x and y, namely, $I(\epsilon_s^x)$ and $I(\epsilon_s^y)$. These are used to calculate the transport of the beam through a system of given section acceptance.

The brightness–current curve is obtained from the function $f(I)$, as explained earlier (Eq. 126); the current–hyperemittance curve, $\epsilon_4(I)$ is likewise obtained by integrating Eq. (127).

Since the projection distribution is proportional to the measured section distribution, it is possible to calculate the parameters of the "equivalent perfect beam" (cf. two-slit method).

All the quantities characteristic of the domain occupied in trace space can therefore be obtained straightforwardly, by a relatively simple experimental procedure—always provided that the assumption about the form of the distribution function is justified.

D. Real-Space Density Profile: "Nondestructive Methods"

In practice, the screen by which the beamlets are selected intercepts almost the entire beam in the foregoing methods, at least during the time required to acquire the necessary information; this will depend on the arrangement chosen and on the beam intensity. Apart from this disturbance in the beam transport, which may be quite brief if the measuring system is retractable, components are required that must be adequately cooled, thick enough to halt the particles and in most cases, movable. As an example, we note that 4.2 mm of steel are needed to stop 50-MeV protons. The means of overcoming these technological difficulties often lead to uncertainty in the spatial position and broadening of the angular spread (cf. Section III,E).

Given these limitations associated with methods involving angular analysis preceded by a selection screen—which we might describe as direct or destructive methods—it is clearly desirable to find some other approach. Such an alternative is offered by the methods based on determination of the density profiles in one or several beam cross sections; these profiles can be obtained by means of destructive arrangements (slit and Faraday cup) but are also furnished by beam profile monitors, which have been invented and improved during recent years with a view to perturbing the beam as little as possible. Such methods are therefore said to be "nondestructive," though it would be more realistic to call them "indirect" since the beam is in fact perturbed in most cases, either by scattering of its particles or by modification of the beam line parameters.

1. Principle of "Nondestructive Methods"

The idea of using its transverse geometrical dimensions to determine the emittance of a beam, without attempting to explore the density distribution in trace space, was first described by Walsh (1960, unpublished report). Several variants have been suggested; these exploit the special features of the transport of a "normal beam" (one having elliptical boundary contours in each trace plane) through a system consisting of linear optical elements with uncoupled motion in each transverse degree of freedom (see Steffen, 1965, Banford, 1966, or Lichtenberg, 1969). Particle transfer then can be treated using the matrix formalism, and, with these initial assumptions, the resulting methods are designed to yield the three parameters defining the emittance boundary ellipse in the directions corresponding to the two symmetry planes (x and y). Using the Courant–Snyder invariant, the equation of such an ellipse may be written

$$\gamma^x x^2 + 2\alpha^x xx' + \beta^x x'^2 = \epsilon^x, \qquad \gamma^x = 1 + (\alpha^x)^2/\beta^x \qquad (144)$$

The maximum value in the x direction, the beam half-width a (Fig. 4) is then

$$a = x_{\max} = \sqrt{\epsilon^x \beta^x} \qquad (145)$$

in which β denotes the "amplitude function" of the emittance ellipse, the area of which is $\pi \epsilon^x$. The transformation of β, γ, and α by a linear optical system is described by a 3×3 matrix (the "Steffen transformation," Steffen, 1965); dispersion and chromatic aberration due to axial momentum spread may also be taken into account. The value of β at a detector situated at z_D, i.e., β_D is therefore related to the ellipse parameters α_0, β_0, and ϵ in some other plane z_p upstream from z_D by an expression of the form

$$\beta_D = \beta_D(z_D, \beta_0, \alpha_0, \epsilon) \qquad (146)$$

which may be derived from the transformation matrix connecting z_p and z_D. In consequence, the equations for α_0, β_0, and ϵ can be solved algebraically given three distinct measurements of β_D. Two variants are in use. The first is the "three-position method," in which the transverse dimensions are measured in three different cross sections along a known beam line, usually a field-free drift space. The other is the "three-gradient method," in which the beam dimensions are measured in a given cross section for three different strengths of a quadrupole lens upstream from the detector. These methods have been developed essentially for studying beam transport in the high-energy range in big accelerators. It is very regrettable that the accounts of this work have received very limited circulation, being restricted to internal reports or notes.

Some work has been devoted to finding the conditions in which these methods will give the emittance parameters of the ellipse most accurately. For the three-position method, it is found that the results are most accurate when one of the measurement positions is close to the minimum of the beam envelope (the waist) while the other two are chosen so that the beam dimensions are about twice the minimum value (Bovet and Guignard, 1968; Metzger, 1969). Parain (1970) has shown that this reasoning can be applied to the three-gradient method; here, one of the three measurements in a single plane corresponds to the waist, the other two to dimensions double the minimum, obtained by suitable choice of the focusing parameters. If the error in measuring the beam dimensions is identical, therefore, the accuracy of the two methods will be comparable, though each has advantages and disadvantages. For the three-position method, the transport optics is not altered, and the measurements can be made in any stage of the beam line, the matching of which to the beam can also be studied (Brummer, 1972; Crandall, 1972); the measurements can be made during a single cycle of the beam, which can thus be checked during each cycle. On the negative sides the successive action of the three detectors on the particle scattering perturbs the beam and introduces errors into the measurements made at the second and third positions; moreover, three detectors are necessary. For the three-gradient method, a single detector is sufficient and the measurements are not fraught with errors due to scattering; on the other hand, the conditions of beam transport are altered and no longer correspond to normal working conditions. In an attempt to render this second method more accurate, Blumberg *et al.* (1969) have developed an automated beam profile monitor, which gives the profiles virtually instantaneously as a function of the quadrupole lens strength. Several measurements of the beam dimensions are thus obtained, and these are matched to the theoretical expressions (Eq. 146) by a least-squares method to give the best-fit values of α_0, β_0, and ϵ. Whatever method is used, problems arise in using the results since the dimensions of the beam are not well defined if the latter does not have a sharp edge. The current collected by a probe of width δx, infinitely long in the y direction, is given by

$$\delta I(x) = C\rho_1(x)\,\delta x = C\,\delta x \int_{-\infty}^{\infty} \int_{-\infty}^{\infty} \int_{-\infty}^{\infty} \rho_4(x, x', y, y')\,dx'\,dy\,dy' \quad (147)$$

and is therefore proportional to the projected density on the x axis, $\rho_1(x)$. Once this density profile is known, the dimensions of the beam corresponding to 90%, 50%, etc. of the total beam intensity—a_{90}, a_{50}, etc.—can be determined. The fractional emittances, ϵ_{90}, ϵ_{50}, etc., can then be established from the set of three dimensions for each of the corresponding percentages. We thus obtain the characteristic curve $I = I(\epsilon^x)$, and likewise $I = I(\epsilon^y)$. The emittance boundary ellipse then can be defined as the ellipse enclosing 90% of the beam (Goodwin *et al.*, 1970) or better still as the ellipse of the "equivalent perfect beam," obtained by taking the value defined in Section II,C for the beam dimension, namely, $a = 2(\overline{x^2})^{1/2}$. This implies that, when quoting the full beam width ($2a$) in this way, 95% of the total current is included within the emittance ellipse if the distribution function $\rho_1(x)$ is Gaussian (Brummer, 1972).

These indirect methods of measuring the emittance therefore seem well suited to the problem of beam transport, since they enable us to determine the ellipse of the equivalent perfect beam. However, they are based on the assumption that the isodensity contours are elliptical, and this may not always be realistic. Nevertheless, their validity can be analyzed on the basis of the theoretical work already quoted (Section II,C), since this establishes the conditions in which a "real beam" and its associated "perfect beam" are equivalent. Goodwin *et al.* (1970) have tested experimentally their validity, by comparing emittance measurements of a 10-MeV proton beam obtained from a two-slit device and from a three-profile monitor arrangement. A fair agreement is reported both for the orientation and for the area of the emittance ellipse obtained from width measurement as compared with that of the isodensity contour having the same width obtained from trace space exploration. At higher energies (200 MeV), where the destructive technique becomes less attractive, it may therefore be expected to obtain emittance from the profile monitor data.

It is assumed that the transfer matrix of the optical element is known, and the latter should have no geometrical aberrations and introduce no coupling between the two directions. If space charge effects in the beam are not negligible, their contribution to the matrix must be included, although this can only be estimated. Furthermore, the distribution of microscopic brightness in T_4 trace space cannot be determined by means of these methods, at least in their present form. In a recent note, however, Häissinki (1978) has shown that ρ_4 can be obtained, without making any particular assumptions about the form of this function, by a more sophisticated type of measurement. The beam profile monitor (consisting of narrow parallel bands) must be variable in orientation between 0 and 180°, so that the projected density $\rho_1(X, \theta)$ in a direction X of azimuth θ can be obtained. By placing a quadrupole doublet upstream from this measuring device an appropriate mathematical treatment of the results yields $\rho_4(x, y, x', y')$ (Swindel and Barret, 1977).

2. Nondestructive Beam Profile Monitors

The density profile of a beam can be measured without modifying its properties by making it interact with a movable wire, a thin film, or a gas and measuring either the secondary electron yield or the radiation emitted during the interaction.

Although the effective secondary emission coefficients are usually much larger at low energy, these arrangements are mostly used for very high-energy electron or ion beams (several tens of megavolts and higher), since the ensuing perturbation of the beam is much less than that at lower energies. We now consider these devices briefly. Secondary electron emission is commonly measured. Thus, in the device known as a "multiwire proportional chamber" (Fig. 18) the beam is intercepted by a planar array of very fine metal wires (a few tens of micrometers in diameter). The secondary electrons emitted by the wires are collected on a thin aluminum foil, about 5 μm thick, positively charged, and situated in a plane parallel to that of the wires. The charge collected by the wires is then measured (Hornstra and Simanton, 1970; Ishimaru et al., 1977; Anne et al., 1978). In practice, the device consists of two arrays, thus permitting the density to be measured in the horizontal and vertical directions. This method can be automated and the time resolution can be good enough for detailed analysis of pulsed beams to be possible (cf. Section III,E,1). The gain can be appreciably increased ($>10^3$) by introducing a neutral gas, since the wires then also collect the ions produced by ionization of this gas (Krauss and Gram, 1978).

Several authors have developed measuring techniques using secondary electrons, quite similar to that described above but replacing the wires

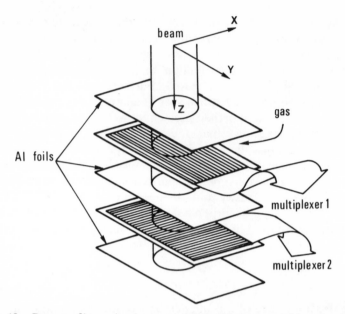

FIG. 18. Beam profile monitor known as the "multiwire proportional chamber"; the secondary electrons emitted by the two perpendicular arrays of wires (x and y) are collected by the high-voltage aluminum foils. The charge on each wire is then separately detected and recorded.

by narrow bands of dielectric such as KCl or CsI (Brummer, 1972; Chehab and Nguyen Ngoc, 1973a,b, 1977). The secondary emission coefficient of the latter is of the order of unity, so that high sensitivity is possible even with low-intensity beams without injection of gas. The effect of the nature of the dielectric on sensitivity has been discussed by Chehab and Nguyen Ngoc (1973a).

In another arrangement, the beam is intercepted by a foil that emits secondary electrons; these are in turn collected on two arrays of detectors placed outside the beam (Aslandies et al., 1973). The thin film can again be replaced by a gas, injected between two very thin windows (Dimov and Dudnikov, 1969; Ishimaru et al., 1977). Residual gas ion monitors are also used, although they are limited in sensitivity (Curtis et al., 1970).

An earlier system used the scanner principle. A hollow cylinder, a few millimeters in diameter, about 20 μm thick, or a wire about 20 μm in diameter, is scanned across the whole beam. This cylindrical probe is positioned by a stepping motor, which displaces it between individual pulses of the beam. The main disadvantage of the scanner, compared with the profile monitors discussed above, is that a series of stable beam pulses are required for measuring the beam profile (Goodwin *et al.*, 1970; Vader and Dermois, 1977; Ishimaru *et al.*, 1977).

Various types of radiation have also been exploited for obtaining the profiles of beams of electrons or positrons: the transition radiation emitted by a thin metal target (silver or aluminum, about 1 μm thick) (Wartski and Marcou, 1973); Čerenkov radiation, which needs bulky equipment (Sholl, 1968); synchrotron radiation, for curved trajectories (Sholl, 1968). In these cases, various receivers with image processing can be used (Vidicon, Plumbicon, image dissector, etc.), thereby giving the particle density at each point of a beam cross section, whereas the profile monitors with wire arrays give only the density projected in a transverse direction (Eq. 147).

Table II, from the work of Chehab and Nguyen Ngoc (1973a), illustrates the advantages and drawbacks of the various types of detectors that might be chosen for measuring the profile of a particular beam, for example, a 1-GeV positron beam.

E. Improvements of Emittance Measurements

1. Automation and Continuous Display Measurements; Time Resolution

By automation, we understand the incorporation of an electronic unit that organizes the measuring procedure *without any intervention by the operator* and processes the results so that the beam characteristics are known *very soon after the measurement*. We first examine such units, then we describe the "fast" or "deflection" emittance meters with which beam diagnostics can be performed on the basis of extremely rapid measurements, ($\sim$40 μsec). We then introduce the notion of the time resolution of an emittance-meter.

The proliferation of minicomputers has enabled wholly automated systems to be develoned, which both organize the displacements and analyze the results extremely rapidly. Quite apart from its intrinsic advantages, the two-slit method is best adapted to complete automation of the measuring process. Figure 12, already discussed, shows the type of probe commonly used in such systems. We now consider the individual steps in a typical measurement:

1. Basic data input: diameter to be studied, step size, etc.

2. In the first measuring stage, the currents collected by the detectors are amplified if necessary, converted into voltages, and time multiplexed before analog–digital conversion (Fig. 19). The angular distribution of the beamlet is then stored in the computer memory.

TABLE II

Comparison of the Characteristics of Different Beam Profile Monitors for Diagnostic of a 1-GeV Positron Beam[a]

Types of detectors	Sensitivity	Gain	Resolution	Spread	Lifetime	Remarks
MES	Good	$1e^-s/e^+p$	1 mm	0.1 mrad	Very good	Use of very thin Al_2O_3 supports
Wire chambers	Good	$>10^3$	2 mm	0.5 mrad	Good	Pre-avalanche regime Gas scanning (magic or not)
Scintillators	Very good	10^4	1 mm	[b]	Medium	2-mm thick scintillator
Čerenkov counter	Good	$1.6\gamma/e^+$	$\simeq 1$ mm	0.4 mrad	Good	10 cm of gas (He, A, air, . . .) between two aluminum windows (10 μm)
Transition radiation	Medium	$1\gamma/100e^+$	[c]	<0.1 mrad	Very good	One aluminum foil (1 μm)
Synchrotron radiation	Medium	$1\gamma/100e^+$	1 mm	null	Excellent	10-cm orbit, 4.3-m radius of curvature $(x/\delta) = 0.13$ m; $(\dot{x}/\delta) = 0.24$ rad

[a] After Chelab and Nguyen Ngoc (1973a).
[b] Depends on screening.
[c] Depends on optics.

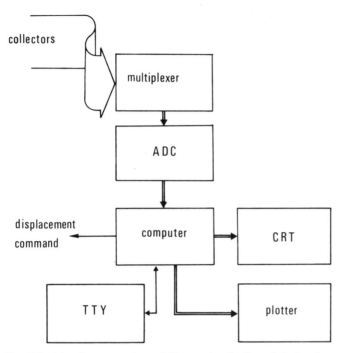

FIG. 19. Principle of automated acquisition and reduction of destructive emittance data, using a probe similar to that of Fig. 12. The graphical display is obtained either on a CRT or $X-Y$ plotter.

3. The probe displacement mechanism is then driven by a stepping motor so that each point is sampled.

4. Once all the measurements have been made, the probe returns to its initial position while the computer performs the calculations, for subsequent visual examination.

5. The results are displayed in various forms, depending on the purpose of the measurement.

Figure 20 is an example of what the operator may see on a cathode ray tube (CRT) screen. Only the information needed to characterize the beam and to match it to the beam line are displayed here. The operator can, however, call the results of intermediate calculations if he wishes, and these show how the beam can be fully described, as explained earlier (see Table I). In practice the entire measuring cycle occupies no more than a few seconds. It is scarcely necessary to dwell on the advantages of such a system, the development of which has been spurred on by the introduction of minicomputers, the price of which is no longer prohibitive; many other methods can likewise benefit from such automation. Suitable com-

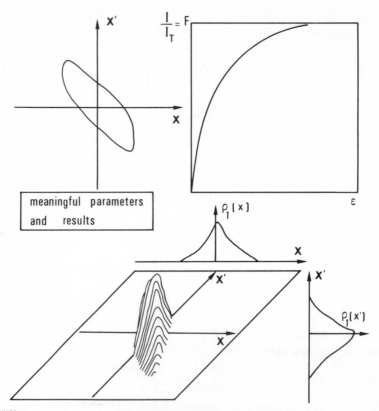

Fig. 20.   A possible graphical display on a CRT of the main results of automated emittance data, from the two-slit method, as adopted by the National Argonne Laboratory group (Goodwin *et al.*, 1970). The following curves can be recognized: (I) The projected density distribution in T_2 trace plane; (II) the emittance contour relative to a threshold density; (III) the projected density profile in the x and x' directions, for second-moment calculations; (IV) the current versus emittance characteristic.

puter interfaces have now been built in several laboratories and technical details are given by Curtis *et al.* (1970), Goodwin *et al.* (1970), Anderson *et al.* (1970), Allison *et al.* (1971), and Ehrich *et al.* (1974).

Although the long and tedious manual analysis of results has now been taken over by computers, acquisition of all the information needed to obtain the emittance diagram from the above arrangement is still a lengthy business owing to the need to shift the probe. Despite the use of highly perfected stepping motors, times longer than 1 sec are still required for a complete measurements, and a long stretch of the beam is therefore involved, or many pulses if the beam is pulsed. Fast methods, enabling us to collect the data on a very short time (less than 1 msec) and to display the result in phase space almost instantaneously on a CRT screen, are therefore of considerable interest. All such methods are characterized by the absence of mechanical displacement. Deflection systems, either electromagnetic or electrostatic, switch the individual beamlets and the whole beam appropriately (Vosicki, 1966; Sluyters *et al.*, 1967; Bordoni *et al.*, 1968; Billen, 1974, 1975; Doucas and Hyder, 1974; Allison, 1977; Ames, 1978).

In the arrangement described by Ames (1978), the two-slit method is adopted (Fig. 21): the beam passes first between two electrostatic deflectors. The slit A will thus transmit only the portion of the beam that was initially a distance $x = kV_1$ off axis, where V_1 is the instantaneous deflector plate voltage. The third electrostatic deflector, driven at a frequency much higher than the two other ones, plus the slit at B pass only particles with divergence coordinate $\theta_x = k'V_2$, where V_2 is the instantaneous voltage of the third deflector. If the voltages V_1 and V_2 are applied to the horizontal and vertical deflectors of an oscilloscope and the grid

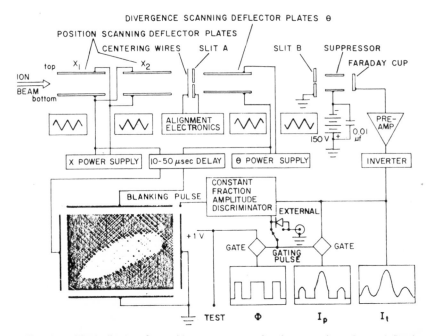

FIG. 21. Block diagram for rapid measurement of emittance using a beam deflection device of the two-slit type (slits A and B); the constant fraction amplitude discriminator allows exploration and display on the CRT of different trace-space isodensity contours. (Courtesy of Ames, 1978, and North-Holland Publishing Co.)

modulated by the current collected downstream from the slit B, the phase domain will be seen directly on the screen, the brightness being proportional to the particle density in this domain. Because of the triangular wave sweep voltage for the position and momentum scans an electronic integration of the phase space area and the partial current is possible. The speed of measurement and the virtually instantaneous display of the phase domain is an advantage that is particularly convenient for adjusting and adapting a particle beam to a beam transport system. Furthermore, these very rapid techniques can be used for high-resolution temporal analysis of the beam, since the variation of the emittance during the passage of a pulse can provide very interesting information. Here the data from the emittance meter must be stored, after high-speed sampling of the current recorded at the collector. Once again, a minicomputer can be used to drive the system, the time resolution of which can be defined as the time required to acquire all the data neeeded to plot the emittance diagram. If this quantity is appreciably shorter than the pulse length, and hence than the period of temporal oscillation of the beam, it will be possible to follow the change in emittance as a function of time. Although such "continuous display devices," as far as we are aware, have not yet been automated in this way, the notion of time resolution has already been introduced for this type of equipment, and is at present of the order of a few tens of microseconds. Beam profile monitors likewise have the advantage that displacements are unnecessary and are well adapted to the time resolution of a beam. Blumberg et al. (1969) have designed an automated system coupled to a secondary emission profile monitor, the time resolution of which is 1.25 msec. In the case of pulsed beams, devices with moving probes could be used, provided that all the pulses are identical. Simultaneous sampling by all the collectors could also be implemented with a variable, programmed delay, the process being repeated as often as necessary for complete analysis of a section of the beam. In this case, the temporal resolution could be less than 1 μsec. Such a process has been reported by Goodwin et al. (1970).

2. Systematic Errors of Measurement

The final dimensions of the diaphragms or collectors represent a compromise between the lower limit set by the detector sensitivity and the desire for better spatial and angular resolution. This leads to some error in the determination of the distribution function and hence in the measurement of emittance. We now consider how the "absolute resolution" of a measuring device can be defined and the error made in measuring emittance estimated. From a practical standpoint, scattering of particles from the edges of the diaphragms modifies the effective dimensions of the latter and broadens the angular dispersion of the transmitted particles. This effect must therefore be avoided, by suitable choice of the material from which the screen is made, of its thickness and of the shape of the opening. Precautions must also be taken to avoid perturbations associated with space charge broadening of the sample beamlet during propagation or upstream from the defining slit, where secondary electrons cause partial neutralization of the space charge of the beam.

a. *Finite-Slit Dimensions: Sensitivity and Resolution.* In connection with each of the principal methods of measurement, we have indicated how the widths of the slits (or diameters of the holes) used for definition and analysis act to determine the element of current $\delta^n I$ passing through the system or the flux per unit area of the receiver. Table III lists the analytic expressions for this current element for the main combinations of aperture shapes, for the special case in which all the apertures have the same size (δs). If a given device records a higher current than another one, it can be used to measure beams of lower total current or alternatively, the slit width can be reduced to improve the resolution and hence the accuracy. This current element can therefore serve as starting point in seeking a compromise between the resolution of a given distribution and the limitation imposed by the sensitivity of the current detectors. Two factors appear in each expression, one characterizing the device, the other, the distribution. Their individual roles can be seen more clearly if we consider a particular distribution corresponding to a uniform density in T_4 trace space, with rectangular projections on each of the T_2 trace planes and half-widths a, b, ψ_x, and ψ_y along the four axes x, y, x', and y', respectively. The current element can then be written in a simplified form (column 3 of Table III), which clearly brings out the relative orders of magnitude of the small quantities $\delta^n I/I_T$, $\delta s/a$, and $\delta s/L\psi_x$, in terms of which the resolution in the measurement of emittance can be expressed.

Let us now consider the two-slit method in more detail; the following remarks can easily be extended to the other combinations. The width δx of the beamlet selection slit characterizes the *spatial definition* (or *discrimination*) of the device: $\Delta x = \delta x$. The *angular definition* (or *discrimination*) involves the widths of both slits, analysis (δX) and selection (δx), and is given by $\Delta x' = (\delta x + \delta X)L$ (Fig. 22). Measurement of the emittance of a beam is therefore meaningful only if each of the quantities to be measured—the width ($2a$) of the beam and the mean angular spread ($2\psi_x$), as given by the second moments of the distribution, for example

TABLE III

SENSITIVITY OF VARIOUS COMBINATIONS OF APERTURES, FOLLOWED BY A FARADAY CUP

Arrangement	Element of current detected[a]			Approximate expression for "singular distribution"[b]
One slit	$\delta I(x) =$	$\rho_1(x)\,\delta s$	$= (\delta s) \iint \rho_4(x, x', y, y')\, dx'\, dy\, dy'$	$\delta I = I_T\,\delta s/a$
Two slits	$\delta^2 I(x, x') =$	$\rho_2(x, x')\,\delta s^2/L$	$= (\delta s^2/L) \iint \rho_4(x, x', y, y')\, dy\, dy'$	$\delta^2 I = I_T \left[\dfrac{\delta s}{a} \cdot \dfrac{\delta s}{L\psi_x} \right]$
Hole–slit	$\delta^3 I(x, x') =$	$D_2(x, x')_{y=0}\,\delta s^2/L$	$= (\delta s^3/L) \int \rho_4(x, x', 0, y')\, dy'$	$\delta^3 I = I_t \left[\dfrac{\delta s}{a} \cdot \dfrac{\delta s}{L\psi_x} \right] \delta s/b$
Two holes (or two pairs of crossed slits)	$\delta^4 I(x, x') =$	$d_2(x, x')_{y=0,y'=0}\,\delta s^2/L = (\delta s^2/L)^2 \rho_4(x, x', 0, 0)$		$\delta^4 I = I_T \left[\dfrac{\delta s}{a} \cdot \dfrac{\delta s}{L\psi_x} \right] \dfrac{\delta s}{b}\, \dfrac{\delta s}{L\psi_y}$

[a] All the apertures have the same dimensions: $\delta x = \delta y = \delta X = \delta Y = \delta s \to \delta x' = \delta y' = \delta s/L$.

[b] $I_T = \iiiint \rho_4(x, x', y, y')\, dx\, dx'\, dy\, dy' \approx \rho_4 ab\psi_x\psi_y$ for the "singular distribution."

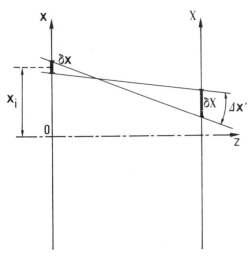

FIG. 22. Diagram illustrating the *angular definition or discrimination* $(\Delta x')$ of a destructive emittance-meter. δx and δX are the widths of the selection and angular analysis slits, respectively.

(cf. Eqs. 51 and 53), is much larger than the spatial or angular discrimination of the device thus:

$$\Delta x = \delta x \ll a, \qquad \Delta x' = (\delta x + \delta X)/L \ll \psi_x \qquad (148)$$

The ratios $\Delta x/a$ and $\Delta x'/\psi_x$ define the *spatial resolution* and the *angular resolution*, respectively, of a particular measurement. The foregoing criteria can be summarized by the following inequality:

$$\delta\epsilon = \delta x(\delta x + \delta X)/\pi L = \Delta x \, \Delta x'/\pi \ll \epsilon \qquad (149)$$

which expresses the condition that the emittance to be measured, ϵ, which is of the order of $a\psi_x$, must be much larger than the product of the spatial and angular discrimination, which we may treat as the *absolute resolution of the emittance-meter*, $\delta\epsilon$. By this, we mean the minimum emittance that the device is capable of resolving. We note that, with this definition, $\delta\epsilon$ is not the same as the acceptance of the device, which is given by $\delta x \, \delta X/\pi L$ and which appears in the calculation giving the current element passing through the system (see Eq. 92 and Table III).

What are the consequences of the finite width of these slits when we attempt to use a measured emittance. The problem is not easy to study theoretically since a function of two variables, x and x', is involved, together with an "apparatus function," which can be represented in the T_2 trace plane (x, x') by a rectangle with sides Δx and $\Delta x'$. To the authors' knowledge, only one preliminary quantitative study has been attempted, for the case in which one of the sides of this rectangle has negligible dimensions and the distributions are parabolic (Guyard and Weiss, 1976). These authors have also shown experimentally that the width of the selection slit has a strong influence on measurements of the rms emittance ($\bar{\epsilon}$) in the case of a beam with constant dimensions (H^+ at 500 keV; see Fig. 23). Owing to the distortion of the distribution function caused by the finite width, only the beam characteristics (ϵ, a, ψ_x) obtained by extrapolating the slit width to zero may be considered to be relatively accurate. The authors showed that if the beam characteristics are then calculated a known distance away from the plane of measurement, only those obtained from these extrapolated values correspond to those measured experimentally in this second plane. The quantitative approach proposed by these authors is in accord with the criteria set out above (Eq. 148) for obtaining meaningful emittance values. We underline the fact that, for measurement of the second moments of a distribution, the errors due to discrete sampling of the distribution may be much larger than those associated with the spatial (or angular) resolution of the measuring arrangement. This finding is illustrated in Fig. 24, which corresponds to sampling of a parabolic distribution. The influence of the wire size on the second moment is relatively small but the error increases steeply if the number of sampling points drops below ten. As a result, the size of the collectors can be chosen so as to obtain easily detectable signals.

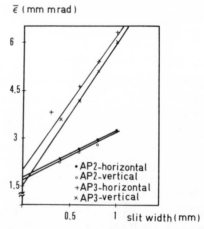

FIG. 23.   Influence of the selection slit width on the measured rms emittance from a two-slit emittance-meter. Measurements are made in two sections of the beam AP_2 and AP_3 separated by a linear beam transformer. It can be seen that the true value of $\bar{\epsilon}$ is obtained by extrapolating the slit width to zero. (Courtesy of Guyard and Weiss, 1976.)

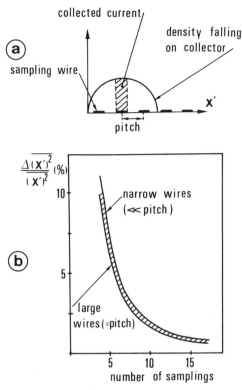

FIG. 24. Simulation of the errors arising in the determination of the second moment of a parabolic distribution by means of discrete sampling with wires (a). The graph (b) shows the influence of the number and width of the sampling collectors. (Courtesy of Guyard and Weiss, 1976.)

It is thus clear that determination of the error made in measuring a fractional emittance of a beam is a far from simple problem. The distortion of the distribution function due to the finite slitwidth causes a laminar beam, which has zero emittance, to have a finite emittance; for any other beam, the measured emittance will likewise be greater than the true value (Fig. 25). A rough estimate of this systematic error can be obtained by extending the procedure suggested by Keever and Yokosawa (1962) for calculating the angular spread of a sample beamlet: here the angular spread that would have been obtained if the beam had been laminar ($\Delta x'$) is subtracted from the measured angular spread (cf. Fig. 25). This yields a lower limit of the angular spread at each point in the beam and a minimum value of the beam emittance can hence be determined. This procedure has been followed by some authors when plotting emittance contours (Wroe, 1967;

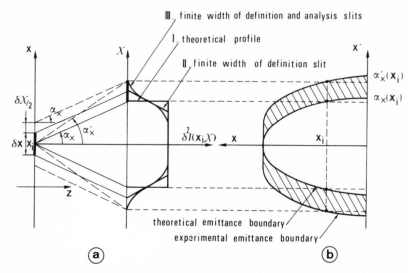

FIG. 25.   (a) Influence of the finite width of the two slits of a destructive emittance-meter on the recorded profile of elemental current $\delta^2 I(x_i, X)$, in the case of a "perfect beam" at its waist; (I) is the theoretical profile; (II) is the profile recorded if the analysis slit width is much smaller than that of the selection slit ($\delta X \ll \delta x$); (III) is the profile recorded if the widths are both finite. (b) Plot of the resulting emittance contour, where the theoretical emittance boundary, which is an upright ellipse, also appears. The method of calculating the true angular limits (α_x) of a beamlet, in order to avoid the influence of finite widths, is illustrated in (a); α'_x is overestimated. In the case of a laminar cylindrical beam, the theoretical emittance vanishes, and the experimental contour then reduces to a rectangle having the same area as the shaded region in graph (b), an area that may be taken as the systematic error in an emittance measurement (Eq. 150).

Gautherin, 1968). If the beam width in the direction in question is denoted by $2a$, the systematic error in an emittance measurement can be estimated as the difference between the excess and default values or approximately

$$\Delta\epsilon = 2a \cdot \Delta x'/\pi = 2a(\delta x + \delta X)/\pi L \qquad (150)$$

The accuracy of measurement is then equal to the angular resolving power of the device: $R = \epsilon/\Delta\epsilon = \psi_x/\Delta x'$. Not many authors quote the accuracy of their measurements, although some do mention an accuracy without explaining how they estimated it (Goodwin *et al.*, 1970; Billen, 1975); others refer to the procedure suggested above (Schubaly *et al.*, 1976).

We recall that in the methods involving a quartz detector or a photosensitive screen, the existence of a threshold sensitivity, which is difficult to specify with any precision, can lead to optimistic results (cf.

Section III,B,1; Collins and Stroud, 1964; Ivanov *et al.*, 1965; Wroe, 1968).

b. *Scattering of Particles by the Aperture Edges.* At high energies the screen thickness needed to stop the particles of the beam becomes considerable. Thus, when the dimensions of the aperture become small in comparison with the screen thickness, particles close to the edge of the aperture can be scattered into the transmitted beam before losing all their energy; they may even represent the major part of the resulting beam, causing an increase in the angular dispersion of the beamlets and forming a halo around the particles that passed through the aperture without striking the edges. In practice, the effect will be serious when small apertures are needed and/or the particle energy is high.

The angular distribution and energy spectra of the scattered particles have been studied by Burge and Smith (1962). An effective increase in slit width may be calculated in terms of the properties of the collimator material. Some elements are particularly favorable and produce only a modest increase in the effective slit width and angular spread. In choosing the material to be used, however, other criteria may also have to be considered: the effective cross section for neutron production, for example (Banford, 1966). Recent work by Nobiling *et al.* (1975) has shown that slit scattering can be suppressed even for very small aperture widths by proper design and manufacture. Thus, high-quality proton beams have been obtained at 1 MeV with diameters and angular divergences as small as 1 μm and 1 μrad, respectively. The halo of scattered particles represents less that 0.1% of the total beam intensity. Conversely, for simple drilled holes or slits, particle scattering generally keeps the geometrical emittance of the collimated beam above 0.1 mm $\times$ 0.1 mrad at these energies, according to the authors. Further discussion about slit profile will be found on p. 349 of this volume, where Martin and Nobiling discuss high-energy probes.

At extremely high energies, these "destructive" methods of measuring emittance must be replaced by the indirect methods discussed in Section III,D.

c. *Space Charge Expansion of the Sample Beamlet.* The space charge of the sample beamlet can cause appreciable broadening of the angular spread over a drift space of length L, if the beam is dense. The problem has been studied for cylindrical pencils (Gautherin, 1968) and strip beamlets (Wroe, 1967; Evans and Warner, 1972). If the ensuing additional angular spread at the analysis plane is denoted by $(\Delta x')_{sc}$, we can use two criteria to decide whether the effect of space charge is negligible.

The first is rather weak:

$$(\Delta x')_{sc} \ll \psi_x \tag{151}$$

while the second is much stronger, involving the angular discrimination $\Delta x'$:

$$(\Delta x')_{sc} \leq \Delta x' \tag{152}$$

These criteria lead to conditions that must be satisfied by the product of aperture size and drift distance. For a strip beam, we find (Evans and Warner, 1972):

$$(\Delta x')_{sc} \ll \psi_x \rightarrow L \, \delta x \ll 2\psi_x/kj_0 \tag{153}$$

$$(\Delta x')_{sc} \leq \Delta x' \rightarrow L\delta x \leq 4 \, \Delta x'/kj_0 \tag{154}$$

where j_0 is the current density and k is a space charge factor,

$$k = q/\epsilon_0 M v_z^3 \tag{155}$$

in which M and q denote the mass and charge of the particle, and v_z its axial velocity. To give some idea of the orders of magnitude involved, we consider the example given by Evans and Warner: a 500-keV proton beam, with current density $j_0 = 100$ mA cm^{-2} and an angular dispersion of 20 mrad ($I_T = 300$ mA for a beam radius of 10 mm). Inequality (153) gives $L \, \delta x \ll 4 \times 10^{-3}$ m², or $L \ll 8$ m for $\delta x = 0.5$ mm; inequality (154), however, gives $L \leq 1.24$ m for $\delta x = \delta X$. In most cases, these conditions are easy to satisfy.

Quite apart from these purely stationary phenomena, Evans and Warner (1972) have shown that important instabilities can develop as the beamlets drift. They have found that the percentage noise level on the sample beamlets is always considerably higher than that of the main beam pulse. The origin of this phenomenon is not yet understood but its effect on the resolution of measurements can be important.

d. *Backstreaming Secondary Electrons.* The secondary electrons emitted by the defining screen due to ion bombardment may disturb the behavior of the beam under test by partial or total neutralization of its space charge. Evans and Warner (1972) have shown that the measured emittance may be appreciably diminished if these secondary electrons are not trapped. The phenomenon becomes important at energies for which the secondary emission coefficient is greater than unity. For protons, for example, it decreases from 4 to 100 keV to 0.5 at 3 MeV. Many ways of trapping these back-streaming secondary electrons have been tested; the simplest is to hold the definition plate at a positive voltage relative to the beam, with a potential difference some three or four times greater than that due to the space charge of the beam.

IV. Conclusion

In the preceding section, we have described the principle of emittance-meters, the main practical variants, and the procedures available for quantitative exploitation of the results. These devices were designed for studying the trace space domain occupied by the points representing particles passing through a cross section of the beam during a given interval. These devices, characterized by the shape and number of diaphragms they use, do not all measure the density distribution function in T_4 trace space. Although this function characterizes very exactly the optical properties of the beam in the cross section in question, it is not essential for solving the basic problems of beam transport with linear optical elements. From the practical viewpoint, however, the difficulty of use of the instrument increases, generally speaking, with the completeness of the information desired, owing to the fact that the number of moving parts needed for exploring trace space increases. The acquisition of the results and the subsequent calculations likewise become exceedingly lengthy and automation is required. In order to help the experimentalist to come to a decision, we have summarized the complicated discussion of Section III in Table IV, in which the main methods of measuring emittance are classified (column 1) as a function of the object of the measurement and any special features of the beam (columns 7 and 5). The information needed to attain this object is listed in column 6, while column 4 indicates the exploration of phase space required to give a representative measurement of the ensemble of particles at the cross section in question, taking into account any special features of the beam. The current element detected in the measurement is given in column 2. In column 3, we indicate what type of graphics plot expresses the main results of the measurement best. For further details of the use to which the results may be put, the reader is referred to the appropriate part of Section III.

This table, which should be used in conjunction with Table III, brings out the advantages and limitations of the various methods of measuring the emittance and brightness of a beam. We recall that the various graphs or quantities that are introduced to characterize the domain occupied in trace space—its projections on the trace planes and the sections by these planes—are not invariants of motion unless certain very restrictive conditions on the beam and beam line are satisfied (in particular, negligible space charge and negligible spread of axial velocity). These conditions are discussed in Section II. In this connection, we once again stress the difference between the fractional emittance, for 90% of the total beam intensity, for example, and the rms emittance. The invariance of the former is a consequence of the validity of Liouville's theorem in a two-dimensional

TABLE IV

POSSIBILITIES AND LIMITATIONS OF EMITTANCE-MEASUREMENT METHODS

I. Measurement methods	II. Current element of flux detected	III. Trace space representation
Direct destructive methods		
1. Multihole–screen ("pepper-pot") (Fig. 14)	$\dfrac{\partial^4 I}{\partial X\, \partial Y} = \left(\dfrac{\delta s^2}{L^2}\right) \rho_4(x, y, x', y')$	Hyperemittance plot $\rho_4(x', y')_{x, y_k}$
2. Hole–screen		Hyperemittance plot $\rho_4(\alpha_r, \alpha_\theta)_{r_i}$
3. Hole–hole ("two pairs of crossed slits) (Fig. 16)	$\delta^4 I(x, x') = \left(\dfrac{\delta s^2}{L}\right)^2 \rho_4(x, x', 0, 0)$	Section emittance plot $d_2(r, \alpha_r)_{\theta=0, \alpha_0=0}$ Section emittance plot $d_2(x, x')_{y=y'=0};\ d_2(y, y')_{x=x'=0}$
4. Hole–slit (Fig. 17)	$\delta^3 I(x, x') = (\delta s^3/L) \int \rho_4(x, x', y, y')\, dy'$	Section-projection emittance plot $D_2(r, \alpha_r)_{\theta=0}$
5. Two slits (Fig. 11)	$\delta^2 I(x, x') = (\delta s^2/L) \iint \rho_4(x, x', y, y')\, dy\, dy'$	Emittance plot of projected density $\rho_2(x, x')$ $\rho_2(y, y')$
6. Two apertures (Fig. 13)	$I = \iiiint_{v_4} \rho_4\, dx\, dy\, dx'\, dy'$	Average density over V_4 $B = \bar{\rho}_4 = I/V_4$
Indirect nondestructive methods		
1. Three positions (wire scanner) 2. Three gradients (wire scanner)	$\delta I(x) = \delta s \iiint \rho_4\, dx'\, dy\, dy'$	Beam density profiles $\rho_1(x)$ $\rho_1(y)$

250

IV. Trace space exploration	V. Special features of beams	VI. Information expected	VII. Purpose of measurements
Direct destructive methods			
1. x, x', y, y'	None: $\rho_4(x, y, x', y')$	Four-dimensional density distribution	Gun improvement
2. $r, \alpha_r, \alpha_\theta$	Axial symmetry: $\rho_4(r, \alpha_r, \alpha_\theta)$	$I = I(\epsilon_4)$ $I = I(B)$	Space-charge and aberration-effect analysis
3. $r, \alpha_r, (\theta = \alpha_\theta = 0)$	Axial symmetry: $\Delta\alpha_r \gg \Delta\alpha_\theta = 0$		
$x, x', (y = y' = 0)$ $y, y', (x = x' = 0)$	Variables separable: $\rho_4 = \rho_4^M F(x, x')\, G(y, y')$		
4. r, α_r $\theta = 0;\ [\alpha_\theta]_{-\pi/2}^{+\pi/2}$	Axial symmetry	Three-dimensional density distribution	Large-beam diagnostics (gun improvement)
5. $x, x';$	None	Two-dimensional projected density distribution	Design and optimization of beam transport systems
y, y'		Equivalent perfect beam	
6. $V_4 = \epsilon_4/\pi^2$	Axial symmetry	*Richtstrahlwert* $I = I(\epsilon_4)$ $I = I(R/B)$	Performance of narrow-angle beams
Indirect nondestructive methods			
$x; y$	"Normal beam"	Equivalent perfect beam	Optimization of very high-energy transport systems

251

space, which in turn assumes that one degree of freedom is uncoupled. Invariance of the rms emittance, however, requires linearity of the transport optics, which must therefore have negligible geometrical aberrations, in the presence of the space charge associated with the density distribution of the "perfect beam." Given this distinction the rms emittance appears to be a more suitable figure of merit of the optical quality of a charged particle beam and of any possible deterioration during propagation; these points will be examined further in a forthcoming review.

Finally, in order to obtain a description of the density distribution function in trace space that is both realistic and well suited to the practical optical problems and beam characterization, it appears that it is convenient to introduce several special definitions and conventions in relation with the concepts of brightness, emittance, and acceptance. In order to prevent any misunderstanding that can arise from lack of standardization in the literature about terminology, notation, and units, we have recapitulated a list of symbols, conventions, and units that we may recommend to users.

SYMBOLS AND CONVENTIONS

Phase Space and Trace Space

Γ_6 six-dimensional phase space; coordinates x, p_x, y, p_y, z, p_z
Γ_4 four-dimensional transverse phase space; coordinates x, p_x, y, p_y
Γ_2^i two-dimensional phase plane associated with the ith degree of freedom ($i = x, y, z$)
T_4 four-dimensional trace space: cartesian coordinates x, x', y, y'; cylindrical coordinates $r, \alpha_r, \theta, \alpha_\theta$
T_2^i two-dimensional trace plane associated with the ith degree of freedom ($i = x, y,$ or r, θ).

Four-Dimensional Domain in T_4 Trace Space

$\rho_4(x, x', y, y')$ density distribution function of microscopic brightness in T_4 trace space
$f_4(x, p_x, y, p_y)$ density distribution function in the Γ_4 phase space
B brightness in units of A rad^{-2} m^{-2}
B_n normalized brightness in units of A $(m_0 c)^{-2}$ m^{-2}
B_p physical brightness in units of A rad^{-2} m^{-2} eV^{-1}
$B_F, B_{n,F}, B_{p,F}$ brightness values associated to $F\%$ of the total beam intensity; meaningful percentages are 0%, 63%, 90%
$R \equiv B_0$ *Richtstrawhlwert:* microscopic brightness along the optic axis
R_n, R_p normalized and physical *Richtstrawhlwert*
V_4 hypervolume of the domain in T_4 trace space
$\mathcal{V}_4$ hypervolume of the domain in Γ_4 phase space

ϵ_4 (geometrical) hyperemittance in units of π^2 rad^2 m^2

ϵ_{4n} normalized hyperemittance in units of π^2 $(m_0 c)^2$ m$|^2$

ϵ_{4p} physical hyperemittance in units of π^2 rad^2 m^2 eV

$\epsilon_{4,F}$, $\epsilon_{4n,F}$, $\epsilon_{4p,F}$ hyperemittance values associated to $F\%$ of the total beam intensity; 90% is representative of the whole beam

$\epsilon_{4,c}$, $\epsilon_{4n,c}$, $\epsilon_{4p,c}$ "hyperemittance constants," representative of the central part of the beam

Y_4 hyperacceptance of a beam-transport system

Y_{4n}, Y_{4p} normalized and physical hyperacceptances

Two-Dimensional Projection Domain in T_2^i Trace Plane $(i = x)$

$\rho_2(x, x')$ projection-density distribution function

A^x area of projection domain

$\mathscr{A}^x$ area of projection-domain in Γ_2^x phase plane

ϵ^x (geometrical) emittance in units of π rad m

ϵ_n^x normalized emittance in units of π $(m_0 c)$ m

ϵ_p^x physical emittance in units of π rad m (eV)$^{1/2}$

$\bar{\epsilon}^x$ rms emittance

$\bar{\epsilon_n}^x$, $\bar{\epsilon_p}^x$ normalized and physical rms emittance

ϵ_{90}^x, $\epsilon_{n,90}^x$, $\epsilon_{p,90}^x$ emittances enclosing 90% of the beam intensity

ϵ_c^x, $\epsilon_{n,c}^x$, $\epsilon_{p,c}^x$ emittance constants (central part of the beam)

Y^x acceptance of the beam-transport system

Y_n^x, Y_p^x normalized and physical acceptances

Two-Dimensional Section Domain in T_2^i Trace Plane $(i = x)$

$d_2(x, x')_{y=0, y=0}$ section-density distribution function

A_s^x area of section domain

ϵ_s^x section emittance

$\epsilon_{s,n}^x$ normalized section emittance

$\epsilon_{s,p}^x$ physical section emittance

$\epsilon_{s,c}^x$, $\epsilon_{s,n,c}^x$, $\epsilon_{s,p,c}^x$ section emittance constants

$\epsilon_{s,90}^s$, $\epsilon_{s,n,90}^x$, $\epsilon_{s,p,90}^x$ section emittances enclosing 90% of the beam intensity

Y_s section admittance

$Y_{s,n}^x$, $Y_{s,p}^x$ normalized and physical section admittances

Two-Dimensional Section Projection Domain in T_2^i Trace Plane $(i = x)$

$D_2(x, x')_{y=0}$ section projection density distribution

A_{sp}^x area of section projection domain

ϵ_{sp}^x section projection emittance

$\epsilon_{sp,n}^x$ normalized section projection emittance

$\epsilon_{sp,p}^x$ physical section projection emittance

$\epsilon^x_{sp,c}$, $\epsilon^x_{sp,n,c}$, $\epsilon^x_{sp,p,c}$ section projection emittance constants
$\epsilon^x_{sp,90}$, $\epsilon^x_{sp,n,90}$, $\epsilon^x_{sp,p,90}$ section projection emittances enclosing 90% of the beam intensity
Y^x_{sp}, $Y^x_{sp,n}$, $Y^x_{sp,p}$ section projection admittance

ACKNOWLEDGMENTS

The authors appreciate the confidence shown in them by Professor A. Septier, editor of this volume, by his invitation to write this article and wish to thank Professor P. Grivet for continual encouragement during its preparation. They are also most grateful to Professor G. Gautherin for many fruitful discussions and to Dr. Chehab of the Orsay Linear Accelerator group, for making available various unpublished documents. Dr. P. W. Hawkes of the C.N.R.S. Laboratory of Electron Optics in Toulouse was kind enough to prepare the English translation and Michèle Keiffer typed the manuscript. Finally, we thank all the authors of papers in this field whether cited or left unmentioned, either by accident or because an alternative reference has been used, for without them this article would have been impossible.

REFERENCES

Abroyan, M. A., Golubev, V. P., Solnyshkov, A. I., and Tarvid, G. V. (1969). *Proc. Int. Conference Ion Sources, 1st, Saclay, 1969* p. 179
Allison, P. W. (1977). Proc. Symp. Production Negative Hydrogen Ion Beams, Brookhaven, 1977, Rep. BNL 50725, p. 119; *IEEE Trans. Nucl. Sci. NS 24-3* p. 1594.
Allison, R. W., Jr., Richter, R. M., and Zajec, E. (1971). *Proc. Symp. Ion Sources Formation Ion Beams, Brookhaven, 1971*, Rep. BNL 50310, p. 103.
Ames, L. L. (1978). *Nucl. Instr. Meth.* **151**, 363–369.
Amman, F. (1970). *In* "Linear Accelerators" (P. Lapostolle and A. Septier, eds.) Part. B.3.5, p. 523. North-Holland, Amsterdam.
Anderson, E. W., Lau, H. C., and Mehring, F. L. (1970). *Proc. Proton Linear Accelerators Conf., 6th, Batavia, 1970* p. 451.
Anne, R., Lefol, A., Milleret, G., and Perret, R. (1978). *Nucl. Instr. Meth.* **152**, 395.
Arakengy, A. (1957). *Am. J. Phys. 25*, 519.
Aslanides, E., Cohen, R. C., Dugan, G., Nagourney, W., Rosenstein, L., Slagowitz, M., and Ziegler, K. (1973). *IEEE Trans. Nucl. Sci. NS-20* **3**, 573.
Aubert, J., Gautherin, G., Gilles, J. P., Grandchamp, J. P., and Lejeune, C. (1976). *IEEE Trans. Nucl. Sci., NS-23-2*, 1088.
Aubert, J., Lejeune, C., and Tremelat, P. (1978). *Proc. Int. Conf. Low Energy Ion Beams. Salford, 1977.* Inst. Phys. Conf. Series, No. 38, p. 282.
Banford, A. P. (1966). "Transport of Charged Particles." Spon, London.
Baumann, H., Bethge, K., and Klein, G. (1976). *IEEE Trans. Nucl. Sci. NS-23-2* 1081.
Becherer, R., and Prévot, F. (1972). *Proc. Int. Conf. Ion Sources, 2nd, Vienna, 1972* p. 150; *Nucl. Inst. Method* **104**, 477–484.
Bex, L., Clark, D. J., Ellsworth, C. E., Estrella, R. M., and Holley, W. R. (1976). *IEEE Trans. Nucl. Sci. NS-23-2* 1077.

Billen, J. H. (1974). *Proc. Symp. Ion Sources Formation Ion Beams, Berkeley, 1974*, Rep. LBL-3399, Paper II-6.

Billen, J. H. (1975). *Rev. Sci. Instr.* **46**, 33–40, and erratum: *Rev. Sci. Instr.* **46**, 1295.

Blumberg, L. N., Barton, M. Q., Fox, J. D., Glenn, J. W., and Repeta, L. E. (1969). Emittance measurements in the AGS slow external beam. Rep A.G.S. DIV 69–12, BNL Upton, New York.

Bordoni, F., Letardi, T., and Placidi, M. (1968). *Nucl. Instr. Meth.* **65**, 72

Bovet, C., and Guignard, C. (1968). Mesure de l'émittance d'un faisceau primaire, Rep CERN/DL/68-7.

Brummer, P. (1972). The method of measurement of the emittance and the betatron phase space parameters in the beam transfer system of the IRS., Rep. CERN-ISR-OP/72-6, CERN, Geneva.

Burge, E. J., and Smith, D. A. (1962). *Rev. Sci. Instr.* **33**, 1371; **34**, 1455 (1963) (erratum).

Chasman, R., Agritellis, C., and Sluyters, Th. (1969). *IEEE Trans. Nucl. Sci. NS 16-3*, 221.

Chehab, R., and Nguyen Ngoc, C. (1973a). Quelques résultats complémentaires sur les profileurs. Laboratoire de l'accélérateur linéaire, Rep. LAL/NI/18–73. Orsay, France.

Chehab, R., and Nguyen-Ngoc, C. (1973b). *IEEE Trans. Nucl. Sci. NS-20, No. 3*, 662.

Chehab, R., and Nguyen-Ngoc, C. (1977). Mesure d'émittance du faisceau de positrons. Rep. LAL/RI/77-1. Orsay, France.

Collins, L. E., and Stroud, P. T. (1964). *Nuclear Instr. Meth.* **26**, 157.

Cooper, W. S., Berkner, K. H., and Pyle, R. V. (1972). *Proc. Int. Conf. Ion Sources, 2nd, Vienna, 1972* p. 264.

Coupland, J. R., Green, T. S., Hammond, D. P., and Riviere, A. C. (1973). *Rev. Sci. Instr.* **44**, 1258.

Courant, E. D., and Snyder, H. S. (1958). *Ann. Phys.* **3**, 1–48.

Crandall, K. R. (1972). *Proc. Proton Linear Accel. Conf., Los Alamos, 1972*, Rep. LA-5115, p. 51.

Curtis, C. D. (1976). *Proc. Proton Linear Accel. Conf. Chalk River, 1976*, Rep. AECL-5677, p. 179.

Curtis, C. D., Dickson, J. M., Goodwin, R. W., Gray, E. R., Livdahl, P. V., Owen, C. W., Shea, M. F., and Young, D. E. (1970). *Proc. Proton Linear Acc. Conf., Batavia, 1970* **1**, 217; *Particle Accelerators* **1**, 93.

Cutler, C. C., and Hines, M. E. (1955). *Proc. IRE* **43**, 307.

Davey, J. P. (1971). *Optik* **33**, 580–590.

Dimov, G. I., and Dudnikov, V. G. (1969). *Instr. Exp. Tech.* **1**, 553.

Doucas, G., and Hyder, H. R. McK. (1974). *Nucl. Instr. Meth.* **119**, 413.

Doucas, G., Hyder, H. R. McK., and Knox, A. B. (1975). *Nucl. Inst. Meth.* **124**, 11.

Doucas, G., Greenway, T. J. L., Hyder, H. R. McK., and Knox, A. B. (1976). *IEEE Trans. Nucl. Science NS-23* 1155–1161.

Ehrenberg, W., and Siday, R. E. (1951). *Proc. Phys. Soc. (London)* **B64**, 1088.

Ehrich, A., Glatz, J., and Strehl, P. (1974). Eine EmittanzmeBeinrichtung am Unilac. Rep. GSI-PB-3-74, Darmstadt, Germany.

Emigh, C. R., Meyer, E. A., Mueller, D. W., and Stevens, R. R. (1971). *Proc. Symp. Ion Sources Formation of Ion Beams, Brookhaven, 1971*, Rep. BNL 50310, p. 113.

Evans, L. R., and Warner, D. J. (1972). *Nucl. Instr. Meth.* **104**, 61–70.

Fink, J. H., and Schumacher, B. W. (1974). *Optik* **39**, 543.

Fink, J. H., and Schumacher, B. W. (1975). *Nucl. Instr. Meth.* **130**, 353.

Fronteau, J. (1967). *In* "Focusing of charged Particles" (A. Septier, ed.), Vol. 2, Chapter 5.4., p. 421. Academic Press, New York.

Fukumoto, S., Inagaki, S., Kobayashi, M., Nishikawa, T., and Takami, S. (1971). *Proc. Symp. Ion Sources Formation Ion Beams, Brookhaven, 1971*, Rep. BNL 50310, p. 121.

Gautherin, G. (1967). Doctoral thesis, Orsay, No. A0 1437, 1967.

Gautherin, G. (1968). *Nuclear Instr. Meth.* **59**, 261.

Glaser, W. (1956). *In* "Handbuch der Physik" (S. Flugge, ed.), Vol. 33, p. 123. Springer-Verlag. Berlin and New York.

Gluckstern, R. L. (1970). *In* "Linear Accelerators" (P. Lapostolle and A. Septier, eds.), Part. C-1-3, p. 827. North-Holland Publ., Amsterdam.

Goldstein, H. (1950). "Classical Mechanics." Addison-Wesley, Reading, Mass.

Goodwin, R. W., Gray, E. R., Lee, G. M., and Shea, M. F. (1970). *Proc. Proton Linear Accel. Conf., Batavia, 1970* NAL, Rep. 1, 107.

Green, T. S. (1974). *Rep. Prog. Phys.* **37**, 1257.

Grivet, P. A. (1965). "Electron Optics." Pergamon, Oxford.

Grivet, P. A. (1972). "Electron Optics," 2nd Engl. ed. Pergamon, Oxford.

Guyard, J., and Weiss, M. (1976). *Proc. Proton Linear Accel. Conf. Chalk River, 1976*, Rep. AECL 5677, p. 254.

Haissïnski, J. (1978). "Commentaire sur la mesure de l'émittance d'un faisceau de particules" (in French), Laboratoire de l'Accélérateur Linéaire, Orsay, Rep. DCI/NI/1-78

Hereward, H. G. (1954) Energy spread and phase focusing in particle accelerators, Rep. CERN,PS/HGH/1.

Hereward, H. G. (1969). How good is the rms as a measure of beam size? CERN, Rep. No. CERN-MPS-DL/69-15.

Hereward, H. G. (1970). *In* "Linear Accelerators" (P. Lapostolle and A. Septier, eds.), Part A.2, p. 19. North-Holland, Amsterdam.

Hoffmann, H. (1972). *Optik* **36**, 494.

Hornstra, F., and Simanton, J. R. (1970). *Nucl. Instr. Meth.* **77**, 303.

Ishimaru, H., Igarashi, Z., Muto, K., and Shibata, S. (1977). *IEEE Trans. Nucl. Sci. NS-24* **3**, 1821.

Ivanov, N. F., Sirkov, Yu, P., and Solnyshkov, A. I. (1965). *Soc. Phys. Instr. Exp. Techn.* **2**, 1043.

Judd, D. L. (1958). *Ann. Rev. Nucl. Sci.* **8**, 181.

Kapchinsky, I., and Vladimirsky, V. (1959). *Proc. Conf. High Energy Accelerators, 2nd, Geneva, 1959*, p. 274.

Keever, R. Mc. and Yokosawa, A. (1962). *Rev. Si. Instr.* **33**, 746.

Kirstein, P. T., Kino, G. S., and Waters, W. E. (1967). "Space Charge Flow." McGraw-Hill, New York.

Kobayashi, M., Takagi, A., and Fukumoto, S. (1972). *Proc. Proton Linear Accel. Conf., Los Alamos, 1972*, Rep. 5115, p. 365.

Kobayashi, M., Nishikawa, T., and Takagi, A. (1974). *Proc. Symposium Ion Sources Formation Ion Beams, Berkeley, 1974*, Rep. LBL-3399, Paper II-5.

Krauss, G. J., and Gram, P. A. (1978). *Nucl. Instr. Meth.* **156**, 365.

Kuhlmann, W., Bojowald, J., Mayer-Böricke, C., Reich, J., and Retz, A. (1970). *Nucl. Instr. Meth.* **80**, 89.

Kuznetsov, V. S., Abroyan, M. A., and Fidelskaya, R. P. (1970). *Nucl. Instr. Meth.* **81**, 296.

Lapostolle, P. (1966). "Quelques relations entre les distributions de type hyperellipsoïodal dans les espaces à 2,3,4 et 6 dimensions." CERN Internal Report ISR-300 LIN/66-32.

Lapostolle, P. (1969). *Proc. Int. Conf. Ion Sources, 1st, Saclay, 1969* p. 165.

Lapostolle, P. (1970). Quelques effets essentiels de la charge d'espace dans les faisceaux continus, Rep. CERN/DI-70-36.

Lapostolle, P. (1971a). *IEEE Trans. Nucl. Sci.* **18**, 1101.

Lapostolle, P. (1971b). Relations énergétiques dans les faisceaux continus, Rep. CERN-ISR-DI/71-6.

Lapostolle, P. (1972). *Proc. Int. Conf. Ion Sources, 2nd, Vienna, 1972* p. 133

Lapostolle, P., Taylor, C. S., Têtu, P., and Thorndahl, L. (1968). Intensity dependent effects and space charge investigations on CERN linear injector and synchrotron, Rep. CERN-68-35.

Larson, J. D., and Jones, C. M. (1977). *Nucl. Instr. Meth.* **140,** 489.

Laslett, L. J. (1967). *In* "Focusing of Charged Particles" (A. Septier, ed.), Chap. 5-3, p. 355. Academic Press, New York.

Lauer, R. (1975). *Z. Naturforsch.* **30a,** 1395.

Lauer, R., and Hanszen, K. J. (1975). Brightness and emittance properties of electron guns. Physikalish-Technische Bundesanstalt Rep. APh-9.

Lawson, J. D. (1975). *Plasma Phys.* **17,** 567–582.

Lawson, J. D. (1976). *Nucl. Instr. Meth.* **139,** 17–24.

Lawson, J. D. (1977). "The Physics of Charged Particle Beams." Clarendon, Oxford (Oxford University Press).

Lawson, J. D., Lapostolle, P., and Gluckstern, R. L. (1973). *Part. Accel.* **5,** 61.

Lee, E. P., and Cooper, R. K. (1976). *Part. Accel.* **7,** 83–95.

Lichtenberg, A. J. (1969). "Phase-Space Dynamics of Particles." Wiley, New York.

Lord, R. S., Mallory, M. L., Stevens, S. S., Duelli, B. L., Newman, E., and Smith, W. R. (1967). *IEEE Trans. Nucl. Sci., NS 14-3* 1151.

Metzger, C. (1969). Mesure des émittances et du centrage des faisceaux dans la ligne de mesure 800 MeV du P.S.B. Rep. CERN/SI/Int. DL/69-10.

Miller, R. H. (1966). *Proc. Linear Accel. Conf., Los Alamos, 1966*, Rep. LA-3609.

Miller, R. H. (1970). *In* "Linear Accelerators" (P. Lapostolle and A. Septier, eds.), Part. B.1.2., p. 115. North-Holland Publ., Amsterdam.

Mills, R. L., and Sessler, A. M. (1958). Liouville's theorem for a continuous medium with conservative interactions, Rep. MURA-433, Stoughton, Wisconsin.

Montague, B. W. (1977). *Proc. Int. School "Beams Accel.," Nov. 1976*, Rep. CERN 77-13, p. 37.

Mueller, D. W., Meyer, E. A., Stevens, Jr., R. R., Coplen, B. C., Paciotti, M. A., and Emigh, C. R. (1972). *Proc. Proton Linear Acc. Conf., Los Alamos 1972*, Rep. LA 5115, p. 378.

Nagy, Gy. A., and Szilágyi, M. (1974) "Introduction to the Theory of Space Charged Optics." Macmillan, New York and London.

Nobiling, R., Civelekoglu, Y., Povh, B., Schwalm, D., and Traxel, K. (1975). *Nucl. Instr. Meth.* **130,** 325.

Osher, J. E. (1977). *Proc. Int. Conf. Low Energy Ion Beams, Salford, 1977*, Institute of Physics, Conference Series No. 38, University of Bristol, p. 201.

Parain, J. (1970). Comparaison de deux methodes pour mesurer l'émittance d'un faisceau. Int. Rep. Dép. Synchrotron Saturne Saclay—SOC/VTI-19, 1970.

Pierce, J. R. (1954). "Theory and Design of Electron Beams" (2nd ed.), Chapter 4. Van Nostrand, New York.

Pierce, J. R. (1959). "Theory and Design of Electron Beam" (3rd ed.), Chap. 8. Van Vostrand, New York.

Rhee, M. J., and Zorn, G. T., Placious, R. C., and Sparrow, J. H. (1971). Oxford, 1971. *IEEE Trans. Nucl. Sci. NS-18*, No. 3, 468.

Rose, P. H. (1974). *Proc. Symposium Ion Sources Ion Beams, 2nd, Berkeley, 1974*, Rep. LBL-3399, Paper VII-1-1.

Rose, P. H., Bastide, R. P., Brooks, N. B., Aviay, J., and Wittkower, A. R. (1964). *Rev. Sci. Instr.* **35,** 1283.

Rostoker, N., and Rosenbluth, M. N. (1960). *Phys. Fluids* **5**, 322.

Sacherer, F. J. (1971). R.m.s. envelope equations with space charge, *IEEE Trans. Nucl. Sci.* **18**, 1105–1107; Rep. CERN/SI/Int. 70-12 (1970).

Schubaly, M. R., Pachner, J., Ormrod, J. H., and Ungrin, J. (1976). *Proc. Proton Linear Accel. Conf., Chalk River, 1976* p. 313.

Self, S. A. (1963). *Phys. Fluids,* **6**, 1762.

Self, S. A. (1965). *J. Appl. Phys.* **36**, 456.

Sessler, A. M. (1972). *Proc. Proton Linear Accel. Conf., Los Alamos, 1972,* Rep. LA 5115, p. 291.

Septier, A. (1967). In "Focusing of Charged Particles" (A. Septier, ed.), Vol. II, Chap. 3.4, p. 123. Academic Press, New York.

Septier, A., Prangère, F., Ismail, H., and Gautherin, G. (1966). *Nucl. Instr. Meth.* **38**, 41.

Sholl, R. A. (1968). In "The Stanford Two-Mile Accelerator" (R. B. Neal, ed.), p. 651. Benjamin, New York.

Simpson, J. A. (1967). In "Methods of Experimental Physics," Vol. 4, "Atomic and Electron Physics" (V. Hugues and H. L. Schultz, eds.), Part A, pp. 84, 124. Academic Press, New York and London.

Sluyters, Th. J. M., Damm, R., and Otis, A. (1967). *IEEE Trans. Nucl. Sci.* **NS-14**, *No. 3* 1143.

Solnyshkov, A. I., Gerasimov, E. I., and Tarvid, G. V. (1972). *Proc. Proton Linear Accel. Conf., Los Alamos, 1972,* Rep. LA 5115, p. 411.

Steffen, K. G. (1965) "High Energy Beam Optics." Wiley (Interscience), New York.

Sturrock, P. A. (1955). "Static and Dynamic Electron Optics," Chap. 2. Cambridge Univ. Press, London and New York.

Swindel, W., and Barret, H. H. (1977). *Physics Today* **30**, 32.

Tanguy, P., and Durand, A. (1978). *Nucl. Instr. Meth.* **148**, 149–156.

Taylor, C. S. (1963). *Proc. Int. Conf. High Energy Accel., Dubna, 1963,* pp. 475–488.

Taylor, C. S. (1970). *Proc. Proton Linear Accel. Conf., Batavia, 1970* **2**, p. 881.

Taylor, C. S., Warner, D. J., Block, F., and Têtu, P. (1966). *Proc. Linear Accel. Conf., Los Alamos, 1966,* LA Rep. 3609, pp. 48–59.

Teng, L. C. (1971). Moment equations of a distribution of particles. NAL Rep. FN 221-0100, National Accelerator Laboratory (Batavia, Illinois).

Vader, R. J., and Dermois, O. C. (1977). *Nucl. Instr. Meth.* **144**, 423.

Van Steenbergen, A. (1965). *IEEE Trans. Nucl. Sci.* **NS-12**, 746.

Van Steenbergen, A. (1967a). *IEEE Trans. Nucl. Sci.* **NS-14**, 641.

Van Steenbergen, A. (1967b). *Nucl. Instr. Meth.* **51**, 245.

Van Steenbergen, A. (1970). In "Linear Accelerators" (P. Lapostolle and A. L. Septier, eds.), Part C.2.4, p. 935. North-Holland Publ. Company, Amsterdam.

von Ardenne, M. (1956). "Tabellen der Electronenphysik, Ionen-physik and Übermikroskopie," Vol. 1, pp. 135–146. VEB Deutscher Verlag der Wissenschaften, Berlin.

von Borries, B. (1948). *Optik* **3**, 321, 389.

Vosicki, B. (1966). *Proc. Linear Accel. Conf., 1966, Los Alamos.*

Walcher, W. (1972). *Proc. Int. Conf. Ion Sources, 2nd, Vienna, 1972* p. 111.

Walsh, T. R. (1960). Ideas on the measurement and shaping of emittances, Rutherford Lab. Internal Rep. HHG/INJ/23.

Walsh, T. R. (1962). *J. Nucl. Energy Part. C. (Plasma Phys.)* **4**, 53–54.

Walsh, T. R. (1963). *J. Nucl. Energy Part. C (Plasma Phys.)* **5**, 17–22.

Warner, D. J. (1972). *Proc. Proton Linear Accel. Conf., Los Alamos, 1972,* Rep. LA 5115, p. 33.

Warner, D. J., and Weiss, M. (1976). *Proc. Proton Linear Accel. Conf., Chalk River, 1976,* Rep. AECL 5677, p. 245.

Wartski, L., and Marcou, J. (1973). *IEEE Trans. Nucl. Sci.* **NS-20,** No. 3, 544.
Weiss, M. (1973). *IEEE Trans. Nucl. Sci.* **NS-20,** 877.
Wilson, R. G., and Brewer, G. R. (1973). "Ion Beams with Applications to Ion Implantation." Wiley (Interscience), New York.
Wroe, H. (1967). *Nucl. Instr. Meth.* **52,** 67.
Wroe, H. (1968). *Nucl. Instr. Meth.* **58,** 213.

ADVANCES IN ELECTRONICS AND ELECTRON PHYSICS, SUPPLEMENT 13A

High-Resolution Scanning Transmission Low-Energy Ion Microscopes and Microanalyzers

RICCARDO LEVI-SETTI

Enrico Fermi Institute and Department of Physics
The University of Chicago
Chicago, Illinois

I. Introduction

While much effort has been placed, at least over the past 20 years, in the development of scanning electron probes of ever increasing resolution, a parallel development of ion probes is still in its infancy. The immediate and wide range of applications of the scanning electron microscope (SEM) as well as its superb performance and technical accessibility have effectively eclipsed the need for the development of a comparable tool using ions (SIM). The advent of the scanning transmission electron microscope (STEM) (Crewe and Wall, 1970) reaching atomic resolution, with

261

its ability to distinguish different types of constrast signals after the interaction of the incident beam with the specimen, has further widened the gap.

Extensive use has been made of low-energy scanning ion beams in the scanning ion microanalyzer (SIPM) (Long, 1965; Liebl, 1967), where atoms at the specimen surface are sputtered by the probe and their mass analyzed in a mass spectrometer. The diameter of the ion probe in the above instruments has generally not been pushed below the limit of a few micrometers, with probe currents reaching up to 10^{-9} A for 30-kV ions. The primary origin of these limitations must be attributed to the limited brightness of the conventional ion sources (e.g., duoplasmatrons) employed. Recent reviews detailing the performance of different types of SIPM are available (Evans, 1972; Anderson and Hinthorne, 1972; Liebl, 1975). X-ray fluorescence induced by proton and ion bombardment has also been explored for trace element analysis and scanning ion microbeams in the several negavolts range developed for this purpose (Cookson et al., 1972; Horowitz, 1978) at resolutions still not better than the micrometer limit. A high-resolution, high-energy ion probe has been proposed (Martin, 1973, 1978).

An increased interest in developing high-resolution scanning ion probes has risen in recent years. This was motivated on one side by the realization (Levi-Setti, 1974) that a scanning transmission ion microscope (STIM) could tap to advantage the multifaceted ion–atom interaction in a variety of structural studies of biological material, and on the other by the fact that a high-resolution SIM was needed to meet new demands in semiconductor technology and microcircuit fabrication (Orloff and Swanson, 1975).

It should be noted that the radical innovation which paved the way for the development of a high-resolution STEM (Crewe et al., 1968) was the use of the field emission (FE) (Müller, 1937) electron source. With its very high specific brightness, due to its small virtual source size, a field emission source provides adequate probe current to approach the theoretical microscope resolution. Along a similar line of thought, the field ionization (FI) (Müller, 1951) source has been advocated (Levi-Setti, 1974) as the suitable choice toward the realization of an ion probe in the nanometer range. Although the resolution attained thus far with a FI proton STIM is still only in the 100-nm range (Escovitz et al., 1978) at 55 kV, with probe currents of $\sim 10^{-14}$ A (of primary concern has been the demonstration and understanding of new contrast mechanisms), the field ion source has been shown to possess the brightness needed for work at much higher resolution. Results supportive of this conclusion were also obtained (Orloff and Swanson, 1975) with a 12-kV FI SIM tested for microfabrication purposes, with which proton and Ar submicron probes of current density in the 10^{-2} A cm^{-2} range were obtained. A veritable revolution in heavy ion probe technology has been the development of practical electrohydrodynamic (EHD) ion sources (Krohn and Ringo, 1975; Clampitt et al., 1975), closely related to field ion sources. Particularly adapted to fulfill the goals of microelectronics (submicron lithography), such liquid metal ion sources exhibit brightness that surpasses that of gas field ion sources. Thus, the most promising results both in terms of probe size (50–100 nm) and current density (1.5 A cm^{-2}) have been attained thus far (Seliger et al., 1979) with a 57 kV SIM which incorporates an EHD liquid Ga ion source.

There is little doubt that the future of scanning high-resolution ion microscopes and microprobe applications must rely on ion sources of the field ionization type. The discussion to follow will then hinge quite heavily on the physical properties of such sources. The relationship that the scanning ion microscopes and microanalyzers bear on other ion-imaging devices will not be taken up in this context. An excellent review of the history and prospects of ion microscopy (Grivet and Septier, 1978) addresses this question exhaustively.

II. FORMATION OF A MICROPROBE IN THE NANOMETER RANGE

The basic optical column of a STIM parallels very closely that of a STEM or SEM. Ions must be extracted from a source, accelerated, and refocused to form a probe. When a field ionization or electrohydrodynamic ion source is used, the source geometry is essentially identical to that of a field emission STEM. With appropriate minor modifications, the considerations which relate the attainable resolution to source brightness, for a desirable performance of the STEM, apply also to a scanning transmission ion microscope or microprobe.

The choice of optimal parameters for the STEM has already been discussed in exhaustive reviews (Crewe, 1974; Zeitler, 1973). A similar analysis extended to the case of a proton (or ion) probe has also been reported (Escovitz et al., 1974).

In both a STIM or a SIPM one wishes to optimize the optical design so as to obtain the maximum probe current in the smallest beam spot size. For both types of instrument, the current in a useful probe must exceed a minimum level determined by the desired function of the device. Thus, in a scanning microscope the probe current must be sufficient to yield an intelligible picture in a reasonable scan time. This threshold current is a fixed input. Similarly, for a microprobe, the probe current must be adequate to perform a particular function, for example, sputtering or writing, within a given exposure time. As a result, the practical resolution that can be attained depends on the available probe current. For a given choice of optical parameters, the latter ultimately depends on the brightness of the source. Since the definition of this and related quantities is often the subject of some confusion, a brief review of the concepts involved is in order.

A. Brightness and Related Beam Quantities

If an area A_s of the source emits an ion current I_s into a solid angle Ω_s at a voltage V_s, and the optical column contains regions at different potential, it is appropriate to consider the *specific* (paraxial) *brightness:*

$$\beta = I_s/A_s\Omega_s V_s \tag{1}$$

When the source is a disk of radius r_s and the semiangle α_s of the emission cone small, we can also write

$$\beta = I_s/\pi^2 r_s^2 \alpha_s^2 V_s \tag{2}$$

and β can be measured, for example, in A cm^{-2} sr^{-1} V^{-1} or ions sec^{-1} nm^{-2} sr^{-1} V^{-1}. Use of this quantity is particularly relevant when the Gaussian image of the source gives a nonnegligible contribution to the final spot size, as is the case at very high resolution (as will become apparent in the following). Furthermore, in a nonrelativistic application of Liouville's (or Helmholtz–Lagrange) theorem to an aberration-free optical system, in absence of limiting apertures, β is invariant for conjugate points of the system. Thus, for an idealized column, β referred to the source is the same as β referred to the final spot size. Also widely used is the *brightness*

$$B = \beta V_s = I_s/A_s\Omega_s = I_s/\pi^2 r_s^2 \alpha_s^2 \tag{3}$$

measured, for example, in A cm^{-2} sr^{-1} or ions sec^{-1} nm^{-2} sr^{-1}. However, even for an idealized system, B differs in regions at different potential. Next in order of decreasing information content is the *intensity:*

$$\phi = BA_s = I_s/\Omega_s = I_s/\pi\alpha_s^2 \tag{4}$$

measured, for example, in A sr^{-1}.

This quantity is relevant for highly aberrated optical systems, namely, when the contributions to the final spot size by the aberrations of the system greatly exceed the size of the Gaussian image of the source (or equivalently when the aberrated final spot size referred to the source plane greatly exceeds the actual or virtual source size, making any reference to the latter irrelevant). It should be emphasized that since the attainable resolution in an ion probe is generally limited by chromatic aberration, the true figure of merit of an ion source should be the chromatic brightness or intensity, namely, any of the quantities defined above divided by the energy spread $e\,\Delta V$ at the source. Finally, relevant to radiation damage or to the effectiveness of a microprobe in sputtering or micromachining is the probe *current density*

$$J_\mathrm{p} = I_\mathrm{p}/A_\mathrm{p} \tag{5}$$

measured, for example, in A cm^{-2}.

Since in this section we will be concerned with the determination of the resolution limits of an ion probe, thus in a region where the gaussian image of the source cannot be ignored, it will be appropriate to base our discussion on the concept of specific brightness.

B. Contributions to the Beam Spot Size

We seek to derive the source specific brightness needed to operate a STIM at a final spot size in the nanometer range. We refer to a highly schematized optical column consisting of a source of radius r_s and a beam transport system (e.g., imaging lens) of overall magnification M, spherical aberration coefficient C_s, and chromatic aberration coefficient C_c (see Fig. 1). It is also assumed that the source yields ions with energy spread $e\,\Delta V$. Subscript s and p refer to source and probe quantities, respectively.

Quite aside from limitations imposed by the aberrations of the system, an attempt to reduce the beam spot size (image) by demagnification of the source (object) encounters limits determined by the finite brightness of the source. This can be seen from Eq. (2) and consideration of Liouville's theorem. In an aberration-free system, if the total emitted current I_s is imaged (no apertures) at magnification M, probe voltage V_p, and final angle α_s',

$$I_\mathrm{s} = \beta\pi^2 r_\mathrm{s}^2 \alpha_\mathrm{s}^2 V_\mathrm{s} = \beta\pi^2 r_\mathrm{s}^2 M^2 \alpha_\mathrm{s}'^2 V_\mathrm{p} = I_\mathrm{p} = I \tag{6}$$

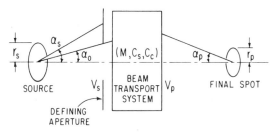

FIG. 1. Idealized optical system defining the quantities used in the text.

Then we can express the radius of the Gaussian image as

$$r_G = Mr_s = (I/\beta V_p)^{1/2} \, 1/\pi\alpha'_s \tag{7}$$

Clearly, even in the ideal case, r_G cannot be made small at will, but only as small as β will allow.

When we now pass to a real system, where we must introduce a beam defining aperture in order to reduce the aberrations, the latter will define a cone of semiangle α_0 through which a current I_0 will be accepted. Correspondingly, the beam will converge at the probe at an angle $\alpha_p \neq \alpha'_s$.

In terms of these quantities, the probe current for a real system is

$$I_0 = \beta\pi^2 r_s^2 \alpha_0^2 V_s = \beta\pi^2 r_G^2 \alpha_p^2 V_p \tag{8}$$

and Eq. (7) becomes:

$$\text{finite source,} \qquad r_G = (I_0/\beta V_p)^{1/2} \, 1/\pi\alpha_p \tag{9}$$

This is the contribution to the final spot size due to the extended nature of the source.

The other contributions are those of a point source imaged through the system. The corresponding theoretical probe radius r_0 is determined by diffraction, and spherical and chromatic aberration, assuming that other geometric aberrations can be avoided or corrected for (e.g., astigmatism). Such contributions are the same as those encountered in electron microscopy (see Grivet and Septier, 1978, for a recent review):

$$\text{diffraction,} \qquad r_d = 0.61 \, \lambda/\alpha_p \tag{10}$$

$$\text{spherical aberration,} \qquad r_s = \tfrac{1}{4} C_s \alpha_p^2 \tag{11}$$

$$\text{chromatic aberration,} \qquad r_c = C_c \alpha_p \, (\Delta V_s/V_p) \tag{12}$$

where, for example, for protons, $\lambda(\text{nm}) = 0.029/V_p^{1/2}$ (V is volts).

[It should be noted that Eqs. (9)–(12) refer to the plane of the probe, the image plane.] There sometimes are advantages in practical optical calculations in expressing the aberration contributions at the probe in terms of the quantities at the source (object) plane. In such a case, calling C_{so} and C_{co} the new aberration coefficients referred to the object plane, r_s and r_c take the form

$$r_s = \tfrac{1}{4} C_{so} M \alpha_0^3 \tag{11'}$$

$$r_c = C_{co} M \alpha_0 \, \Delta V_s/V_s \tag{12'}$$

For use in the next section, we also define the ratio of the Gaussian image radius r_G to that of the Airy disk (to the first zero) r_d from a point source (Crewe, 1973):

$$\epsilon = r_G/r_d = MR_s/r_d \tag{13}$$

and from Eq. (8) we can write

$$\epsilon^2 = I_0/\pi^2\beta r_d^2\alpha_p^2 V_p = I_0/\pi^2\beta^2 V_p(0.61\lambda)^2 \tag{14}$$

When I_0 is expressed in protons sec^{-1}, for example, and β in protons sec^{-1} nm^{-2} sr^{-1} V^{-1},

$$\epsilon^2 = I_0/(0.305 \times 10^{-2}\beta) \tag{15}$$

C. Optimum Design Parameters in Terms of Optical System Aberrations

To seek the optimum value α_{opt} of α_p, which reduces the overall probe radius r_p to its optimum value r_{opt}, we assume that the various contributions may be added in quadrature (Grivet, 1972). In limiting situations, the resulting expressions take a simple and meaningful form:

1. When spherical aberration is dominant

$$\alpha_{opt} = (\alpha_0)_s(1 + \epsilon^2)^{1/8}, \qquad r_{opt} = (r_0)_s(1 + \epsilon^2)^{3/8} \tag{16}$$

where

$$(\alpha_0)_s = C_1\lambda^{1/4}C_s^{-1/4}, \qquad (r_0)_s = C_2\lambda^{3/4}C_s^{1/4} \tag{17}$$

with $C_1 = 1.08$ and $C_2 = 0.63$.

The expressions for $(r_0)_s$, $(\alpha_0)_s$ correspond to the optimum semiangle and spot size in the case of a point source. The coefficients C_1 and C_2 obtained in this derivation (Excovitz et al., 1974) differ slightly from those obtained in the more rigorous calculations of Haine and Mulvey (Haine and Mulvey, 1954), $C_1 = 1.4$, and $C_2 = 0.43$, respectively. Adding the contributions in quadrature seems to overestimate somewhat the final spot size.

2. When chromatic aberration dominates, as is the case in a STIM that uses a FI or an EHD ion source (where $e\,\Delta V$ can range typically between 1 and 10 eV), the expressions for α_{opt} and r_{opt} simplify considerably by expansion if the following condition is met:

$$9C_s(0.61\lambda)(1 + \epsilon^2) \ll 4(C_c\,\Delta V_s/V_p)^4 \tag{18}$$

The result is in this case

$$\alpha_{opt} = (\alpha_0)_c(1 + \epsilon^2)^{1/4}, \qquad r_{opt} = (r_0)_c(1 + \epsilon^2)^{1/4} \tag{19}$$

where

$$(\alpha_0)_c = C_1'\lambda^{1/2}(C_c\,\Delta V_s/V_p)^{-1/2}, \qquad (r_0)_c = C_2'\lambda^{1/2}(C_c\,\Delta V_s/V_p)^{1/2} \tag{20}$$

and $C_1' = 0.78$ and $C_2' = 1.1$.

It should be pointed out that the above derivations implicitly assume that the aberration coefficients C_s and C_c are independent of the magnification M, and this is generally not true. We are, however, exploring a limiting situation in which the probe is close to the focal plane of, say, a strong objective lens. In this case (Oatley, 1972) the present approach is still valid.

As can be appreciated from Eqs. (14), (16), and (19), the theoretical probe radius $(r_0)_s$ or $(r_0)_c$ can only be attained for $\epsilon \to 0$, namely, specific brightness $\beta \to \infty$. In practice the available β will severely limit the useful range of probe sizes, if the probe current I_0 is required to exceed a lower bound. With this formulation we can now proceed to determine the best current-limited resolution of an ion probe.

D. The Probe-Current-Limited Resolution: Brightness Requirements

We are now in a position to estimate the source brightness required to obtain a particular probe radius with a given probe current I_0, given λ, C_s, and C_c. The conclusion of the above analysis is that the attainable resolution is indeed brightness—or probe current—limited. As an example, we will refer to the requirements of imaging with a STIM. In order to obtain an acceptable picture with a proton probe in a 100-sec scan made out of 500×500 point elements with 10 protons per point element, a probe current of 2.5×10^4 protons sec^{-1} is required. For better statistics per point element, or finer mesh of point elements, the current needed will have to be scaled accordingly. A good picture may require a probe current of, say, 2.5×10^5 protons sec^{-1}.

In order to explore the resolution limits of a 100-kV proton probe, it is assumed (Levi-Setti, 1974) that a superconducting lens may be employed, operating at 80 kG, with an excitation parameter $k^2 = 0.5$, NI = 1.2×10^5 A-turn. Such lens should attain a focal length of 1.2 cm with aberration coefficients $C_s = 1.2$ cm and $C_c = 0.8$ cm. Use of these parameters (Escovitz et al., 1974) (which satisfy the condition expressed by Eq. 18) yields the set of curves in Fig. 2, which give β as a function of the optimum probe radius for a range of ΔV values such as those encountered in field ionization sources (Tsong and Müller, 1964; Jason, 1967). For two values of β, 4×10^6 and 4×10^7 protons sec^{-1} nm^{-2} sr^{-1} V^{-1}, the optimum probe radius is plotted in Fig. 3 as a function of probe current I_0, for $e \, \Delta V = 0$ and 5 eV, respectively.

Clearly the curves of Figs. 2 and 3 portray the behavior of a rather idealized system and may only serve the purpose of defining relevant ranges for the quantities involved. In addition to applying to an extreme

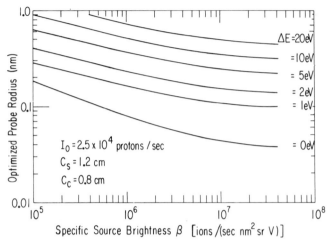

FIG. 2. Estimate of the attainable probe radius versus specific source brightness when a probe current of 2.5 × 10⁴ ions sec⁻¹ is required. This is the lowest beam current to yield an acceptable picture in a proton STIM. (From Escovitz *et al.*, 1974.)

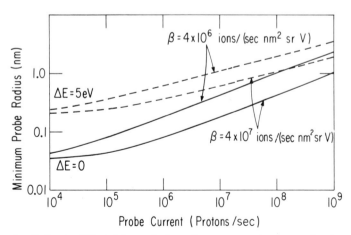

FIG. 3. Estimate of the minimum probe radius versus probe current for the conditions specified in Fig. 2. (From Escovitz *et al.*, 1974.)

STIM design (in terms of objective lens performance), they do not take into account the additional contributions to the final spot size arising from the aberrations of other components of the system, for example, the accelerating gun, deflection system, and mechanical vibrations.

Nevertheless, the goal of reaching the nanometer range with an ion probe has been framed in terms of basic source brightness requirements and demands on the system aberrations. At best, to reach a probe radius of 0.5–1.0 nm, useful for microscopy purposes, will require a source with β in excess of $\approx 10^7$ protons sec^{-1} nm^{-2} sr^{-1} V^{-1}.

In practical designs of electrostatic optical columns, as will be shown later, this lower limit increases by as much as two orders of magnitude. Specific brightness figures such as these become comparable with those that apply to the requirements of the STEM (Crewe, 1973), when multiplied by a factor of order 10^2. This factor represents the number of beam particles needed to obtain a signal contributing to contrast. For thin specimens (no attenuation) this corresponds to the ratio of proton versus electron cross section for the contrast originating process.

Conventional accelerator or microprobe ion sources, including radiofrequency (rf), duoplasmatron, and Penning discharge-type sources, do not provide the specific brightness needed for a high-resolution STIM. With perhaps a few exceptions (pulsed operation), the values of β appropriate to these sources (Septier, 1967) are several orders of magnitude smaller than the desirable range of 10^7–10^9 ions sec^{-1} nm^{-2} sr^{-1} V^{-1} ($\beta V >$ $\sim 10^6 - 10^8$ A cm^{-2} sr^{-1} at $V_s = 10^4$ V).

Instead, due to their small virtual source size, field ionization and EHD ion sources exhibit β values in the required range. In view of the inherent energy spread of these sources, the smallest attainable probe size will be essentially limited by the chromatic aberrations of the system.

III. Sources of High Specific Brightness

A. *Field Ionization Sources*

Steady ion currents up to 10^{-8}–10^{-7} A can be obtained in a gaseous atmosphere at a pressure of several milliTorr, when a finely pointed metal needle tip is placed at a high positive potential (with respect to some electrode acting as a cathode). This phenomenon was first used (Müller, 1951) in the field ion microscope, which is essentially a field emission microscope (Müller, 1937) operated with reverse polarity and filled with gas.

While in the field ion microscope, the ionization of the molecules of an "imaging" gas in the vicinity of the tip is exploited to project a highly magnified image of the surface of the tip itself on, for example, a fluorescent screen, in the present applications field ionization is exploited to obtain a quasi-point source of ions which are subsequently accelerated and focused to form a probe. Field ion sources are extensively used in a similar configuration, in mass spectrometry (Beckey, 1971).

1. *Mechanism of Field Ionization*

A quantitative and detailed understanding of the field ionization of gases is presently available and described in extensive monographs (Gomer, 1961; Müller and Tsong, 1969). Based on these presentations, only a summary of the essential concepts relevant to the behavior of field ion sources will be touched upon here.

Field ionization of a gas atom or molecule in the vicinity of a metal surface, in the presence of a high electric field, consists in the tunneling of electrons from the atom into the metal. Figure 4 shows how the constant potential seen by a 1s electron of an H atom is modified by an applied electric field in the vicinity of a tungsten surface. When the field is large enough to raise the ground state of the atom above the Fermi level, tunneling through the potential barrier can occur with appreciable probability. For a given applied field, there exists a critical distance of closest approach of the atom to the surface, x_c, that must be exceeded for tunneling to be energetically possible:

$$x_c \simeq (I - \Phi)/F \qquad (21)$$

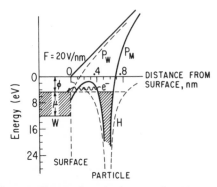

FIG. 4. Potential energy diagram for a 1s electron of an H atom in a field of 20 V nm^{-1}, at a distance of 0.55 nm from a tungsten surface. Broken lines show the Coulomb potential in the absence of an external field. Also indicated are: μ, the Fermi energy; ϕ, the work function; P_M, the atom potential; P_W, the superposition of applied and pseudoimage potential. (From Gomer, 1961, courtesy of R. Gomer and Harvard University Press.)

where I is the ionization potential of the atom, Φ the work function of the metal, and F the applied field. Image charge effects modify this relation slightly. Thus, for example, for the hydrogen atom near a tungsten surface, $I = 13.6$ eV, $\Phi = 4.5$ eV, and $F = 20$ V nm^{-1}, the critical distance is ~ 0.46 nm.

Explicit expressions for the barrier penetration factor D, and estimates of the rate of electron arrival of the barrier ν, leading to the mean lifetime for ionization

$$\tau = 1/D\nu \tag{22}$$

are given in the monographs mentioned above. Depending on the ionization potential, the ionization fields for the production of useful ion currents range between ~ 10 and 45 V nm^{-1}.

Fields in this range can be easily obtained in the vicinity of a sharp metal tip. For a tip schematized as consisting of a conical shank with hemispherical termination of radius r_t the surface field is

$$F \simeq V/5r_t \tag{23}$$

The numerical factor may vary with the cone angle. Typically, a field of 20 eV nm^{-1} can be obtained for $r_t = 100$ nm and $V = 10^4$ volts.

2. Ion Current

In general, one can anticipate the ion current to depend on the supply function of gas atoms or molecules to the tip and on the ionization probability. The latter, as typical of barrier penetration phenomena, will depend initially on the barrier thickness, hence on the local field. Also the time spent by a gas atom in the region at high field, but beyond the critical distance x_c, will be an important factor. In fact the ionization probability depends on the time in the field as

$$P(t) = 1 - e^{t/\tau} \tag{24}$$

In practice, both the supply function and the ionization probability depend in a complex manner on various factors involving intrinsic properties of the gas molecules, for example, the electric polarizability, the temperature of the tip, and the field.

There are various regimes for the ion current determined by these parameters. For the present purposes, a qualitative understanding of the basic interpretation of these regimes may suffice. In fact, although a detailed theoretical treatment is available, neither the temperature dependence nor the voltage dependence of the ion current are fully accounted for. Three main regions can be distinguished with reference to a representative empirical log I–log V curve in Fig. 5 (e.g., for H_2 or He at 78 K).

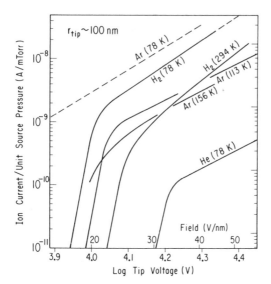

FIG. 5.   Typical log I–log V characteristics of field ionization sources. The curves were normalized to a tip radius of 100 nm by translating at constant field, as illustrated in the text, the curves fitting data for other tip radii.

At low fields, below the knee, the current is determined by the equilibrium concentration c_t of gas molecules near the tip and the mean lifetime τ for ionization. In this region, the total ionization does not decrease c_t appreciably. The latter exceeds the zero field concentration by a Boltzmann factor determined by the polarization energy of the gas molecules in the field. As a result, the current is a very sensitive function of the applied voltage and tip temperature. In this region, the observed slopes of the log I versus log V plots at 78 K may be as high as 30 for He on W (Southon and Brandon, 1963) or 40 for H_2 on W (Turner, 1967). This region is definitely to be avoided in any application where a steady intense ion current is desired.

At high fields, well above the knee, the ion current is limited by the supply function only. All molecules in the vicinity of the tip are ionized. The supply function is dominated by the effective tip cross section, which exceeds the geometric cross section by a large factor due once again to the attraction of the gas atoms or molecules to the tip by polarization forces. This enhancement factor is predicted to depend on $1/T$. However, gas supply from the shank may also contribute, and a detailed dependence of the ion current on the tip radius, temperature, and applied field is in general not predicted accurately by theory. The slopes at the log I–log V curves in this region, at 78 K, vary between ~3 and 5 (Southon and Brandon, 1963; Tsong and Müller, 1966; Turner, 1967), depending on the tip cone angle, which may vary between 40 and 10°, respectively. At the upper end of the range, the log I–log V curves terminate at the evaporation field for the metal tip (~ 57 V nm^{-1} for W). At constant fields, the ion current depends on the tip radius r_t as r_t^n, with $n \sim 2.5 \div 3$.

The high field region is clearly where one would like to operate practical field ion sources for microprobe applications, to obtain the highest probe current density. However, as will be discussed shortly, extreme fields have a drawback if high resolution is required. In fact, the energy spread of the extracted ions increases with the field, so that the chromatic brightness (brightness for unit ΔE at the source) may not actually be as favorable as at somewhat lower fields. This brings into focus a third regime at intermediate fields, in the vicinity of the knee in the log I–log V curves. This is the region where the best image voltage (BIV) is located in the language of field ion microscopy. In this regime, ionization occurs predominantly quite close to the critical distance x_c, while gas atoms or molecules hop toward the highest field regions of the tip, after having been attracted to the latter by polarization and dipole forces. Thermal accommodation, in particular on a cooled tip, slows down the particles so that they become effectively trapped by the tip and ionization during hopping is ensured. This mechanism limits the energy spread $e \Delta V$ of the ions and also reduces the extent of the virtual source size. In practice, the design of a STIM column must rely on the brightness of a FI source in, say, the lower portion of the high-field regime. Based on the above information, the empirical expression

$$I_2 = I_1 (r_2/r_1)^n (F_2/F_1)^m \qquad (25)$$

relates the current field characteristics for tips of different radii r_2 and r_1, respectively, in the region of interest here.

Since $F \sim V/r$, Eq. (25) becomes, in terms of the applied voltage V,

$$I_2 = I_1 (r_2/r_1)^{n-m} (V_2/V_1)^m \qquad (26)$$

The curves in Fig. 5, normalized to a tip radius of 100 nm, were actually constructed by translating at constant field (using Eq. 25 with $n = 2.5$), curves fitting available data for other tip radii [Southon and Brandon, 1963 (He); Turner, 1967 (H_2: 78 K, Ar: 113 K and 155 K); Tsong and Müller, 1966 (H_2: 294 K); Orloff and Swanson, 1978 (Ar: 78 K)]. Because of the method employed for their normalization, and because of the inhomogenous origin of the data, the curves in Fig. 5 may not reflect relative magnitudes correctly. However, in view of the scatter shown by such characteristics depending on individual tips, Fig. 5 may still be taken as representative of the expected behavior of field ion sources.

It should be noted that Fig. 5 is based on ion current data, which did

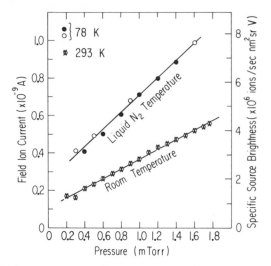

FIG. 6. Field ion current versus H_2 source pressure for a typical W tip at 7.5 kV. The specific brightness scale, valid for operation at 78 K, assumes a virtual source diameter of 0.7 nm. (From Escovitz et al., 1978; courtesy of New York Academy of Science.)

not include secondary electron current. Only for the Ar (78 K) log I–log V plot (Orloff and Swanson, 1978), a correction for this contribution had to be estimated and applied to the data.

The Ar (78 K) plot differs from the characteristics for other gases in that condensation of the gas on the tip at this temperature is most likely to have occured. In H_2 at 4.2 K it is known (Jason et al., 1970) that gas condensation extends the supply limited regime to much lower fields than ionization from the gas phase. A similar behavior is suggested by the log I–log V plot for Ar in Fig. 5.

The ion currents in Fig. 5 refer to unit source pressure. This is an appropriate normalization at least for the supply limited regime. In fact the supply function is predicted to depend linearly on the gas pressure, and this is well borne out of the experimental data as shown in the example of Fig. 6 (Escovitz et al., 1978).

3. Virtual Source Size and Brightness

In order to relate the ion current to the brightness of a field ion source, information on the size of the emitting region of the tip and angular distribution of ion emission is required.

The effective or virtual source size corresponds very closely to the disk of confusion at the tip surface, which determines the resolution in a field emission or field ion microscope. In the idealized case of a smooth hemispherical tip termination, the symmetry of the field would require ions found in the vicinity of the tip surface (for zero transverse velocity) to be accelerated radially outward. An observer looking at the tip would see the ions originating from a virtual point source at the center of the spherical emitter. If the ions leave the tip with a thermal transverse component of the velocity, however, the virtual source will not be a point any more, but will appear as a finite disk of radius r_s still much smaller than the actual tip radius r_t. From conservation of angular momentum along the ion trajectory (see, e.g., Gomer, 1961),

$$r_s = 4\beta r_t \, (kT/eV_s)^{1/2} \propto (r_t T/F)^{1/2} \tag{27}$$

where β is a numerical factor $\simeq 1.5$, which accounts for the deformation of the field due to the tip shank.

There are other contributions to the resolution of a field ion microscope, relevant to the visualization of the structure details, for example, atomic sites, at the tip surface (Gomer, 1961; Müller and Tsong, 1969). The basic dependence of the virtual source size on the tip radius and temperature are, however, contained in Eq. (27).

The brightness versus log V curves for H_2 (78 K) on W tips of different radii shown in Fig. 7, have been constructed using for r_s in Eq. (3) the val-

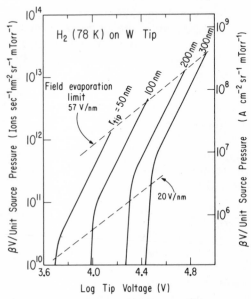

FIG. 7. Brightness βV versus log V of a H_2 field ion source for W emitters of different radii. The curves are derived from Fig. 5, by making a number of assumptions as discussed in the text.

ues of the theoretical resolution ($\times\frac{1}{2}$) given by Müller and Tsong (1969). The latter are somewhat larger than the values predicted by Eq. (27), which are on the conservative side. It was also assumed that ion emission occurred typically (Orloff and Swanson, 1975) within a cone of aperture semiangle $\alpha_s = 0.3$ rad. It is to be understood that Fig. 7 may give at best an order of magnitude estimate of the brightness of a practical H_2 field ion source.

The brightness $\beta_2 V_2$ for a source of radius $r_t = r_2$ relates to that ($\beta_1 V_1$) of a source of radius r_1, at constant field (from Eqs. 3, 25, and 27) as

$$\beta_2 V_2 = \beta_1 V_1 (r_2/r_1)^{n/2-1} \tag{28}$$

Since $n \simeq 2.5-3.0$ (Southon and Brandon, 1963), Eq. (28) indicates some advantage in brightness with ion source operation using larger tip radii (while maintaining constant ion current regime determined by a certain applied field). This in turn will require correspondingly higher applied voltages.

4. Energy Distribution of Field Ions: Beam Mass Composition

The fact that field ionization of gas molecules can occur over a range of distances from the metal surface, beyond the critical distance x_c, causes the accelerated ions to exhibit some energy spread. In principle, the energy of an ion originating at distance x from the tip surface will differ from that of an ion originating at x_c by an amount $eF(x - x_c)$, where F is the field strength near the tip surface. The problem has been extensively investigated and quantitatively understood (for a review, see Müller and Tsong, 1969).

The particular field ionization regime will clearly affect the energy distribution. The lowest energy spread will occur in a regime in which the ionization layer is thin and close to the critical distance x_c. This is the case for the hopping of thermally accommodated molecules on a cold tip, for example in the vicinity of the BIV in field ion microscopy, slightly above the knee in the log I–log V characteristics. The shape of the energy distributions is generally Maxwellian and for most gases, for example, the full width at half-maximum (FWHM) is close to 1 eV near the knee. A slight pressure broadening is observed (Tsong and Müller, 1964), approximately linear with gas pressure. As the field increases in the supply-limited region, ionization can take place farther and farther away from x_c, and the FWHM of the energy distribution increases accordingly to several electron volts, even for He and Ar. The field broadening is more pronounced for Ne, H_2, and other molecules.

In particular, beyond the field ionization threshold region, the field ion energy spectra of these gases exhibit an increasingly important secondary structure of peaks separated by several electron volts (Jason, 1967). Such structure is interpreted in terms of the formation of field—and surface potential—induced resonant states. While the H_2^+ energy distribution is still dominated by the "zero energy" peak, with an FWHM of ~ 1–2 eV up to fields of ~ 25 V nm^{-1}, at fields beyond 30 V nm^{-1} the secondary structure becomes dominant, extending to 60–100 eV.

Depending on the field strength, field-induced molecular dissociation may also occur. Unless the ion beam is momentum analyzed, this effect will increase the apparent energy spread at the source. For example, the beam from an H_2 ion source contains in general both H^+ and H_2^+ ions and a small admixture of H_3^+ at low fields (for a review see Müller and Tsong, 1969). As originally observed by Inghram and Gomer (1954), H_2^+ is dominant at low fields (~ 20 V nm^{-1}), while H^+ production rapidly takes over at higher fields ($\gtrsim 23$ V nm^{-1}). An unseparated energy spectrum of H ions exhibits two peaks separated by ~ 3 eV, the lower corresponding to H^+, the higher to H_2^+ (Tsong and Müller, 1964). Operating an H_2 field ion source at low field is then advantageous on two accounts, from the viewpoint of reducing the source energy spread: (1) to avoid the resonant broadening, and (2) to eliminate the additional spread from the H^+–H_2^+ admixture. In so doing, however, the selected ion species is H_2^+.

5. Noise

The ion current in a field ion probe is subject to relatively strong, statistical, short-time fluctuations (Beckey, 1971). These are present even if the applied voltage is highly stabilized (small changes in field strength cause large current variations due to the slope of the log I–log V characteristics). The effect is related to the small number of emitting sites in the surface area of the tip, which are viewed within the solid angle of acceptance of the probe-forming optical system. For high-resolution probes, only a fraction equal to 10^{-5}–10^{-4} of the emitted current at the tip is transmitted. Thus for a tip of 100-nm radius, the tip surface intercepted by the acceptance cone may amount to only 1–10 nm^2. Since field ionization at a microscopic level is promoted by the local field enhancement at surface protrusions, for example, atomic sites, the time evolution of the surface "granularity" reflects itself in statistical fluctuations of the ion current. The actual statistics of emitting centers in the above viewed area may be quite small; hence, the fluctuations are severe.

An analysis of the frequency spectrum of the ion current in a FI SIM (Orloff and Swanson, 1977) reveals essentially $1/f$ noise, entirely contained within the range 0–30 Hz independently of tip temperature. To reduce the noise, one must clearly maximize the statistics of emitting centers within the viewed surface area of the tip. In turn this calls for a high acceptance angle at the tip, a large tip radius, and a smooth tip surface. Further details of this phenomenon are reported in the monograph by Beckey (1971).

6. Best Operating Conditions

To achieve high resolution with a FI STIM there are several reasons to favor operation of the field ion source close to the knee (or BIV) in the log I–log V characteristics, at *high voltages* and with relatively *blunt tips*. From the previous discussion, these are:

1. The source brightness increases with approximately the $\frac{1}{4}$–$\frac{1}{2}$ power of the tip radius (at constant field).

2. It is desirable to operate at fields as low as possible to reduce the energy spread of the extracted ions and consequently increase the chromatic brightness.

3. With molecular ions, the additional spread caused by field-induced dissociation may be reduced or practically eliminated.

4. The $1/f$ noise is reduced at larger tip radii due to the improved statistics of emitting sites.

B. Field Ion Emitters for STIM Applications

A wealth of information concerning practical aspects in the realization of field ion sources is reviewed by Beckey (1971). However, while a variety of emitter geometries may be employed for mass spectrometric applications, for present purposes the discussion will be limited to single wire tips. Clearly much of the technology developed in the preparation and operation of tips for field ion microscopy (reviewed in Müller and Tsong, 1969), equivalent in many aspects to that for the utilization of field emission tips in the SEM and STEM (Crewe, 1971), can be directly transferred to STIM applications. Particular developments of field ion sources for the latter purposes have been recently undertaken (Levi-Setti, 1974; Orloff and Swanson, 1975; Schwarzer and Gaukler, 1977). Only a summary mention of the most relevant aspects of the problem will be taken up here.

1. FI Tips: Practical Aspects

Thus far, only tungsten (Escovitz *et al.*, 1975a; Schwarzer and Gaukler, 1977) and iridium (Orloff and Swanson, 1977) emitters have been employed in operating probe-forming systems (aside from mass spectrometric applications). Because of its high tensile strength, high melting point, high evaporation field limit (57 V nm^{-1}), and other metallurgical properties, tungsten is a natural choice as a field ion emitter for a high-resolution scanning transmission ion microscope (STIM). Furthermore, anodic electropolishing and etching of W wires to obtain the desired tip shape is particularly easy. One drawback of tungsten is its vulnerability to reactive gas etching, in particular from water vapor and nitrogen (Müller and Tsong, 1969), resulting in rapid blunting and degradation of the emitter. The use of W tips is, therefore, restricted to very clean vacuum systems.

The W tip fabrication technique adopted by the Chicago STIM group is essentially that employed by Crewe *et al.* (1968) for their STEM field emission tips. In turn, the latter follows closely the method of Dyke *et al.* (1953). A piece of 0.125-mm diameter tungsten wire (preferably an oriented single crystal) a few millimeters long is spot welded on to a 0.2-mm diameter tungsten filament in the shape of a hairpin. The W wire is then electrolytically etched in a 1 N NaOH solution. A typical filament-mounted W tip is shown in Fig. 8. Much of the technique of etch-

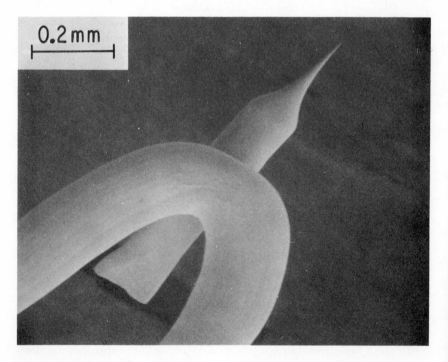

Fig. 8.   Tungsten FI (or FE) tip spot welded onto a hairpin filament, as used in the Chicago STIM. (Micrograph taken at the E. Fermi Institute SEM User's Laboratory.)

ing tips is an art, which is optimized in every laboratory and subject to an extended range of variants. It is most convenient to rely on the field emission properties of newly fabricated tips, to follow their evolution during subsequent treatment, and to determine finally their radius. Thus, a new tip is placed in a test chamber at $\sim 10^{-9}$ Torr, essentially a field emission microscope, so that the emission current can be measured and the field emission pattern observed on a fluorescent screen. By sending a current pulse through the hairpin filament, the tip is flashed at increasingly higher temperatures. Such thermal treatment (forming), at zero field, rounds off the tip to an approximately hemispherical shape by surface migration of tungsten on tungsten under surface tension forces. While flashing is always an effective method to clean a W tip from the accumulation of contaminants, a well-known alternate approach for the formation of a smooth symmetrical tip termination is that of field evaporation (Müller and Tsong, 1969). This is normally carried out while the test chamber operates as a field ion microscope, by applying a timed overvoltage to the tip.

The final determination of the tip radius is most conveniently obtained in the field emission mode from the slope of a Fowler–Nordheim plot (Gomer, 1961; Müller and Tsong, 1969). If, however, the tip is being tested in a high-resolution field ion microscope, a more direct method, outlined by Müller and Tsong (1969), can be used. This consists of counting the number of rings between two poles of known angular separation in a field ion micrograph. If the spacing between successive planes is known, the tip radius can be determined much as that of a lens using the spherometer.

Iridium is perhaps next in terms of desirable mechanical and refractory properties. It is practically unaffected by water etching (Orloff and Swanson, 1975) which is an attractive feature with nonbakable, diffusion pump level vacuum systems. Etching of iridium tips is, however, considerably more difficult that that of W tips. Electropolishing or etching recipes for iridium are given in Müller and Tsong (1969). Good results are obtained, following a suggestion by Swanson, using a dilute solution of NaClO (household chlorine bleach).

An auxiliary technique, which, in the experience of the Chicago STIM group, is invaluable in prolonging the useful lifetime of a tungsten tip generally subject to progressive blunting due, for example, to gas reactive etching, is that of remolding or thermal-field buildup. This will also be relevant to the problem of beam confinement as mentioned in the next section and applies to oriented single crystal emitters. Once again the technique is inherited from the practice with field emission sources (Martin et al., 1960; Crewe et al., 1968). For example, if a W tip is brought momentarily to a temperature in the range 2000–2500°C in the presence of a strong electric field ($5-10$ V nm^{-1}), surface migration of W atoms is promoted by electrostatic forces preferentially along certain crystal planes (Sokolovskaia, 1956; Bettler and Charbonnier, 1960). In constrast to surface migration at zero field, which is dominated by surface tension and rounds off the tip termination, field-induced surface migration acts in the opposite direction. A net transport of surface atoms to the region of highest field gradient "builds up" the tip termination into a faceted body with regions of sharper curvature than that obtained at zero field. Faceting by remolding lowers the voltage required to obtain a particular tip current, both in field emission and field ionization.

Although specific procedures for remolding may vary, and one may wish, for example, to carry out the process in a test chamber, this can be very profitably carried out on a STIM-installed tip. The required tip temperature is achieved by flashing the tip, while the electric field is provided by a typical positive dc tip voltage within the range of normal field ionization regime for the source. It has been found extremely valuable to have the capability to reverse polarity and use the STIM as a STEM or SEM (this requires a vacuum in the 10^{-9} Torr range). The large and easily measured field emission current serves as an indicator of the progress of the remolding process, which is repeated until, for example, certain required characteristics have been restored. Thus, the routine remolding of a W tip prior to any STIM run has enabled reproducible STIM operation for several hundred hours, and most likely this may be extended to an indefinite time. Invariably, catastrophic tip failure is caused by arcing during high-voltage breakdown in some other part of the STIM system.

2. Crystal Orientation and Angular Confinement of Ion Emission

Any field ion micrograph shows that, even for a rounded emitter, the brightness of ion emission is highly nonuniform over the emitting area. Particular sites related to the crystal structure of the emitter appear brighter than others. As thoroughly discussed by Müller and Tsong (1969), the regional image brightness pattern is partly due to variations in the local radii of curvature, which enhance gas supply and field ionization probability in such regions. Many other factors may contribute. Anisotropies of this kind can be exploited to maximize the effective source brightness, by the use of oriented single crystal emitters. This is achieved by making the preferred crystallographic axis coincide with the emitter axis so that the angular region of brighter emission falls within the acceptance angle of the optical system.

A similar situation occurs in field electron emission that is enhanced along those crystal axes for which the work function is lowest. Although field ionization is much less sensitive than field electron emission to local variations in the work function, it turns out that the same crystal orientations that are favored to give enhanced on-axis electron emission are also favorable in field ionization. This is mostly due to the ensuing symmetry with respect to the emitter axis of the most active sites for field ionization. Furthermore, such sites can be built up by remolding.

As a result of the above considerations, the polar and aximuthal angular distribution of both field electron and field ion emission are related and dependent on crystal orientation with respect to the emitter axis. Of course, whenever local anisotropies are washed out, such as may be the case with a polycrystalline emitter, one would expect that the angular distribution of emission were dominated by the field distribution at the emitting region determined by the geometry of the tip and its shank. For example, in a situation of this kind (Beckey et al., 1966), the angular distributions for field electron emission (tip covered by absorbate gas layer) and ion emission are quite similar, approximately bell shaped, and contained within a cone of semiangle $\approx 0.5-0.7$ rad.

Much more confined distributions are observed with oriented crystals and various methods to enhance the angular confinement have been explored (Crewe et al., 1968; Swanson and Crouser, 1969). The primary method is that of remolding or thermal-field (T–F) buildup already referred to, effective both in field electron emission and field ionization. For tungsten, commonly used emitter orientations are along the $\langle 310 \rangle$, $\langle 111 \rangle$, and $\langle 100 \rangle$ crystal axes. The angular confinement in field electron emission following T–F buildup along the $\langle 100 \rangle$ axis is very pronounced. Typically, angular distributions which extend to $0.2-0.3$ rad for smooth emitters, become confined to a range of less than 0.1 rad. Similar results have been noted in field ionization (Swanson and Crouser, 1969) for the $\langle 100 \rangle$ orientation, and as practiced by the Chicago STIM group, the remolding of $\langle 111 \rangle$-oriented tips is consistently effective in restoring paraxial ion emission. For $\langle 110 \rangle$ oriented iridium, Orloff and Swanson (1978) report T–F buildup confinement from ~ 0.35 rad (annealed tip) to ~ 0.13 rad.

The brightness plots of Fig. 7 were constructed assuming emission within a cone of semiangle $\alpha_s = 0.3$ rad. This is characteristic of annealed oriented crystal emitters. Other methods of emitter processing such as zirconium coating of a $\langle 100 \rangle$-oriented crystal emitter and field evaporation (Swanson and Crouser, 1969) have been shown to confine the cone of field electron emission. Since such methods rely primarily on the selective lowering of the work function along the $\langle 100 \rangle$ plane, they do not have a significant effect on field ionization. The Chicago STIM group is presently investigating the behavior of carbon coated tungsten emitters. Extreme confinement of field electron emission is observed, as expected, and the acquired resistance to gas reactive etching of tungsten makes this technique attractive in field ionization as well.

Another type of anisotropy in field ion emission occurs at high fields when the gas has condensed on a cold emitter. In this situation the rate of field ionization in the axial region of the tip may exceed the rate at which the liquid film on the shank "feeds" the tip. The result is a ring-shaped region at emission with a marked on-axis depletion (Jason *et al.*, 1970; Beckey, 1971). This provides an additional reason to prefer a low-field regime in ion source operation, relevant if gas condensation on the emitter may occur.

C. Electrohydrodynamic Ion Sources

Intense ion currents can be extracted from a liquid metal surface in a strong electric field. Following the first investigation (Krohn, 1961) of ion emission from molten metals, a number of applications of the phenomenon have been proposed. These have been recently reviewed (Krohn and Ringo, 1975; Clampitt and Jefferies, 1978a).

Ion sources of high brightness have been developed along two basic configurations. In one approach (Krohn and Ringo, 1975), ions are extracted from a Taylor's cone (Taylor, 1964) of liquid metal protruding from a capillary. In the other (Clampitt and Jefferies, 1978a, b), ions originate at the tip of a metal needle wetted by a liquid metal film. The latter is supplied by a pool of liquid through which the needle protrudes.

Owing to their low melting point, cesium and gallium have provided the preferred liquid metal sources. Ion beams from a number of other molten metals have been obtained, however (Clampitt and Jefferies, 1978b).

1. Mechanism of Current Generation

If a sufficiently high field is applied to a field ion emitter, atoms of the emitter may be ejected and subsequently ionized. This phenomenon (field evaporation) was discovered by Müller (1956) and recognized as a special case of field desorption, a process by which absorbate atom layers on the surface of a field ion emitter are evaporated. A detailed treatment of these processes have been given by Gomer (1959) and Gomer and Swanson (1963). The field strengths required for desorption of absorbate atoms are higher than those required for field ionization of the same atom from the gas phase. Field evaporation of tungsten at 78 K occurs for fields in excess of 57 V nm^{-1}.

Gomer (1979) has considered the mechanism of electron and ion emission from Taylor's cones of liquid metal. Ion emission is understood in terms of field desorption at low ion currents and by thermal evaporation followed by field ionization at high ion currents.

The basic steps in the process of ion current generation from a capillary filled with liquid metal, as a function of a positive applied voltage, are the following:

1. The first step is the formation of a Taylor's cone. The balance of electrostatic and surface tension forces leads to the formation of a cone of half angle 49.3° at a critical voltage V_c which depends on electrode geometry and spacing. Beyond V_c the cone is unstable, and this may lead to ejection of droplets or liquid jets. The supply of liquid to the cone is always sufficient to sustain currents up to the milliampere region.

2. The ion current onset occurs at V_c already in a space-charge limited regime so that the current is expected to increase with $V^{3/2}$. The currents observed at onset, on the order of several microamperes, the actual values of V_c that have been observed, jointly with the field requirements for field desorption, require that the radius of the cone termination be as small as 1–2 nm. The ion energy distribution for this regime is expected to be narrow in the region of ~ 1 eV. Space charge provides a stabilizing, negative feedback on the balance between apex field and apex radius.

3. As the voltage is increased so that the current may exceed ~ 10 μA, heating caused by field desorption will raise the cone temperature to a region where thermal desorption of neutral atoms becomes dominant. To account for the magnitude of the ion current, field ionization of the evaporated atoms must be invoked over a region much larger than the apex surface. Large energy spreads of the field ions are expected in this regime, which then is not seen as profitable for high-resolution STIM applications.

Actual current voltage characteristics for some EHD sources are shown in Fig. 9. The data for a Cs Taylor's cone (Clampitt and Jefferies, 1978b) had been previously fitted by Krohn (1974) to a form

$$I \propto V^{1/2} (V - V_c) \tag{29}$$

where V_c is the threshold voltage.

The space-charge-limited regime extends well beyond the limit of ~ 10 μA envisioned by Gomer, although it is not known to what extent secondary electron emission may have contributed to the measured current. As pointed out by Clampitt and Jefferies (1978b), the threshold voltage is very sensitive to the size, shape, and proximity of the ion extraction aperture, among other factors, and may vary between ~ 2 and 6 kV, depending on extractor apertures in the range 100–1000 μm.

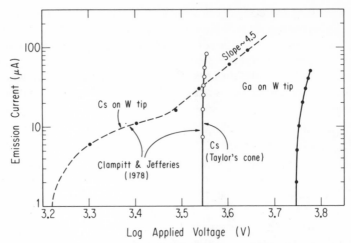

FIG. 9.   Log I–log V characteristics for some EHD sources. (Unpublished data for Ga on W tip courtesy of R. L. Seliger.)

A needle configuration for Cs (Clampitt and Jefferies, 1978b) provides an excursion through the various regimes outlined above even though Gomer's treatment refers to an "unsupported" Taylor's cone. In particular, it is significant to note the asymptotic slope, ~ 4.5 of the log I–log V plot in Fig. 9 for this EHD emitter. This is well within the range of the corresponding slopes observed for field ionization, and may be taken as evidence in favor of Gomer's interpretation of the high current regime.

The data for gallium refers to the source developed by Seliger *et al.* (1979) and kindly made available to me by Dr. Seliger. Although the configuration is of the needle type, its behavior is quite similar to that of a Taylor's cone near threshold, namely, in the space-charge limited regime. Large fluctuations are observed in the threshold voltage, and an initial overvoltage is required to "ignite" emission. I–V data are generally obtained while lowering the voltage until the source cuts off.

Seen in retrospect, the large currents exhibited by EHD sources in comparison with those of conventional gas phase field ion sources may well be attributed primarily to the much larger supply function present with liquid metal wetted needles or Taylor's cones. One may speculate that the behavior of field ion sources in which the gas has condensed into a liquid film on the tip shank could be made to approach that of EHD sources, provided the supply of liquid to the tip were enhanced by contact with a reservoir of liquified gas. Such an approach could conceivably extend the spectrum of ions that could be obtained from EHD sources beyond that of liquid metals.

The above views have been recently explored in a systematic investigation by the group of R. Castaing (Sudraud *et al.*, 1978a) at Orsay. In attempts to increase the supply function, both liquid-fed field ionization sources and field desorption sources have been studied. In the former, capillary contact is established between a reservoir of liquid (e.g., glycerol, acetone, pyralene) and a standard field ion tip. In the latter, a condensate (rare gases, CO_2, ethyl alcohol, etc.) is made to form directly on the tip at an appropriate temperature. Ring emission patterns are observed with the field desorption sources much as originally noticed by Jason *et al.* (1970) with H_2 condensate. Ion currents enhanced by a factor $10^1 - 10^2$ over those typical of gas phase field ion sources have been measured in a stable and reproducible performance. Electrodynamical instabilities in liquid-fed sources lead to a somewhat erratic ion extraction regime, of the general form $V \propto I^{1/2}$. The currents observed in these conditions are also enhanced a hundredfold over those of gas phase sources. Furthermore, the same group has investigated, in unprecedented detail (Sudraud *et al.*, 1978b; and private communication), the mechanism of high-temperature metal ion emission from solid and liquid phases. Different regimes have been investigated, including field evaporation from W and Cu tips subjected to the remolding process, field evaporation from solidified Au Taylor cones throughout the melting transition, and the EHD regime both with an Au Taylor cone and an Au-wetted W needle. Of particular interest is the study of a new regime, local EHD, occurring just below the melting point. This is interpreted as arising from the formation of current promoted local melting, with ensuing formation of a liquid microcone, which becomes the site of stable, confined ion emission in the range $10^{-10} - 10^{-9}$ A. Emission currents, in the full EHD regime for Au, up to the microampere range have been observed.

2. *Brightness: Comparison with Field Ion Sources*

Several estimates of the brightness of EHD sources have been reported. On the basis of the measured beam current in a focused probe from a liquid gallium Taylor's cone source, and an inferred source radius of 25 nm, Krohn and Ringo (1976) reported a source brightness βV of 1.4×10^6 A cm^{-2} sr^{-1} at 21 kV. A value of 3.3×10^6 A cm^{-2} sr^{-1} has been reported by Seliger *et al.* (1979) for the probe brightness of a needle-type liquid gallium source, based on the measurement of the probe current in a focused spot of 100-nm diameter at 57 kV. Since the actual spot size corresponds to the aberrated Gaussian image of the source, the actual source brightness may be considerably in excess of the quoted value. In order to provide a common basis of comparison between field ionization and EHD sources, an estimate of the brightness of the latter has been obtained based on the primary ion current data of Fig. 9, a virtual source of 1-nm radius (following Gomer's estimate) and an emission cone of semiangle $\alpha_s = 0.3$ rad. The results are shown in Fig. 10, as a function of applied voltage. For comparison, βV versus V plots for H_2 field ion sources of different tip radius operating at 10^{-2} Torr are also shown. The assumption of a virtual source of 1-nm radius for EHD sources may be optimistic, and the set of corresponding curves may well overestimate the brightness by an order of magnitude or more. Even so, the brightness of a field ion source operating in a rather strenuous regime barely overlaps that which can be achieved at much lower voltages with EHD sources.

Concerning the energy spectra of the extracted ions, a FWHM of 12 eV for Ga and 15 eV for Cs at 10 μA have been measured (Krohn and Ringo, 1975) for a Taylor's cone. For a needle-type Ga source also operating at 10 μA, a FWHM of 14 eV has been inferred (Seliger et al., 1979) from the observed size of the chromatically aberrated beam spot, in substantial agreement with the Taylor's cone value. These figures are an order of magnitude higher than the corresponding energy spreads for a field ion source operating near the knee of the log I–log V characteristics. If chromatic brightness is taken as the figure of merit, then field ion sources may still be competitive toward the goal of achieving extreme resolution. Sudraud et al. (1978a, b) have made a careful study of the energy spectra of the ions emitted by the variety of sources they have inves-

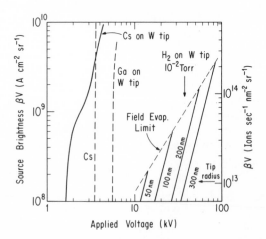

FIG. 10. Source brightness βV versus applied voltage from the data for EHD ion sources in Fig. 9, and an assumed virtual source radius of 1 nm. Data derived from Fig. 7 for a H_2 FI source are also included for comparison.

tigated. Full widths at half-maximum of 10–20 eV have been measured for field desorption sources, whereas in the EHD regime the FWHM is 50–100 eV for example, for Au^{2+} and Au^+ ions, respectively.

IV. The Design of Optical Systems for
SIM and STIM: Aberrations

The particular source geometry and extraction field requirements of FI and EHD sources set well defined input boundaries on the practical design of accelerating and focusing optical systems for the formation of a probe. The problem has been discussed (Beckey, 1971) in relation to the use of FI sources in mass spectrometric applications.

In view of the overall symmetry between a FE SEM or STEM and a FI SIM or STIM, it is most profitable to take advantage here of the remarkable development which has recently taken place in the design of FE electron probe systems (Crewe, 1971). The part of the optical system that clearly is more critically dependent on the source geometry is the field emission or field ion gun.

A. Field Ion Guns

As illustrated by Crewe et al. (1968) and in more detail by Crewe (1971), and reworded in this context in terms of ions, a FI gun must contain a minimum of three electrodes. A voltage V_s between the emitter and the second extracting electrode provides the field required for field ionization and extraction of ions from the source region. A third accelerating electrode at potential V_p with respect to the emitter, defines the final probe energy. Suitable apertures in the extracting and accelerating electrodes allow the ions to be transmitted and form a probe. A variety of possible electrode configurations and shapes that have been explored are shown in Fig. 11 (Munro, 1973). The goal of optimizing the gun performance was approached from first principles in the analysis by Crewe (1971). It was required that the electric field on either side of the two apertures, in the extracting and accelerating electrode, respectively, be as close to zero as possible so that the only focusing action on the beam would be caused by the accelerating field between the two electrodes. The latter had to be shaped to minimize the aberrations of the accelerating system. A solution that minimized the spherical aberration of the gun was obtained by Butler (1966) for parabolically shaped electrodes. The boundary condition that the electric field be zero near the apertures is satisfied when the aperture is placed at the apex of a conical cavity of semiangle $\arctan \sqrt{2}$. Families

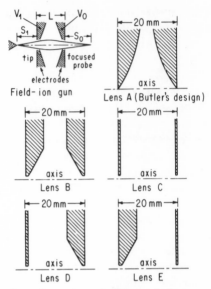

FIG. 11.   Configurations of two-electrode FE guns in the comparative study by Munro
(1973). The same configurations relate in the present context to FI guns. (Courtesy of E.
Munro and Academic Press, Inc., London, Limited.)

of curves illustrating the first-order optical properties and the aberration
constants for a Butler's gun are available (Crewe, 1971, 1973). Using a
finite element program, a number of alternative electrode geometries
(those shown in Fig. 11), including Butler's, have been analyzed by
Munro (1973). Munro's calculated values of C_{so} and C_{co} (referred to the
plane of the emitter), as a function of the magnification M for the electrode geometries of Fig. 11, and a probe distance $S_0 = 10$ mm, are reproduced in Fig. 12.

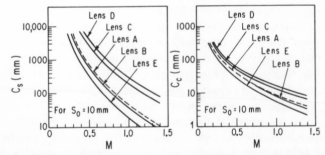

FIG. 12.   Spherical and chromatic aberration coefficients C_s and C_c versus magnification M for the two-electrode gun configurations of Fig. 11, as calculated by Munro (1973).
(Courtesy of E. Munro and Academic Press, Inc., London, Limited.)

For a system such as sketched in Fig. 11 or Fig. 1, the magnification is defined by the Helmoltz–Lagrange relation as

$$M = \alpha_o/\alpha_p(V_s/V_p)^{1/2} \qquad (30)$$

The asymmetrical electrode configuration of lens E yields somewhat lower aberration coefficients than the Crewe–Butler design. However in both cases the arctan $\sqrt{2}$ taper condition at the first aperture is critical. From the values of C_{so} and C_{co} in either Fig. 12 or, for a wider range of object and image positions (Butler's gun), in one of Crewe's papers referred to above, the contributions to the probe size by the aberrations of the gun (referred to the probe or image plane) are calculated from

$$r_s = \tfrac{1}{4}C_{so}M\alpha_o^3 = \tfrac{1}{4}C_{so}M^4\alpha_p^3 R^{3/2} \qquad (31)$$

$$r_c = C_{co}M\alpha_o \, \Delta V_s/V_s = C_{co}M^2\alpha_p R^{3/2} \, \Delta V_s/V_p \qquad (32)$$

where $R = V_p/V_s$.

As discussed by Escovitz et al. (1974), an optimum optic design for an ion gun of the type under discussion is severely constrained by the first-order focal properties that depend on the ratio R of operating voltages. As a result, the magnification M is fixed for a given choice of R and probe position, and equations like (16) or (19) have only partial minima of no practical consequence. In practice, acceptable aberration coefficients for the family of two elements lenses of Fig. 11 obtain only at magnifications close to unity, and these can only be reached (for source and image distances within a few centimeters from the lens electrodes) for values of R in excess of ~ 6–7 (see, e.g., Crewe, 1971). Thus, the range of operating voltages is severely constrained and since FI sources require V_s to exceed 8–10 kV, the probe voltages must exceed ~ 50 kV. The probe current-limited radius as a function of the ion probe current that can be attained with a Butler gun (object distance 2.5 cm, image distance 7.6 cm) have been calculated by Escovitz et al. (1974). This is shown in Fig. 13, where several isobrightness curves for $e \, \Delta V_s = 5$ eV have been plotted. The probe angle α_p required to obtain the probe radii indicated is also shown. An example will illustrate the limits of resolution of a system of this kind. Assume that a probe radius of 10 nm is desired. From Fig. 13, a probe angle of $\sim 5 \times 10^{-5}$ rad is indicated. If the FI source has a specific brightness β of 4×10^7 ions sec^{-1} nm^{-2} sr^{-1} V^{-1} (within the range given by Fig. 7) a probe current of $\sim 2 \times 10^4$ ions sec^{-1} will be obtained. A higher source brightness will give a correspondingly higher probe current; however, for $R = 10$ as in this example, the source regime above 10 kV is in practice out of reach, and β can at most be made to increase by a factor 5–10, giving in the limit a probe current of 1–2×10^5 ions sec^{-1}, adequate for microscopy. With an EHD source instead (from Fig. 10) currents up to

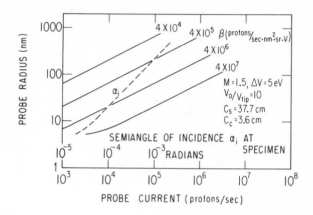

FIG. 13.   Fig. 13.   Estimate of the probe radius versus probe current attainable with the Butler's gun as operated in the Chicago STIM. The object distance is 2.5 cm; the image distance is 7.6 cm. (From Escovitz *et al.*, 1974.)

10^7 ions sec^{-1}, in the picoampere range are predicted. This corresponds to current densities near 1 A cm^{-2}.

At least an additional electrode is clearly required to obtain the flexibility of varying the emitter voltage independently of the probe voltage, while maintaining fixed source and image positions. This is essential to exploit the full range of FI source operation. Aware of these considerations, and seeking to reduce in particular the chromatic aberration in view of ion microprobe applications, Orloff and Swanson (1979) have recently proposed a physically and voltage asymmetric three element lens of attractive properties. This lens is similar in design to the einzel lenses explored by Riddle (1978) for the purpose of minimizing spherical aberrations, for use in a FE electron gun. The proposed lens has low chromatic aberration $C_c/f \lesssim 0.5$, when operated in the accelerating mode, over a range of voltage ratios R and as low as 2. A critical comparison of the performance of the new three element lens with that of two element lenses of the Munro type is also given by these authors.

Using the computational technique developed by Butler (1966), now encompassed in a system program CLOPT-4 (Butler, 1974), optical calculations have been performed at Chicago on a number of two- and three-electrode guns and multiple-lens columns to ascertain their relative merit. Table I compares relevant data from the new search with those systems already in operation. From Eqs. (31) and (32), and in view of the relatively large energy spread $e \, \Delta V_s$ of FI or EHD sources the figure of merit of an optical system is essentially represented by the product

TABLE I

Optical Data for Two- and Three-Electrode Ion Guns and for Selected Two- and Three-Lens Columns

System type	Object[a] distance (cm)	Image[b] distance (cm)	V_p/V_s	V_s (kV)	M	C_{so} (cm)	C_{co} (cm)	MC_{co}/V_s ($\times 10^{-4}$ cm V^{-1})
Two-electrode guns:								
Butler's type (Escovitz et al., 1974)	2.5	7.6	10	6.5	1.5	37.7	3.6	8.3
Munro's type (Seliger et al., 1979)	2.2	4.0	10	5.7	1.0	39.6	3.3	5.8
Three-electrode guns:								
Symmetric einzel lens	1.4	4.9	1.0	10.0	2.63	218	9.0	23.7
Asymmetric accelerating Orloff and Swanson lens	0.5	1.0	5.5	10.0	1.18	8.13	6.6	7.8
	0.5	1.0	2.75	20.0	1.64	19.4	8.8	7.2
	0.5	1.0	1.83	30.0	2.02	27.4	9.9	6.7
	1.5	5.0	2.0	15	3.2	54[c]	2.1[c]	4.5
Two-lens systems:								
Two symmetric einzel lensies (Orloff and Swanson, 1977)	0.55	3.3	1.0	12	6	400	7.5	37.5
Asymmetric accelerating O–S lens and one einzel lens	0.5	1.0	5.5	10	0.24	1421	17.4	4.2
	0.5	1.0	2.75	20	0.41	892	21.8	4.4
One crossover	0.5	1.0	1.83	30	0.50	722	24.1	4.0
Three-lens systems:								
Butler gun and two einzel lenses	2.5	0.5	6.1	9	0.30	208	8.2	2.8
No crossover								

[a] From the entrance plane of lens.
[b] From the exit plane of lens.
[c] As calculated by Orloff and Swanson (1979b).

MC_{co}/V_s. For the two- and three-lens systems included, to be illustrated later, effective aberration constants for the entire column are given, referred to the source, so that Eqs. (31) and (32) can still be applied.

As apparent from the entries in the last column of Table I, symmetrical einzel lenses have definitely a worse figure of merit than two-electrode guns or asymmetrical three-electrode lenses. The performance of either of the latter is, however, comparable within a factor of two. It should be noted, however, that the asymmetrical three-electrode lens offers the flexibility lacking in two-element guns.

B. Systems with Two or More Optical Elements

A two-element proton probe to reach the nanometer range, using a FI source, was proposed by Levi-Setti (1974). Since the construction of such a device was deemed too ambitious at a time when the feasibility of several concepts still had to be demonstrated, the proposal is still on the drawing board. Seen in retrospect, after a few years of development in the

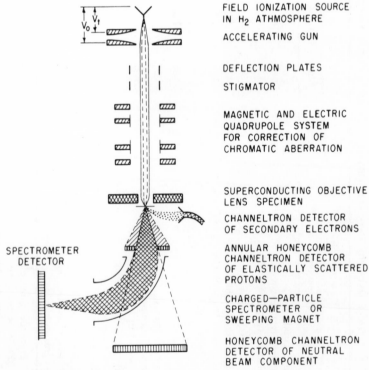

FIELD IONIZATION SOURCE
IN H_2 ATHMOSPHERE

ACCELERATING GUN

DEFLECTION PLATES

STIGMATOR

MAGNETIC AND ELECTRIC
QUADRUPOLE SYSTEM
FOR CORRECTION OF
CHROMATIC ABERRATION

SUPERCONDUCTING OBJECTIVE
LENS SPECIMEN

CHANNELTRON DETECTOR
OF SECONDARY ELECTRONS

SPECTROMETER
DETECTOR

ANNULAR HONEYCOMB
CHANNELTRON DETECTOR
OF ELASTICALLY SCATTERED
PROTONS

CHARGED—PARTICLE
SPECTROMETER OR
SWEEPING MAGNET

HONEYCOMB CHANNELTRON
DETECTOR OF NEUTRAL
BEAM COMPONENT

FIG. 14.   Schematic design of a 1-nm STIM. (From Levi-Setti, 1974, courtesy of IIT Research Institute.)

use of FI sources for probe applications, the original optical design still holds promise to represent a sort of ultimate proton probe device. The optical column of the proposed probe is reproduced in Fig. 14. Ions from a FI source are accelerated to 100 kV by a Butler gun to form a parallel beam, which is then brought to a focus by a superconducting lens. The original design parameters of the probe, given in Table II, come close

TABLE II

DESIGN PARAMETERS FOR 100-kV TWO-ELEMENT PROTON PROBE
(BUTLER GUN AND SUPERCONDUCTING LENS)[a]

Column parameters:

Overall magnification	$M = 0.2$
Semiangle at source	$\alpha_o = 1.06$ mrad
Semiangle at probe	$\alpha_p = 2$ mrad
Accepted solid angle	$\Delta\Omega = 3.5 \times 10^{-6}$

Butler gun parameters:

V_p/V_s	$R = 7$
Spherical aberration coefficient	$C_{so} = 22.2$ cm
Chromatic aberration coefficient	$C_{co} = 2.91$ cm
Object distance (tip-to-gun entrance aperture)	$S_o = 2.52$ cm

Superconducting lens parameters:

Focal length	$F = 1.2$ cm
Image distance	$S_p = 1.2$ cm
Excitation parameter	$k^2 = 0.5$
Excitation	$NI = 1.2 \times 10^5$ A-turn
Bore diameter	$D = 1.6$ cm
Field strength	$B = 80,000$ G
Spherical aberration coefficient	$C_s = 1.2$ cm
Chromatic aberration coefficient	$C_c = 0.8$ cm

FI source parameters:

Tip radius	$r_t = 100$ nm
Source voltage	$V_s = 14.3$ kV
H_2 pressure	$P = 2$ mTorr
Tip temperature	$T = 78$ K
Brightness	$\beta V = 10^7$ A cm^{-2} sr^{-1}

Probe parameters:

Final accelerating voltage	$V_p = 100$ kV
Current	$I_p = 1.35 \times 10^{-13}$ A
Contribution to probe radius due to:	
Gaussian image of source	$r_G \simeq 0.07$ nm
Diffraction	$r_d \simeq 0.03$ nm
Spherical aberration of gun	$r_{s,g} \simeq 0.02$ nm
Spherical aberration of lens	$r_{s,l} \simeq 0.05$ nm
Chromatic aberration of gun	$r_{c,g} \simeq 0.43 \times e\ \Delta V$ nm ($e\ \Delta V$ in eV)
Chromatic aberration of lens	$r_{c,l} \simeq 0.17 \times e\ \Delta V$ nm

[a] From Levi-Setti (1974).

enough to the optimum optic parameters discussed in Section II,C not to warrant modification. The final spot size is dominated by the chromatic aberration contributed by the gun and the final lens. The source data are consistent with those discussed in Section III,A,3. The superconducting lens parameters were obtained by extrapolating (and converting to the proton case) data by Génotel *et al.* (1968) for electrons. Over the explored range of the excitation parameter k^2 (~0.1–0.45 for protons), the values of C_s/R and C_c/R were found to be consistent with those given for magnetic electron lenses by Liebmann and Grad (1951) (for $S/D = 1$). Although not a trivial problem, the construction of the required objective lens seems within reach of present technology. The design of Fig. 14 also indicates a magnetic and electric quadrupole system for the corrections of chromatic aberration. Recourse to such devices seems unavoidable to achieve probe sizes below 1 nm.

Following a recent experience at Chicago with the magnetic analysis of the beam in a FI source-operated STIM, it became apparent that the partial neutralization of the extracted beam by the source gas poses a problem that cannot be overlooked. The precautions to be taken to reduce this phenomenon may deeply affect the overall design of an optical column. It should be realized that the rate of beam neutralization in the vicinity of the source increases with the square of the gas pressure, hence of the source brightness. The traversal of several centimeters of gas at a pressure in the milliTorr range may originate an intolerable continuous background of nonfocussed off-time neutral particles at the probe position. Thus, to make a design such as that of Fig. 14 workable, the source gas should be confined to the immediate vicinity of the tip, while maintaining the optical column at high vacuum.

As mentioned in Section IV,A, a search for optical configurations leading to low chromatic aberrations was recently carried out at Chicago, with the help of J. W. Butler, for a system of electrostatic lenses. The search hinged on a number of requirements. It was deemed desirable to:

1. Decouple the FI source voltage constraints from the final probe voltage.
2. Maintain a fixed object and image position while varying source and probe voltages.
3. Minimize the chromatic aberration of the column.
4. Provide a crossover where a small aperture could be placed without affecting the transmission of the column. Such an aperture would stop a large fraction of the residue of nonfocused, neutralized, and energy-degraded beam particles that would still originate in the source region, in particular, when working at pressures of several mTorr.

The above requirements are met by the "constant angular magnification" mode of operation proposed by Veneklasen and Siegel (1972). At the same time it was thought desirable to take advantage of the properties of the asymmetrical triode gun of Orloff and Swanson (1979), when used in the accelerating mode. A compromise solution, comprising an Orloff–Swanson triode gun leading to a crossover in field-free space close to the gun exit, and a final einzel objective lens, was obtained. The parameters of this system are given in Table I for tip voltages 10, 20, and 30 kV and probe voltage 55 kV. A schematic diagram of the system, with a ray tracing and axial potential distribution, is shown in Fig. 15. As seen in Table I, the column can operate over a range of source voltages without

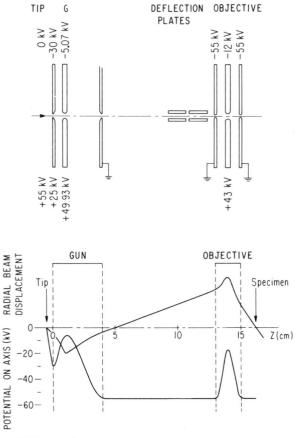

Fig. 15. Radial beam displacement and axial potential distribution for a two-element optical system, providing a crossover. Aberration data for this column are contained in Table I.

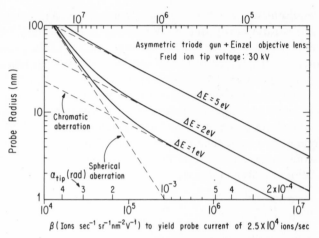

FIG. 16. Probe radius versus probe current attainable with the optical system shown in Fig. 15. [Probe current (ion/sec) for specific source brightness $\beta = 10^7$ ions sec^{-1} sr^{-1} nm^{-2} V^{-1}.]

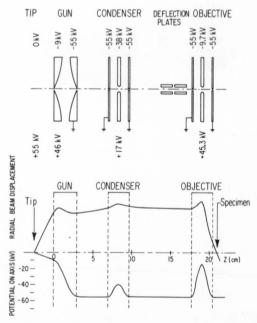

FIG. 17. A three-element optical system yielding low chromatic aberration. The results of the optical calculation are given in Table I.

affecting noticeably its effective overall chromatic figure of merit MC_s/V_s. The latter, however, is not significantly different from that of a gun microscope. What is really gained with the addition of another lens, for constant beam transmission and final spot size is a lower magnification for the system, in addition to the crossover.

A probe radius versus probe current plot for this system when operating at $V_s = 30$ kV is given in Fig. 16. Curves for three values of $e \Delta V$ are shown, 1, 2, and 5 eV, respectively. For the lower $e \Delta V$ values, a 1-nm probe could be obtained with currents still sufficient for microscopy, ($\sim 2.5 \times 10^4$ ions sec^{-1}) even with a FI source operating, for example, at 1 mTorr (required $\beta V = 3 \times 10^{11}$ ions sec^{-1} nm^{-2} sr^{-1} from Fig. 16 and required source pressure from Fig. 7).

Conversely, if high current densities are demanded, with this system operation of the FI source, for example, at 10 mTorr could yield a current density of ~ 0.5 A cm^{-2} in a spot of 10-nm radius. In other words, the proposed system would bring FI sources to yield probe current densities comparable to those obtainable with a simple gun microscope using EHD sources. This may be particularly desirable to extend the range of ion species which could be used for practical microlithography.

Data for an optical column comprising a Butler gun and two einzel lenses (condenser and objective) are also included in Table I. The chromatic figure of merit is indeed the smallest obtained; however, in this design there would be no crossover. The schematics, ray path, and potential distribution for this system are shown in Fig. 17. It may prove more suitable for EHD sources in view of the relatively low source voltage. In practice, not much seems to be gained with the increased complexity of this design, in comparison with the performance of a gun microscope, when EHD sources are employed.

A design study for a 200-kV, high-resolution ion microprobe has been reported by Singh et al. (1976) and in more detail by Cho et al. (1978). This has been by and large inspired by the approach to the problem as outlined by Levi-Setti (1974) and further developed on the basis of early information provided by the Chicago group. Detailed beam optical calculations and engineering considerations are contained in the papers referred to above.

V. Results with Operating Systems

In actual practice, the scanning ion microscopes or microprobes which have thus far been constructed, even using FI or EHD ion sources, still fall short of the intrinsic potential of these sources for the formation of a truly high-resolution probe such as those outlined in Section II. The initial steps have been taken mostly in the direction of exploring the performance of relatively simple optical systems, such as single lens accelerating and focusing ion guns at low resolution, whose properties have been discussed in Section IV.

A comparison of probe data for the operating systems discussed in this section is contained in Table III.

It should be emphasized that for the purposes of transmission ion microscopy, a large probe current density is the antithesis of what is desired to limit radiation damage. Conversely, the ultimate radiation damage (sputtering) is the goal of microfabrication. Therefore, the wide gaps between the performances of different systems in Table III reflect only in part actual instrumental limitations.

A. Gun Microscopes with FI Sources

1. The Chicago STIM: Operation and Performance

The first STIM using a H_2 FI source has been constructed by the Chicago group, and various steps in its development have been recently summarized (Escovitz et al., 1978). In its present version, the instrument is schematized in Fig. 18. The optics of the 65-kV STIM is similar to that of a gun STEM developed by Crewe et al. (1968) and makes use of a 3-cm Butler's gun whose detailed properties have been described in Section IV,A. An aperture of 30 μm defines the beam semiangle at the specimen, equal to 0.15 mrad. The theoretical minimum probe radius limited by the chromatic aberration, is (6.5 × e ΔV) nm, where e ΔV is the source energy dispersion in electron volts.

The electrostatic scanning deflection system and stigmator (Crewe, 1971) consists of eight plates in a symmetric arrangement. The $X-Y$ scanning raster voltages are applied to two pairs of plates respectively. At the same time two linearly independent quadrupole fields, rotated by 45° with respect to each other, can be superimposed on the deflection plates for the correction of astigmatism. A second identical set of plates can be used for dc deflection of the beam.

The optical column incorporates a 90° sector double-focusing magnetic spectrometer, which is used to separate the neutral from the charged beam components and to analyze the latter. The measured spectrometer resolution is 0.1% in energy, in agreement with the design estimate. Its angular acceptance is ±30 mrad. The 5000-gauss water-cooled magnet has precision machined Permendur pole pieces and fringe field clamps

TABLE III

A COMPARISON OF SOURCE AND PROBE DATA FOR EXISTING STIM AND SIM SYSTEMS

	Gun microscopes			Other
	Escovitz et al. (1976)	Schwarzer and Gaukler (1977, 1978)	Seliger et al. (1979)	Orloff and Swanson (1977, 1978)
Type of source	FI	FI	EHD	FI
Gas or metal	H_2	Air	Ga	H_2, Ar
Source pressure (mTorr)	~1	~1	—	~10
Emitter	$\langle 111 \rangle$ W	W	Ga	$\langle 110 \rangle$ Ir
Emitter radius (nm)	50–100	Up to 200	—	150
Emitter temperature (°K)	77	293	~303	77
Probe voltage (kV)	55–65	30	57	10–20
Probe semiangle (mrad)	0.7	1	0.38	2
Probe radius (nm)	100–200	750	100	325 (H_2), 100 (Ar)
Probe current (A)	1.1×10^{-14}	4×10^{-12}	1.2×10^{-10}	5×10^{-11} (H_2), 2×10^{-11} (Ar)
Probe current density (A cm^{-2})	3.5×10^{-5}	2.3×10^{-4}	1.5	1.5×10^{-2} (H_2), 6.4×10^{-2} (Ar)
Probe brightness (A cm^{-2} sr^{-1})	23	73	3.3×10^6	1.2×10^3 (H_2), 5.1×10^3 (Ar)

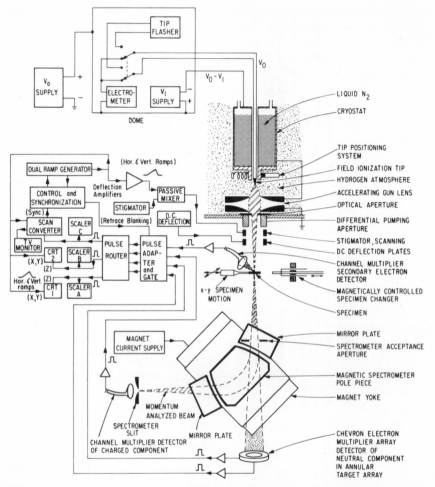

FIG. 18.   Schematic of the latest operating version of the Chicago STIM. Only the electronic instrumentation related to video display is shown.

(mirror plates). Careful magnetic shielding of the optical column and of the magnet preserves good microscope imaging properties, while the magnetic field is swept from zero to the upper limit of the useful range. Thus, it is possible to collect images of the specimen through any selected momentum window, for example, corresponding to a preset range of beam energy loss, or to a particular ionic species. The alignment of the apertures in the system is performed with a laser beam, prior to the installation of the tip and the bottom flange. Importantly, the system is completely symmetric with respect to operation with ions or electrons (with the tip in the FE mode) as an STEM.

a. *Ion Source and Vacuum System.* The field ionization tip is made of $\langle 111 \rangle$ oriented tungsten wire mounted on a hairpin filament as described in Section III,B,1, and is placed 2.5 cm away from the first aperture of the gun. The tip holder is in thermal contact with a liquid N_2 dewar, and the entire assembly is at voltage $V_p - V_s$ with respect to the microscope body. The tip can be flashed by sending a current pulse through the hairpin filament. A spring-loaded frame positioned by two driving sapphire spheres provides accurate and reliable tip-positioning control. Hydrogen gas is admitted to the source region through a palladium leak, and a constant pressure can be maintained, through feedback from an ionization pressure gauge, against the getter action of the pump sublimator (with the ion pump turned off). The source region is separated from the remainder of the column by a differential pumping aperture consisting of a tube of 0.5-mm diameter, 3 cm long. This maintains a pressure ratio of $10^3 - 10^4$ between the two chambers.

In view of the high vacuum requirements for alternate FE operation of the tip, to reduce reactive gas etching of the tip during FI operation, and to maintain a clean specimen environment, the entire system must be evacuated to $\sim 10^{-9}$ Torr before admitting H_2 in the source. This is accomplished with a 150-liter sec^{-1} ion pump in the source region, an 80-liter sec^{-1} ion pump in the specimen and spectrometer region, and a 20-liter sec^{-1} ion pump in the specimen changer vacuum interlock system. The entire microscope must be baked to $\sim 150°C$, at least once after having been opened to air. Purging of the system and bakeout of the source region after each run is necessary to maintain reproducible source operation.

b. *High Voltage.* The FI tip voltage is provided by a stable (~ 10 ppm) -10-kV power supply that is "floated" at V_p in an isolated dome. This also contains the power supply and capacitor bank required for flashing the tip as well as a ± 3-kV supply for FE operations and an electrometer for current monitoring. The STIM probe voltage V_p is obtained from a 100-kV supply stabilized by feedback from a voltage divider to $\gtrsim 10$ ppm. A 25-kV 10-ppm supply provides the voltage for the STEM mode.

Although seldom mentioned, as an engineering triviality, the problems encountered in bringing the system to operating voltage in the range 50–70 kV are quite serious. Part of the difficulty is caused by having a liquid N_2 dewar at high voltage inside the microscope chamber. Extreme precautions had to be adopted in the design of the dewar geometry to reduce causes of vacuum and gas arcing. In spite of these, a slow electrode conditioning process, during which whiskers growth is progressively reduced, is necessary after breaking vacuum. The presence of a number of protecting devices still fails at times in preventing distruction of the tip caused by whisker-induced arcing.

c. *Detectors.* Three output signal channels are available. A channel electron multiplier is used to detect secondary electrons in the SIM or SEM mode of operation. The same detector can be rotated to intercept the entire beam in the transmission mode. This is extremely useful in a number of adjustments such as focusing, correction of astigmatism as well as to obtain overall absorption images. A bias of ± 300 V on the front plate of this detector is used to either attract or repel secondary electrons, depending on the operation mode. A second channel electron multiplier is used to detect ions (or electrons) at the spectrometer exit. Here again, appropriate biasing of the front plate rejects unwanted low-energy particles. A chevron electron multiplier array is used to detect the neutral beam component and provide angular information on the transmitted charged or neutral beam. The array channels are 12 μm in diameter (15 μm center to center).

The gain of the detectors is typically 3×10^6 for the channel multipliers, and 10^7 for the chevron array. The pulse width and maximum random counting rate of the channel multiplier are 30 nsec and 2 MHz, respectively. The chevron array can count up to 1 MHz cm^{-2} of exposed surface. The observed noise is < 1 count sec^{-1} for the channel multiplier, < 10 counts sec^{-1} for an exposed surface of 4.7 cm^2 in the chevron array. For both types of detectors, the detection efficiency is close to 100%. Only pulse mode detection is being used.

d. *Scanning.* The electronic instrumentation related to image display is summarized in Fig. 18. Two CRTs can simultaneously display images obtained from two of the three output signal channels. Either one can be stored in a scan converter connected to a TV monitor. The horizontal scan repetition rate is $\frac{1}{9}$ of TV rate (15,750/9 Hz), the vertical repetition rate is $\frac{1}{8}$ of TV rate (60/8 Hz). Such a vertical repetition rate, rapid for a scanning microscope, is very effective in eliminating the $1/f$ FI current noise, which would otherwise give rise to a banded intensity pattern of the recorded image.

e. *Measuring Instrumentation.* Additional instrumentation not included in Fig. 18 is devoted to the uses of the STIM as a measuring instrument. The counts detected by any of the output channels, for example, during a line scan over a specimen and control region, can be recorded and displayed by a four-input 1024 channels multichannel analyzer. Similarly, mass and momentum beam spectra of the component analyzed by the magnetic spectrometer can be automatically recorded and displayed via a programmed sweep of the magnet current, after having arrested the beam scan at any predetermined location on the specimen under investigation. Coincidence circuits enable the detection of time-related events from any pair of the microscope output channels. A beam-switching circuit can be used to alternately (~ 5 kHz) direct the beam through two selected specimen regions. The signals from the two regions are synchronously routed to two inputs of the multichannel analyzer. Two spectra are thus simultaneously obtained and compared. If one of the two regions is chosen to be a hole, by this method an on-line comparison can be made between primary beam intensity and mass composition versus the momentum analysis of the transmitted beam.

f. *Imaging and Measuring Performance.* The earliest phase of the STIM development was oriented toward establishing the basic imaging capabilities of the instrument. The feasibility of scanning transmission ion microscopy using a field ion source at low resolution was demonstrated (Escovitz *et al.*, 1975a) by the successful operation of the gun microscope at 55–65 kV for extended periods of time in a reproducible manner. It was established that the use of $\langle 111 \rangle$-oriented W crystal wire FI tips gave significant improvement in source performance, such that it became possible to optimize focusing using the microscope stigmator. Images of biological specimens (myofibrils, nuclei of lymphocytes, human metaphase chromosomes) were obtained at resolutions of 100–200 nm (see Figs. 19 and 20), with a probe current of 10^3–10^4 ions sec^{-1}. This was consistent with the design resolution for the probe semiangle adopted at that time (0.7 mrad) and an energy dispersion of the source ions (H$^+$ and H$_2^+$) of 2–3 eV. The mechanism responsible for image contrast in this early exploration was either total or partial absorption of the incident beam in specimen layers of thickness 0.04–0.06 mg cm^{-2}.

In the microradiograph of Fig. 19, critical range absorption (Levi-Setti, 1973, 1974) enhances the contrast between single and double myofibril strands, since the combined thickness of the latter exceeds the range of the incident protons in the specimen (~ 500 nm). In Fig. 20, critical range absorption yields differentiation over a range of areal densities in the structure of metaphase chromosomes. In these early attempts, the channel multiplier detector intercepted all transmitted particles, including those elastically scattered during specimen traversal. In a second phase, imaging of thin specimens (2–10 nm) was explored using contrast mechanisms due to elastic scattering and hydrogen ion neutralization (Escovitz *et al.*, 1976a). The latter process had been singled out by Chanson and Magnan (1954) as a promising source of contrast in the microscopy of unstained organic materials.

For these purposes, the channel multiplier detector was placed farther downstream of the specimen so that a sweeping magnet could be inserted

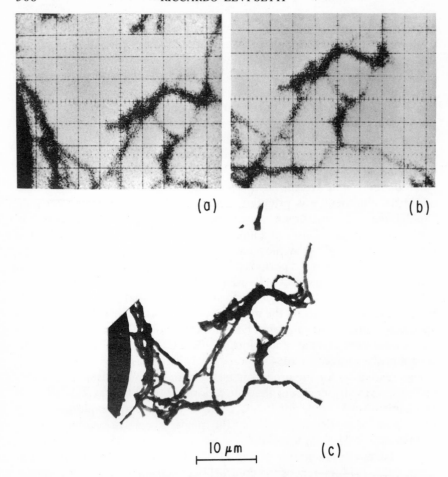

(a)

(b)

10 μm

(c)

FIG. 19. Comparison of images of myofibrils obtained with the STIM [(a), (b)], with (c), a TEM view (Hitachi HV-12) of the same specimen. (From Escovitz *et al.*, 1978, courtesy of New York Academy of Sciences.)

to remove the charged component of the transmitted beam (Fig. 21). At the same time, the detector aperture filtered out beam particles scattered outside a ~6-mrad cone. This yielded conventional bright-field contrast. Detailed images of thin biological specimens, such as erythrocyte membranes (Fig. 22), were obtained using the copious neutral hydrogen signal.

Beyond the qualitative demonstration of imaging capabilities using various contrast mechanisms, further progress in the development of scanning transmission ion microscopy could only be achieved through a better understanding of the basic physical processes involved in the traversal of an ion beam through thin foils of condensed matter.

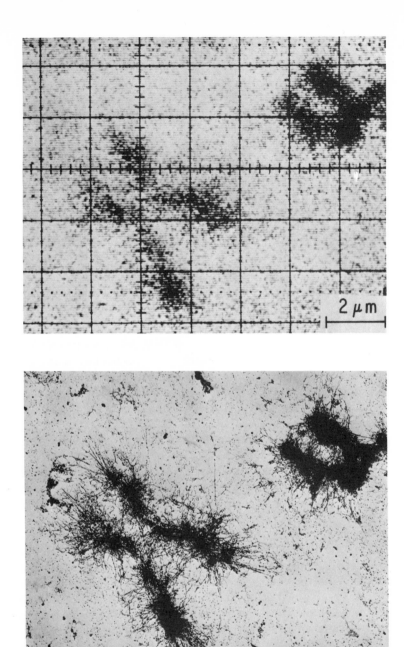

Fig. 20. Comparison of a STIM micrograph of unstained human metaphase chromosomes (above) with (below) a TEM view (Philips EM 200) of the same specimen. The TEM micrograph was taken after a proton irradiation of 5×10^4 protons μm^{-2}, and shows no evidence of catastrophic damage. (From Escovitz et al., 1975b, courtesy of Ultramicroscopy.)

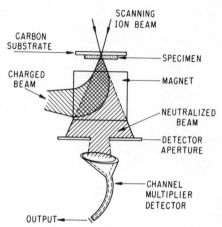

FIG. 21.   Schematic diagram of experimental arrangement to detect the neutralized beam component in the STIM. (From Escovitz *et al.*, 1976a, courtesy of *Ultramicroscopy*.)

Old as this problem may seem, very scanty experimental information is available that is relevant to microscopy, in particular, in the energy region of interest (20–80 kV), close to the Bohr velocity. In this region, at the transition between the validity of classical and quantum mechanical approximations, theoretical calculations are also not entirely reliable.

To explore, then, the potential of the STIM for quantitative ion microscopy, the Chicago group has undertaken a program of systematic study of ion–solid interactions, making use of the magnetic spectrometer as analyzing instrument. Admittedly, this decision has been taken at the expense of further work, for the time being, toward improving the resolution of the microscope. As it turns out, the STIM with its alternate STEM mode and the opportunity to handle microscopic ultrathin targets represents a tremendous asset in conducting atomic and molecular beam–foil experimentation (Escovitz *et al.*, 1979a,b). By recourse to electron or proton energy loss spectra, the target thickness and density can be readily determined. With the wide-acceptance spectrometer employed, electron spectra can be obtained at beam energies between 5 and 25 keV. With H ions, the beam energy range 10–70 kV is accessible to measurement.

Typical incident beam and transmitted beam momentum spectra (obtained simultaneously by beam switching) relative to the traversal of 25-keV H ions through a 4.5-nm carbon film, are shown in Fig. 23. Such spectra are obtained with a wide momentum sweep and are useful to determine the mass composition of the incident beam. For a more detailed study of energy loss spectra, a narrower sweep around particular spectral lines is performed.

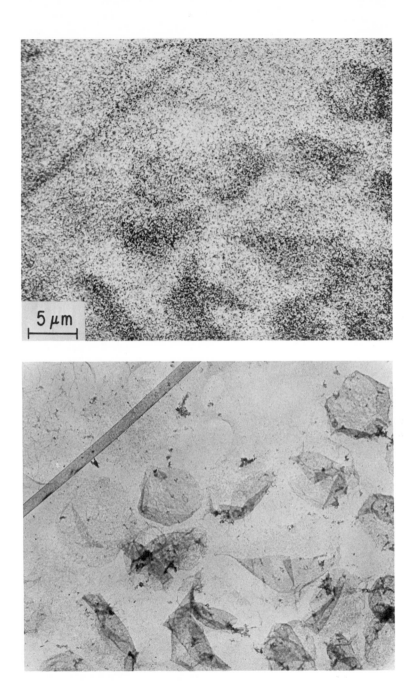

FIG. 22.   (Top) images of unstained human erythrocyte membranes, supported on thin carbon film, as obtained in the STIM using the neutral hydrogen signal. (Bottom) TEM view (Hitachi HV-12) of the same specimen. (From Escovitz *et al.*, 1976a, courtesy of *Ultramicroscopy*.)

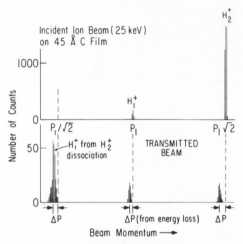

FIG. 23. Typical momentum spectra of the incident beam (top) and transmitted beam (below) as recorded with the magnetic spectrometer of the Chicago STIM. The FI source was operated at low field (~ 20 V nm^{-1}) where H_2^+ is the dominant component. (From Escovitz et al., 1979b.)

Clearly, an overwhelming range of beam–foil measurements is open to investigation using the STIM at the present time. With regard to the reliability of operation of the system, one W tip (remolded prior to each run) has operated for several hundred hours over the past nine months, partly in the FI and partly in the FE mode, without appreciable degradation of performance.

2. The Tübingen Probe

Among the options for the optical system of a gun microscope, a three-electrode einzel lens was chosen for a scanning microprobe constructed by Schwarzer and Gaukler (1977, 1978). The figure of merit for a lens of this kind under typical operating conditions (see Table I) is somewhat unfavorable compared with the other systems discussed previously. Nevertheless, the experiments by these authors are of interest representing an exploration of undemanding working conditions. Thus, the FI tip operates at room temperature, and the system is pumped by a 100-liter sec^{-1} oil diffusion pump. The FI tip protrudes from the orifice nozzle cap through which the source gas is made to flow. A high gas supply is thus provided to the vicinity of the emitter. Only moderate differential pumping (by a factor of 5) is provided through the first gun aperture. The FI source operates at 30 kV with tips of a radius up to 200 nm. This region of source operation approaches the conditions deemed desirable in the discussion of Section III,A,6. The beam current is measured with a specimen grid within a Faraday cup by a high-speed current amplifier. Visual observation of the beam for alignment and coarse focusing is obtained on a scintillation screen. Various source gases, H_2, Ar, O_2, and air have been used. The source and probe data for this system have been listed in Table III.

B. Gun Microscopes with EHD Sources

A high-intensity, high-resolution 57-kV SIM that operates with a liquid gallium EHD source has been constructed at Hughes Research Laboratories (HRL) by Seliger et al. (1978). The schematic of the probe-forming column is shown in Fig. 24. The optics of the system are quite similar to that of the Chicago STIM, and make use of a Munro-type two-element gun already discussed in Section IV,A. The system's operating characteristics have been summarized in Table I.

The ion source consists of a liquid gallium-wetted tungsten needle supported in a reservoir tube (Clampitt et al. 1975). The performance of this source has been discussed in detail in Sections III,C,1 and III,C,2.

The electrostatic deflection system can be programmed under computer control to write a line pattern at a slow scanning speed (20–80 μm sec^{-1}), or to scan in a raster at high speed (5×10^4 μm sec^{-1}) for SIM operation. In the latter mode, secondary electrons are detected by a channel multiplier, to generate an analog signal for video display. With this facility, submicron patterns can be sputtered and promptly visualized. The variation of the probe diameter with the angle of acceptance α_0 at the source was investigated for three settings defined by different object apertures. The resolution was measured from line scans across a test pattern sputtered into a gold film. The results are shown in Fig. 25. The experimental points fit Eq. (32) well for a source energy dispersion e $\Delta V = 7$ eV ($= $ FWHM$/2$). As the authors cautiously suggest, this result most likely confirms the expectation that the resolution is chromatic aberration limited.

The probe currents were found to vary as α_0^2, in agreement with Eq. (8). For source currents of 10 μA, probe currents of 0.7 and 3.0 nA were measured (with target biased so as to suppress secondary emission) in spots of 250- and 500-nm diameter, respectively. This corresponds to a beam current density of 1.5 A cm^{-2}. At current densities such as these, direct line writing by sputtering becomes practical. Chevron patterns sputtered on 40-nm gold films on aluminum substrates are shown in Fig. 26, with line thickness 0.32 and 0.54 μm. Figure 27 shows that repeated passes of a 100-nm probe do not widen appreciably the written line. This indicates

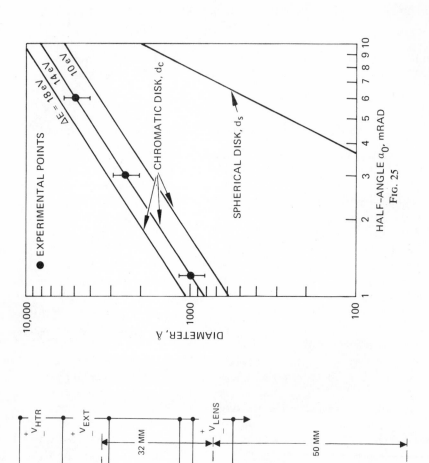

FIG. 24. Schematic of the 57-kV HRL gallium scanning ion probe. (From Seliger et al., 1978, courtesy of R. L. Seliger.)

FIG. 25. Probe diameter versus source half-angle for the SIM of Fig. 24. (From Seliger et al., 1978, courtesy of R. L. Seliger.)

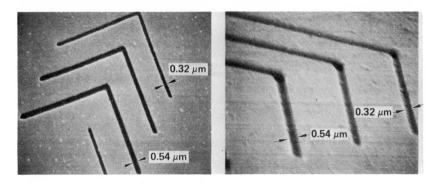

Fig. 26. SEM micrographs of submicron test patterns sputtered in a 400-nm Au film on Al substrate with the Ga⁺ HRL probe. (From Seliger et al., 1979, courtesy of R. L. Seliger.)

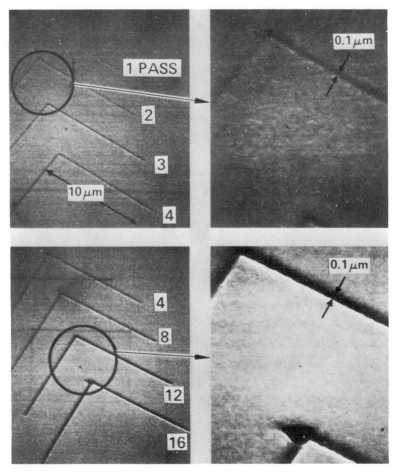

Fig. 27. SEM micrographs of test pattern micromachined by repeated passes of a 100-nm Ga⁺ probe. (From Seliger et al., 1979, courtesy of R. L. Seliger.)

that the probe current density profile is quite rectangular. Evidence of astigmatism with the 100-nm probe is observed when reducing the source current from 10 to 2 μA. The narrow dimension reaches 38 nm in this case. A stigmator should improve the attainable resolution considerably.

On the basis of the mechanism proposed by Gomer (1979) for current generation in EHD sources, one should expect that much smaller probe sizes could be achieved with this remarkable instrument, by simply reducing the beam-defining aperture. From the data summarized in Table III, it is unquestionable, however, that the goals of submicron microlithography have already been met and thus far, only by the HRL device.

Prior to the work of Seliger et al. (1979), focused beams of Cs and Ga ions have been obtained by Krohn and Ringo (1975, 1976) from a Taylor-cone type EHD source. The optical system in this microprobe consisted of an einzel lens followed by a stigmator–deflector. Operating at a magnification of ~75, this system was designed to explore the effective source size rather than to obtain a probe of small dimensions. Nevertheless, the Ga probe was shown to have a brightness of 1.4×10^6 A cm^{-1} sr^{-1} at 21 kV, quite consistent with the results of Seliger et al. (1979). On the basis of these results, a 15-nm multielement 100-kV microprobe was proposed (Krohn and Ringo, 1976, 1978).

C. Multielement Columns

A FI SIM making use of two einzel lenses, as objective and projector, respectively, has been built and operated by Orloff and Swanson (1977, 1978) at the Oregon Graduate Center in Beaverton, Oregon. Relevant optical data for this column have been included in Table I and ion source and probe data in Table III. A schematic of the instrument is shown in Fig. 28. The multielement design offers the desirable flexibility ensuing from the decoupling of source operation from probe focusing. However, the use of symmetrical einzel lenses yields an overall chromatic figure of merit for this column that seriously limits the attainable resolution.

Most appropriately, the source design contains the beam path through the high–pressure source gas (up to 20 mTorr) within 1–2 mm. The differential pumping aperture coincides with the aperture in the extracting electrode, part of a metal cap surrounding the emitter. The use of iridium tips enables operation of this instrument at modest (oil diffusion pump) vacuum requirements. Much of the information relevant to the operation of this system has already been referred to previously, as it pertains to various aspects of this discussion. Among the FI STIMs or SIMs, the Oregon device has thus far yielded the largest probe current densities, 1.5×10^{-2} A cm^{-2} for H$_2$ and 6.4 $\times$ 10^{-2} A cm^{-2} for Ar ions. In fact, this

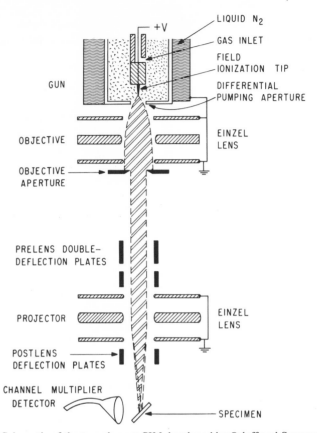

FIG. 28.   Schematic of the two-element SIM developed by Orloff and Swanson (1977).

data, which refers to the operation of a FI source in conditions approaching maximal brightness, lend support to the design expectations set forth in Section IV,B. With a chromatic figure of merit for the electrostatic column, a factor of ten smaller (see Tables I and III), probe currents in the A cm^{-2} range and resolutions in the 10-nm range seem well within reach. Scanning ion micrographs of radiolarians, obtained by Orloff and Swanson with Ar ions, are shown in Fig. 29.

VI. FUTURE DEVELOPMENTS

Notwithstanding the fact that this article is meant to deal with high-resolution scanning ion probes and microscopes, none of the devices thus far built has really entered the high-resolution domain. The design of sev-

FIG. 29.   Micrographs of radiolarians obtained with the SIM of Fig. 28, using 12-kV Ar⁺ ions. (Courtesy of J. Orloff and L. W. Swanson.)

eral systems that should reach the 10-nm range has been discussed; other more speculative systems indicate that even a 1-nm resolution, or better, may be attainable. The ion sources and the technology to attain this goal are, in principle, available.

We are presented here with a dichotomy of purposes that will determine, to a large extent, the amount of effort that will be placed in the future toward approaching such resolutions. As already mentioned, on the one hand it is desired that probes of high-current densities for microsputtering be developed; on the other, high-resolution probes are wanted for microscopy that should not damage the target.

The resources currently devoted to the development of microsputtering probes are considerable. The push originates in the goals for the next generation of microelectronic devices. It would be most desirable if such a thrust could be maintained to go one step further than is actually practical for production and control purposes in the submicron range.

In contrast to the above situation, the development of a high-resolution STIM toward the goals of basic structural microscopy is not as popular. Ironically, one of the major concerns in this development had to be that of demonstrating that an ion probe can also be used in a nondestructive manner (Levi-Setti, 1974; Escovitz *et al.*, 1975b, 1976b). Another major prerequisite that may determine the future of the development is that of providing evidence that a STIM may yield additional information that a STEM is unable to gather. It is for this reason that the author's program is still oriented toward the exploration of new contrast mechanisms and basic beam–foil interactions, rather than pursuing the goal of high resolution. These are considerations that are quite remote from the aspect of feasibility, but the 40-year lead of electron microscopy represents an almost overwhelming advantage, that is difficult to contend with.

If curiosity should prevail, then some of the systems proposed in Section IV could actually be built. Although the solutions proposed are not radically new, they point in several of the directions considered promising in a recent discussion of the prospects for high-resolution ion microscopy by Grivet and Septier (1978). Among the suggestions made by these authors, with regard to the improvement of conventional transmission ion microscope devices, is the use of a high-resolution energy filter of the Castaing–Henry type (Castaing and Henry, 1962, 1964). Such a system could also be employed in a STIM to select a narrow band in the energy spectrum of ions extracted from a FI source, prior to the formation of the probe. This would be a very effective method for improving the chromatic aberration limited resolution.

In the extreme, a system of magnetic and combined electrostatic–magnetic quadrupoles could be used to correct the chromatic aberration at low energy. With the use of EHD sources, a considerable margin for improvement of the resolution may still be available by stopping down the beam defining aperture further. Similarly, devices to increase the supply function in FI sources, resulting in a brightness increase over the present limits, would allow this "brute force" approach to be exploited. It seems that a number of relatively simple options can still be brought to bear before truly sophisticated methods to improve the resolution may be the only resource left.

Shortsighted as it may be, the basic issue at the present moment remains one of motivation and support. Is there a need for a 0.1–1.0-nm probe? The author is still trying to prove that indeed there is such a need, being well aware of the fact that truly outstanding applications may well emerge only postfacto.

ACKNOWLEDGMENTS

This work was supported by the National Institutes of Health and the National Science Foundation. The author is very much indepted to Dr. R. L. Seliger and Dr. L. W. Swanson for contributing most relevant data prior to publication and unpublished photographs. Dr. Gomer has kindly communicated his results on the mechanism of ion emission from EHD sources, also prior to publication. For this, and several illuminating discussions, sincere thanks are due. The undefatigable help and criticism of W. H. Escovitz and T. R. Fox is acknowledged with much appreciation. The author also wishes to thank Dr. J. W. Butler for his computations and for many useful discussions.

REFERENCES

Andersen, C. A., and Hinthorne, J. R. (1972). *Science* **175**, 853.
Beckey, H. D. (1971). "Field Ionization Mass Spectrometry." Pergamon, Oxford.
Beckey, H. D., Dahmen, J., and Knoppel, H. (1966). *Z. Naturforsch.* **21a**, 141.
Bettler, P. C., and Charbonnier, F. M. (1960). *Phys. Rev.* **119**, 85.
Butler, J. W. (1966). *Proc. Int. Conf. Electron. Microsc. 6th, Kyoto, 1966* **1**, 191.
Butler, J. W. (1974). *Proc. Int. Cong. Electron Microscopy, 8th, Canberra, 1974* **1**, 136.
Castaing, R., and Henry, L. (1962). *C. R. Acad. Sci. Paris* **255**, 76.
Castaing, R., and Henry, L. (1964). *J. Microsc.* **3**, 133.
Chanson, P., and Magnan, C. (1954). *C. R. Acad. Sci.* **238**, 1707; *Proc. Int. Conf. Electron Microscopy, London, 1954* p. 294.
Cho, Z. H., Singh, M., and Huth, G. C. (1978). *Ann. N. Y. Acad. Sci.* **306**, 223.
Clampitt, R., and Jefferies, D. K. (1978a). *Nucl. Instr. Meth.* **149**, 739.
Clampitt, R., and Jefferies, D. K. (1978b). *Inst. Phys. Conf. Ser. No. 38* p. 12.
Clampitt, R., Aitken, K. L., and Jefferies, D. K. (1975). *J. Vac. Sci. Technol.* **12**, 1208.
Cookson, J. A., Ferguson, A. T. G., and Pilling, F. D. (1972). *J. Radioanal. Chem.* **12**, 39.
Crewe, A. V. (1971). *In* "Electron Microscopy in Material Science" (U. Valdre, ed.), p. 163. Academic Press, New York.
Crewe, A. V. (1973). *Prog. Optics* **XI**, 225.
Crewe, A. V. (1974). *J. Microsc.* **100**, Pt 3, 247.
Crewe, A. V., and Wall, J. (1970). *J. Mol. Biol.* **48**, 375.
Crewe, A. V., Eggenberger, D. N., Wall, J., and Welter, L. M. (1968). *Rev. Sci. Instr.* **39**, 576.
Dyke, W. P., Trolan, J. K., Dolan, W. W., and Barnes, G. (1953). *J. Appl. Phys.* **24**, 570.
Escovitz, W. H., Fox, T. R., and Levi-Setti, R. (1974). *Proc. Conf Appl. Small Accelerators, 3rd, North Texas State Univ.*, U.S.E.R.D.A. Conf.—741040-P2, p. 125.
Escovitz, W. H., Fox, T. R., and Levi-Setti, R. (1975a). *Proc. Nat. Acad. Sci. USA* **72**, 1826.
Escovitz, W. H., Fox, T. R., and Levi-Setti, R. (1975b). *Ultramicroscopy* **1**, 79.
Escovitz, W. H., Fox, T. R., and Levi-Setti, R. (1976a). *Ultramicroscopy* **1**, 271.
Escovitz, W. H., Fox, T. R., and Levi-Setti, R. (1976b). *Ultramicroscopy* **1**, 383.
Escovitz, W. H., Fox, T. R., and Levi-Setti, R. (1978). *Ann. N. Y. Acad. Sci.* **306**, 183.
Escovitz, W. H., Fox, T. R., and Levi-Setti, R. (1979a). *IEEE Trans. Nucl. Sci.*, NS-26, 1147.
Escovitz, W. H., Fox, T. R., and Levi-Setti, R. (1979b). *IEEE Trans. Nucl. Sci.* NS-26, 1395.
Evans, C. A. (1972). *Anal. Chem.* **44**(13), 67A.
Génotel, D., Laberrigue, A., Payen, F., and Séverin, C. (1968). *Proc. Europ. Reg. Conf. Electron Microsc., 4th, Rome, 1968* p. 187.
Gomer, R. (1959). *J. Chem. Phys.* **31**, 341.
Gomer, R. (1961). "Field Emission and Field Ionization." Harvard Univ. Press, Cambridge, Mass.
Gomer, R. (1978). *Appl. Phys.* **19**, 365.
Gomer, R., and Swanson, L. W. (1963). *J. Chem. Phys.* **38**, 1613.
Grivet, P. (1972). "Electron Optics," 2nd Engl. ed. Pergamon, Oxford.
Grivet, P., and Septier, A. (1978). *Ann. N. Y. Acad. Sci.* **306**, 158.
Haine, M. E., and Mulvey, T. (1954). *J. Sci. Instr.* **31**, 325.
Horowitz, P. (1978). *Ann. N. Y. Acad. Sci.* **306**, 203.
Inghram, M. G., and Gomer, R. (1954). *J. Chem. Phys.* **22**, 1279.
Jason, A. J. (1967). *Phys. Rev.* **156**, 266.
Jason, A. J., Halpern, B., Inghram, M. G., and Gomer, R. (1970). *J. Chem. Phys.* **52**, 2227.
Krohn, V. E. (1961). *Prog. Astronaut. Rocketry* **5**, 73.

Krohn, V. E. (1974). *J. Appl. Phys.* **45**, 1144.

Krohn, V. E., and Ringo, G. R. (1975). *Appl. Phys. Lett.* **27**, 479.

Krohn, V. E., and Ringo, G. R. (1976). *Int. J. Mass Spectr. Ion Phys.* **22**, 307.

Krohn, V. E., and Ringo, G. R. (1978), *Ann. N. Y. Acad. Sci.* **306**, 200.

Levi-Setti, R. (1973). *Proc. Symp. Adv. Technol. Arising from Particle Phys. Res.*, Argonne Nat. Lab. Rep. ANL-8080, p. 4.1.

Levi-Setti, R. (1974). *In* "Scanning Electron Microscopy/1974" (O. Johari and I. Corvin, eds.), Part I, p. 125. IIT Research Institute, Chicago, Ill.

Liebl, H. (1967). *J. Appl. Phys.* **38**, 5277.

Liebl, H. (1975). *J. Phys.* **E8**, 797.

Liebmann, G., and Grad, E. M. (1951). *Proc. Phys. Soc.* **B64**, 956.

Long, J. V. P. (1965). *Br. J. Appl. Phys.* **16**, 1277.

Martin, E. E., Trolan, J. K., and Dyke, W. P. (1960). *J. Appl. Phys.* **31**, 782.

Martin, F. W. (1973). *Science* 179, 173.

Martin, F. W. (1978). *Ann. N. Y. Acad. Sci.* **306**, 262.

Müller, E. W. (1937). *Z. Phys.* **106**, 541.

Müller, E. W. (1951). *Z. Phys.* **131**, 136.

Müller, E. W. (1956). *Phys. Rev.* **102**, 618.

Müller, E. W., and Tsong, T. T. (1969). "Field Ion Microscopy." Elsevier, New York.

Munro, E. (1973). *In* "Image Processing and Computer-Aided Design in Electron Optics" (P. Hawkes, ed.), p. 284. Academic Press, London and New York.

Oatley, C. W. (1972). "The Scanning Electron Microscope," Part I. Cambridge Univ. Press, London and New York.

Orloff, J. H., and Swanson, L. W. (1975). *J. Vac. Sci. Technol.* **12**, 1209.

Orloff, J. H., and Swanson, L. W. (1977). *In* "Scanning Electron Microscopy, 1977" (O. Johari and R. P. Becker, eds.), Vol. I, p. 57. IIT Research Institute, Chicago, Ill.

Orloff, J. H., and Swanson, L. W. (1978). *J. Vac. Sci. Tech.* **15**, 845.

Orloff, J. H., and Swanson, L. W. (1979). *In* "Scanning Electron Microscopy/1979," Part I, p. 39. Scanning Electron Microscopy Inc., Chicago, Illinois.

Riddle, G. H. N. (1978). *J. Vac. Sci. Technol.* **15**, 857.

Schwarzer, R., and Gaukler, K. H. (1977). *Proc. Int. Vac. Conf. Solid Surfaces, 7th, Vienna, 1977* p. 2547.

Schwarzer, R., and Gaukler, K. H. (1978). *Vak. Tech.* **27**, 2.

Seliger, R. L., Ward, J. W., Wang, V., and Kubena, R. L. (1979). *Appl. Phys. Lett.*, **34**, 210.

Septier, A. (1967). *In* "Focusing of Charged Particles" (A. Septier, ed.), Vol. II, p. 123. Academic Press, New York.

Singh, M., Melvin, J., and Cho, Z. H. (1976). *IEEE Trans. Nucl. Sci.* **NS23**, 657.

Sokolovskaia, I. L. (1956). *Sov. Phys. Tech. Phys.* **1**, 1147.

Southon, M. J., and Brandon, D. G. (1963). *Phil. Mag.* **8**, 579.

Sudraud, P., Van de Walle, J., Colliex, C., and Castaing, R. (1978a). *Surface Sci.* **70**, 392.

Sudraud, P., Van de Walle, J., Colliex, C., and Trebbia, P. (1978b). *Proc. Symp. Int. Field Emission, 25th, July 17–22, Albuquerque, N.M.*

Swanson, L. W., and Crouser, L. C. (1969). *J. Appl. Phys.* **40**, 4741.

Taylor, G. I. (1964). *Proc. Roy. Soc. London* **A280**, 383.

Tsong, T. T., and Müller, E. W. (1964). *J. Chem. Phys.* **41**, 3279.

Tsong, T. T., and Müller, E. W. (1966). *J. Appl. Phys.* **37**, 3065.

Turner, P. J. (1967). Field ion microscopy at low field strengths. Thesis, University of Cambridge, England.

Veneklasen, L. H., and Siegel, M. (1972). *J. Appl. Phys.* **43**, 4989.

Zeitler, E. (1973). Lectures presented at Center for Scientific Culture, Erice, Sicily. Unpublished.

Note Added in Proof

Since completion of this article, new results have been reported which provide answers to several of the issues raised herein.

The suggestion in Section III,A,6 that high brightness and low noise in the operation of FI sources may be best achieved with relatively blunt tips and high voltages is now supported by experimental results (Orloff and Swanson, 1979). These authors report angular intensities of H ions as high as 1 μA/sr with $\langle 110 \rangle$ Ir tips of 200-nm radius operated at 21 kV, temperature of 78 K, and pressure of 10 mTorr. The operation of an H_2 FI ion source at temperatures lower than 20 K has been reported (Hanson and Siegel, 1979). The most encouraging results have been obtained at low fields (16 V/nm) with relatively blunt tips, much as anticipated in the discussion of Sections III,A,2 and III,B,2. Ring patterns are usually observed in these operating conditions, with emission sites of angular intensity up to 10 μA/sr, occasionally as high as 60 μA/sr. Notwithstanding the promise of this mode of FI source operation, it is to be anticipated that the emission cones of the brightest sites may not always be accepted by a highly collimated, high-resolution focusing column.

A wealth of new information has become available concerning the operation of EHD sources, discussed in Section III,C. Relevant to the latter are studies by Swanson et al. (1979a,b) reporting beam angular intensities of 20–60 μA/sr from a Ga-wetted W tip yielding currents in the range 1–25 μA. A FWHM of the energy spectrum of the emitted Ga ions of ~4.5 eV was observed, at a tip current of 1 μA for operation at 300 K. Bismuth ion beams were also obtained (Swanson et al., 1979b) with FWHM of ~9 eV at 600 K, 1-μA tip current, and angular intensity comparable to those obtained with Ga. Detailed studies of the ionization mechanism of Ga on a W field emitter have been reported by Sakurai et al. (1979) and by Culbertson et al. (1979). This work explores the regimes which occur for Ga through the melting transition, much as done by Sudraud et al. (1978b) and Sudraud (1979) for Cu and Au. The energy spread of field-evaporated ions from solid Ga, as well as from an intermediate regime preceding the EHD regime, are remarkably low (1.5 eV) (Culbertson et al., 1979). The latter regime, observed for Ga at temperatures $\gtrsim 500°C$ but at fields lower than those yielding EHD emission, yields stable currents of ~10^{-9}A.

By and large, the new data on the performance of FI and EHD sources reinforce several of the views expressed in this article. Based on the angular intensity data given by Orloff and Swanson (1979a,b), the expected performance of an optical column such as that of Fig. 15 has been updated (Levi-Setti and Fox, 1980). Probe currents adequate for STIM operation near the 1-nm level, and current densities adequate for microprobe applications over the range 10–100 nm, are the expectation from such a new instrument.

References

Culbertson, R. J., Robertson, G. H., and Sakurai, T. (1979). J. Vac. Sci. Technol. 16(6), 1868.
Hanson, G. R., and Siegel, B. M. (1979). J. Vac. Sci. Technol. 16(6), 1875.
Levi-Setti, R., and Fox, T. R. (1980). Nucl. Instr. Meth. 168, 139.
Orloff, J. H., and Swanson, L. W. (1979). J. Appl. Phys. 50, 6026.
Sakurai, T., Culbertson, R. J., and Robertson, G. H. (1979). Appl. Phys. Lett. 34(1), 11.
Sudraud, P. (1979). Thesis (unpublished). Université Paris-Sud, Orsay, France.
Swanson, L. W., Schwind, G. A., and Bell, A. E. (1979a). In "Scanning Electron Microscopy/1979," Part I, p. 45. Scanning Electron Microscopy Inc., AMF O'Hare, Ill.
Swanson, L. W., Schwind, G. A., Bell, A. E., and Brady, J. E. (1979b). J. Vac. Sci. Technol. 16(6), 1864.

ADVANCES IN ELECTRONICS AND ELECTRON PHYSICS, SUPPLEMENT 13A

High-Energy Ion Microprobes

BERND MARTIN AND RAINER NOBILING

Max-Planck-Institut für Kernphysik
Physikalisches Institut der Universität Heidelberg
Heidelberg, West Germany

I. SURFACE ANALYSIS BY HIGH-ENERGY IONS

During the last decade the rising understanding of the importance of trace elements in nature, for example, in geology, mineralogy, biology, and medicine, has led to the search for new and better detection techniques.

Among the many processes that occur when a beam of energetic ions or neutral particles hits a surface are the backscattering of some of the incident particles, the sputtering of atoms, molecules, and ions from the surfaces, the secondary emission of electrons, and the production of X rays as a result of the collision process with the target atom (Fig. 1). The use of Rutherford backscattering and nuclear reaction techniques for surface analysis and trace element determination has been the subject of numerous conferences (Mayer and Ziegler, 1974; Meyer *et al.*, 1976; Wolicki *et al.*, 1978) and review articles (e.g., Morgan, 1975; Valković, 1977). The Rutherford backscattering analysis has developed into a very useful tool for measuring concentrations and depth profiles of high-Z elements on low-Z substrates. To obtain depth profile information about low-Z atoms on surfaces of higher-Z substrates, nuclear reactions with positive Q values such as the (d, α) and (d, p) reactions have been used. Since the

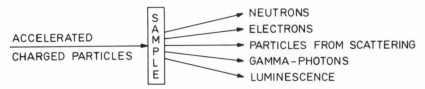

FIG. 1.   Schematic representation of radiations emitted during sample bombardment with charged particles.

Rutherford backscattering distribution can interfere with the (d, α) and (d, p) analysis because of its much higher yield, thin absorber foils, electrostatic deflectors, or magnetic analyzers can be used to eliminate the elastically backscattered particles from being detected. On the other hand, the Rutherford backscattering distribution contains considerable information about the concentrations and depth profiles of the surface constituents. Using high-resolution solid-state detectors and pulse-pileup rejection, the (d, α) and (d, p) reaction peaks can be recorded even in the presence of the Rutherford backscattering distribution with a yield orders of magnitude higher. The Rutherford backscattering and reaction data complement each other since the Rutherford backscattering yields more accurate depth information, while the reaction data give more positive identification of the surface constituents.

The techniques mentioned above are possible complements to the particle- or proton-induced X-ray emission method (PIXE) (Johansson, 1977). The latter is appropriate for samples for which one needs a rapid identification of the trace elements present in the probe. PIXE is a multi-element tracing technique that may also be used with particle beams of micrometer dimensions (Cookson et al., 1972, 1973) owing to the large X-ray production cross sections for protons and charged particles (Garcia et al., 1974).

As a tool for trace element analysis PIXE enables high detection sensitivities in cases where only small samples are available, for example, moon rocks or biological cells. It has been pointed out by Goulding and Jaklevic (1973) and by Folkmann (1975) (Fig. 2) that the minimum detection limits attainable in PIXE are principally given by the production cross sections of the characteristic X rays of the trace elements and, as a result of the interaction of the charged particle beam with the sample, by the continuous background radiation. Characteristic X-ray emission for light projectiles is well understood and can be described theoretically by the inner-shell vacancy production (Garcia et al., 1974) and fluorescence yields (Bambynek et al., 1972). Continuous background radiation mainly consists of secondary electron bremsstrahlung and projectile bremsstrahlung of the bombarding particles slowed down in close collisions

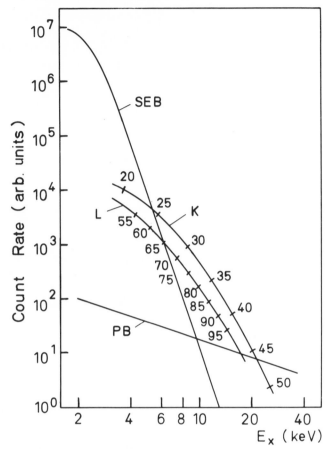

FIG. 2.   Calculated X-ray detector response for a 2-MeV proton beam striking a C matrix (1 mg cm^{-2}) with trace elements (1 ng cm^{-2}). Total characteristic K and L X-ray intensities are shown for the K_α photon energy for target Z values. Bremsstrahlung background yields per 200 eV are given for 1 mg cm^{-2} C. (From Folkmann, 1975.)

with the matrix nuclei. The cross sections of both have been calculated (Folkmann *et al.*, 1974). At higher bombarding energies Compton scattering of γ rays from nuclear reactions between projectiles and matrix nuclei also contributes to the background radiation. The background due to Compton scattering becomes especially predominant for heavy ion bombardment. For the analysis of the X-ray spectra in terms of element concentrations knowledge on X-ray absorption, the detector efficiency, and the solid angle is required. Uemura *et al.* (1978) report on a new way of determining concentrations in the PIXE trace element analysis using the peak-to-background ratio in the spectra.

Once analytical methods such as PIXE have been established, conversion of the technique from macrosample (approximately millimeters in diameter) examination to microsample (≤ 100 μm in diameter) analysis may be achieved by focusing the incident ion beam and providing suitable sample handling facilities. The combination of an energy-variable accelerator for protons or heavy ions and a microprobe facility as described in Section II provides a powerful tool for trace element analysis because the analysis of restricted areas may be carried out in much the same way as with the electron microprobe.

Up to now the nuclear microprobe has found extensive application in the examination of metallurgical specimens (Pierce and Huddleston, 1974). In addition to rocks and minerals, lunar samples and inclusions in various crystals have been examined. So far relatively few biological applications have been reported for the proton or particle microprobe (Horowitz *et al.*, 1976; Johansson, 1977; Bosch *et al.*, 1978b; Wilde *et al.*, 1978). But since the micro-PIXE enables analyses from 0.1 to 1 ppm (weight) for a wide range of atomic numbers, this nondestructive method is invaluable for the determination of trace element concentrations in biological cells, for example, in the human organism with the purpose of detecting and treating human diseases. Its significance has been demonstrated in several publications (Johansson, 1977; Wolicki *et al.*, 1978).

II. Optical Systems for Ions in the Megaelectron-Volt Energy Range

A. General Considerations

There are two possible approaches to constructing a microprobe with ion beams of about $1-5$ MeV u^{-1}. A microprobe or microbeam facility we call any device that can produce ion beams with diameters of less than about 10 μm. This number seems arbitrary at first, but we will give arguments for it in the following.

It is sometimes assumed that the technologies of ion sources and accelerators generally available at institutes of nuclear physics are unsuitable for microprobes, and thus it is concluded that novel approaches to constructing ion sources and accelerators are needed (Cho *et al.*, 1975; Singh *et al.*, 1976; Martin, 1978). We want to point out, however, that van de Graaff and tandem van de Graaff accelerators have a brightness that is sufficient to generate reasonable intensities in microbeams with a phase-space volume of $1-10$ μm^2 $\times$ $10-100$ mrad^2. Theoretical considerations (Folkmann, 1975) and experimental work (Johansson and Johansson, 1976) proved that accumulated charges between 10 and 1000 nC are necessary for relevant measurements. The beam current of 100 pA employed in Table I represents in arbitrary value which in some cases may be too low if measuring times of less than 1000 sec are required for a single analysis.

The possible lateral resolutions with such phase space volumes are as low as about 1–5 μm if the beam is focused on the sample. Beams that are merely collimated require a divergence of no more than $(0.1 \text{ mrad})^2$ if the beam diameter given by the last collimator aperture shall define the lateral resolution of the microbeam (1 mrad stands for an increment in beam radius by 1 μm per 1 mm distance between collimator and target). Contrary to Horowitz and Grodzins (1975), we claim that specially designed ion sources are required if lateral resolutions of less than 10 μm are to be obtained. Standard electrostatic accelerators yield $1000-100$ $(\mu m)^2$ with a beam current of 100 pA. This implies that it will generally be necessary to focus the ion beam. This also facilitates background suppression. Beam-limiting collimators, which often are a source of background or line-peak interference, are now positioned at such a distance from the target that shielding of the X-ray detector is easily accomplished.

The geometric emittance of the existing ion sources and accelerators, however, have such large values ($\epsilon = 1-10 \text{ mm} \cdot \text{mrad}$) that focusing to a few hundredths of a millimeter in diameter results in unacceptably large divergences of several 100 mrad ($\sim 5°$). The phase space thus has to be

TABLE I

REQUIRED PHASE SPACE FOR 100 pA
WITH STANDARD ELECTROSTATIC ACCELERATORS

Accelerator/ion source	Brightness (A cm^{-2} sr^{-1})	Required phase space for 100 pA[a] in a microbeam[b]
Tandem van de Graaff/duoplasmatron	5–50	200–2000 μm^2 · mrad^2
van de Graaff/standard RF source	500–2000	5–20 μm^2 · mrad^2
van de Graaff/optimized ion source[c]	>10^4	<1 μm^2 · mrad^2

[a] The probe current 100 pA is an example; the current has to be adjusted to each specific problem, that is, poor heat conductivity of the sample may forbid current densities higher than 5 pA μm^{-2}, detection limits better than 1 ppm in 1000 sec may require 1 nA or more.

[b] The phase space is given as the product $\epsilon_x \cdot \epsilon_y$, where ϵ_x and ϵ_y represent the horizontal and vertical emittances given in μm · mrad. From this one may easily estimate the lateral resolution in micrometer and the focal depth; additionally, one must consider that semidivergences higher than 50 mrad will cause aperture aberrations as well as chromatic aberrations more than 1 μm.

[c] Septier (1967), Woköck (1977).

restricted by collimators. The intensity loss resulting from collimation is tolerable (see Table I).

The collimators and lenses may be constructed and arranged in the following ways: The beam diameter may be successively confined in subsequent steps as shown in Fig. 3a. Those parts of the beam having too large divergences for the acceptance of the following beam transport system will be cut off by apertures. As in the electron microprobe, the apertures are positioned near the largest beam dimensions, that is, right in front of the lenses. The alternative solution shown in Fig. 3b consists of placing the defining aperture at one of the crossovers of the beam. A reduced image of this aperture is produced by means of one lens. Additional collimators may be used to limit the phase space in the x' and y' components.

The advantages and disadvantages of both methods are discussed briefly. The focal length of lenses for ion beams in the energy range of some megaelectronvolts is hardly less than 10–20 cm. At least 1.5–2.0 m in drift length between object and image is required for a single-stage 100-to-1 area reduction. The very long apparatus necessary to focus a 1-mm² ion source in, for example, two stages on only 100 μm² gives rise to several difficulties.

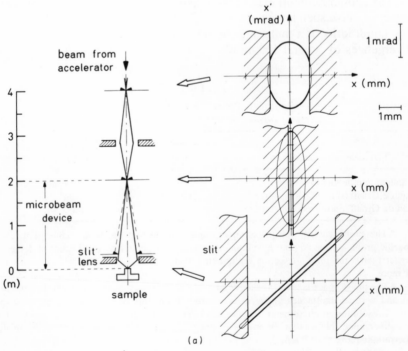

FIG. 3. (Legend on p. 327.)

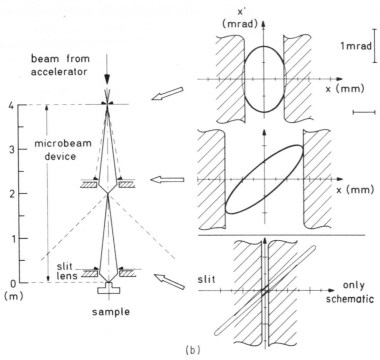

FIG. 3.   Beam profiles and corresponding phase space ellipses. (a) Focusing in two steps; at the intermediate image no collimator is placed. (b) Focusing in one step; a narrow collimator is placed at a crossover and the reduced image of this collimator is formed on the sample.

1. Achieving mechanical stability as well as precision in the micrometer region will be the more difficult the longer the drift lengths between object and image.

2. The increment of phase space resulting from residual gas scattering increases. Since the mean free path of high-energy particles in the atmosphere is of the order of 10^{-7} m, the gas layer between the source and the sample must be on the order of 10^{-7} Torr · m if no more than 10^{-3} particles are to be emitted from the phase space by residual gas scattering. More thorough calculations and experimental work (Nobiling *et al.*, 1975) confirms this rough estimate.

3. Aberrations, for single-step focusing devices usually of less than 1 μm, will increase in every following stage (Heck, 1978a).

Owing to these difficulties focusing in two stages is rarely applied. Examples for this technique exist in Zurich (Bonani *et al.*, 1978) or at an installation for testing purposes in Los Angeles (Cho *et al.*, 1974). Instead single-stage focusing is most often adopted for constructing a microprobe. It consists of mounting a small aperture (holes 10–50 μm in diameter) at a crossover of the ion beam. Since in this approach the x and y components of the beam are decreased drastically, area reductions of the order of 100 are sufficient for obtaining lateral resolutions of 1–5 μm. Slit scattering, however, may deteriorate the beam quality. Together with residual gas scattering and possibly lens aberrations this slit scattering gives rise to a halo around the focused microbeam and degrades the lateral resolution. These considerations indicate the necessity for special collimators, which keep slit scattering small, and for lenses with a short focal length for a compact microprobe construction.

In the following, the essentials for constructing a collimator and a focusing system for proton and heavy ion beams of about 1–5 MeV u^{-1} are discussed.

B. Collimator Systems

A collimator for ion beams usually consists of apertures or a set of edges that restrict the phase space of the beam. At the collimator edge particles may be scattered, and the slit scattering generally prevents geometric emittances from being less than 0.1 mm × 0.1 mrad. Beams that are limited by normal collimators, that is, by simple drilled holes or slits with milled surfaces, have a halo of scattered particles (Armstrong and Wegner, 1971) owing to slit scattering.* This restricts the efficiency of such beams for microanalysis. A microprobe that is to supply information on a microscopic structure should fulfill the condition that at least 99% of the beam intensity hit the region of interest. With a more intense scattering halo around the beam, however, one either has to perform time-consuming control measurements or else, in the case of strong concentration gradients of some elements, the results are completely obscured. In order to build a microprobe with a good quality beam one must pay special attention to the collimator system, particularly if one wants to construct a compact microprobe. As shown above, for this purpose a carefully designed collimator should be arranged at a crossover of the beam from a standard accelerator for 1–5-MeV u^{-1} protons or heavy ions.

This design should reduce slit scattering to such a degree that a microbeam with a halo of less than 0.1% of the beam intensity will be obtained. Slit scattering has been studied with a H_3^+ molecular beam of 1-MeV energy from a van de Graaff accelerator (Nobiling et al., 1975). With this

---

* The following considerations give only geometric arguments; depending on the special case of application, we also have to consider processes other than elastic scattering, for example, (p, n) reactions (Burge and Smith, 1962).

method it was possible to measure the intensity of the beam and of particles that had been scattered at the slits and at the residual gas simultaneously, and to differentiate between them. According to the results of this slit scattering study (Fig. 4) a halo of about 1×10^{-4} from slit-scattered particles is expected at slit widths of about 30 μm in this particular experimental arrangement.

Two aspects are essential for the quality of the collimator slits: a good surface quality and a correct geometry of the slits. With the proper mater-

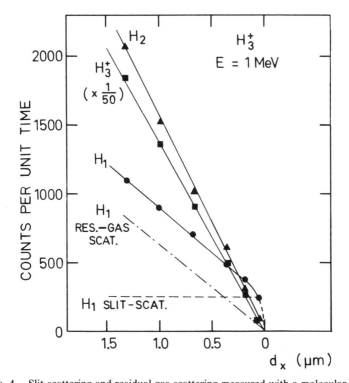

FIG. 4. Slit scattering and residual gas scattering measured with a molecular beam of H_3^+ particles from a van de Graaff accelerator. The energy of the particles is measured by means of a surface-barrier detector. The beam passes through a line-shaped collimator with a hole of $d_y = 6$ μm $\times$ d_x, d_x being varied. This geometry provides an almost constant source for slit scattering and a variable beam intensity. The acceptance angle of the solid-state detector (15 μsr) is of the same order of magnitude as the acceptance of the focusing lens of the Heidelberg microprobe. The dashed and dashed–dotted curves are obtained by decomposing the observed H intensities into a constant and a d_x-proportional term. From this one can calculate the probabilities for slit scattering and residual gas scattering each. The drift length is 1.06 m, the residual gas scattering amounts to 3.5% of the beam intensity at $5 \cdot 10^{-5}$ Torr, where the fraction of slit scattering at, for example, 1 μm was about 0.35% of the beam intensity. (From Nobiling et al., 1975.)

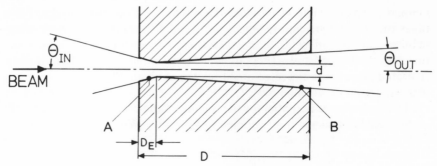

Fıg. 5. Schematic view of the discussed slit profile. Both surfaces A and B are polished to a peak-to-valley height of 0.05 μm. The values for the slits in use at the Heidelberg microprobe are θ_{in} = 15°, θ_{out} = 4°, D = 5 mm, D_E = 0.2 mm.

ial* a peak-to-valley height of the surface better than 0.1 μm is easily obtained by thoroughly polishing the beam-defining surfaces. At the Heidelberg microbeam the collimators are made out of Widia metal (tungsten carbide). With this material a much better polishing quality can be achieved than with antimagnetic steel.

Polishing, however, can merely reduce slit scattering; equally important is the geometry of the slit profiles (Fig. 5) for which the following points have to be considered:

1. Only protons that are scattered at the surface A into angles larger than θ_{in} reach the second part of the collimator behind the edge. To reduce the number of scattered particles θ_{in} should be as close to 90° as possible.

2. For the same reason θ_{out} should be as small as possible in order to stop particles that have passed the collimator edge.

3. On the other hand, the angle α between both polished surfaces should be as close to 180° as possible to keep the transparency for protons small. This transparent area of the slits depends on the particle energy and on the slit material and is typically some 0.1 μm at an angle α of 160° and with 1–4 MeV protons.

4. θ_{out} has to be greater than the maximum semidivergence of the incoming beam to avoid that transmitted particles are scattered at the exit surface B.

In trying to fulfill these conditions one has to compromise. An angle θ_{in} of about 10–20° provides a small scattering probability and an angle of 2–4° for θ_{out} fulfills the "antiscatter condition" (2) for slit widths up to 1–2 mm if D of the collimator is of the order of 5 mm, where D_E is small (0.1–0.3 mm). For practical purposes it is useful to vary the slit width.

* See footnote on p. 328.

This may increase the beam intensity and lower the detection limits but may result in worse lateral resolutions. In addition, nonquadratic beam geometries may be used with an optimal current density.

A second set of slits or apertures is applied to match the emittance of the collimator system with the acceptance of the following lens. With an average lateral reduction factor of, for example, 10 the semidivergences should be on the order of 0.2–2.0 mrad. Thus the collimating system will produce emittances ϵ_x and ϵ_y of 10–100 μm $\cdot$ 0.1–2.0 mrad from a standard accelerator beam. Beams with emittances of this order can be focused in such a way that lateral resolutions of 1–5 μm are obtained with one-stage focusing.

C. Focusing Elements

As mentioned earlier, the beam after passing the collimator system has to be focused in order to obtain good lateral resolutions of ≤ 10 μm and sufficient current densities. In the following, the different types of focusing lenses for charged particles are examined as to whether they are suited to produce ion beams with diameters of less than 10 μm.

Axially symmetric lenses, as frequently used in electron optics, have the advantage of a simple construction but they are limited in their reflective power: a coil with a focal length of 10–15 cm requires a field of 3–5 T if only 2-MeV protons with a momentum of 60 MeV c^{-1} are to be focused (Glaser, 1952). For this case a superconducting coil is needed and at higher momenta than about 80 MeV c^{-1} several problems will arise, even with superconducting coils. Moreover, aberrations are generally greater than for lenses that are not axially symmetric (Scherzer, 1936; Dymnikov et al., 1965a).

Nonaxially symmetric lenses such as quadrupole lenses have a more complex geometry, but their reflective power is much better suited for focusing heavy ions with velocities of some megaelectron volts per atomic mass unit. For particles with lower velocities than 1.0–1.5-MeV u^{-1} electrical quadrupoles may be used (Augustyniak et al., 1978). In this case the required field gradient is proportional to the particle energy, where for magnetic lenses the required gradient scales only with $E^{1/2}$. At higher velocities (≥ 1 MeV u^{-1}) we should thus use magnetic systems. To obtain good field geometries and high gradients, generally iron or ferromagnetic material with high saturation is used for the pole pieces and pole tips (Septier, 1960). On account of saturation, iron becomes the limiting factor for the field gradients. In many cases normal conductive coils are sufficient for excitation. Superconducting quadrupoles are used mainly when wide apertures are required (Geraskin et al., 1973). But usually the apertures in microbeam systems are so small that lenses with narrow apertures can be used that increase the maximum field gradient in conventional quadrupoles to values of about 500 T m^{-1}. This is sufficient for focusing also particles heavier than protons, for example, 40-MeV ^{16}O.

The existing systems exclusively employ quadrupole focusing. Frequently (Cookson et al., 1972; Wilde et al., 1978; Brune et al., 1977; McKenzie, 1978) an arrangement of four quadrupoles is used, as proposed by Dymnikov et al. (1965b). The advantage of this arrangement, an orthomorphic image, can only be utilized if the shape of the first collimator, the object, is reproduced exactly on the sample.

From the considerations on collimators given above it follows that instead of pin holes crossed slits should generally be used as source apertures. Since the horizontal and vertical direction can thus be varied independently, stigmatic imaging is no longer necessary. Therefore the lens system can be optimized according to other points of view, for example, a short, simple construction.

Although the drift length should be as short as possible, 5–10 cm between sample and lens are needed for a monitor microscope, detectors, and, perhaps, electrostatic or magnetic deflectors. In most cases an area reduction of the first collimator of about a factor of 100 is needed to achieve the desired beam intensity. For one-stage focusing this will be a drift length of about 1.5–2.0 m. From such a mechanical length of the apparatus we can expect sufficient stability, and the vacuum system requires no specially developed technology to achieve less than 10^{-3} for scattering probabilities at the residual gas. A pressure of $p \sim 10^{-7}$ Torr is sufficient.

Estimates for a quadrupole doublet and triplet and imaging features of these lenses are given in Table II. The required field gradients, as mentioned, may be obtained easily by means of a narrow aperture of about 5 mm. To avoid aberrations caused by mismachining we must carefully design and build these quadrupoles, and we will discuss in Section II,D what we find to be essential in their design.

D. Microprobe Facilities

1. The Harwell Microprobe

The first high-energy proton microprobe built in Harwell (Cookson and Pilling, 1970) utilizes the "Russian quadruplet" arrangement for focusing and circular apertures for collimating. A schematic view of the setup is given in Fig. 6. Both collimators consist of drilled holes causing slit scattering to contribute to the halo around the beam. The halo inten-

TABLE II

COMPARISON BETWEEN QUADRUPOLE DOUBLET AND TRIPLET[a,b]

	Quadrupole lens	
	Doublet	Symmetric triplet
Effective length (mm) and gradient G (T · m^{-1}) of:		
Element 1 (3)	$l = 40, G = 88$	$l = 22.5, G = 132$
Element 2	$l = 40, G = 136$	$l = 40, G = 132$
Drift length between Elements (mm)	31	31
Area reduction factor	156	84

[a] The calculations have been performed with the Fortran code OPTIC II (Larson, 1971).
[b] Common parameters used for both systems are: particles with 100 MeV c^{-1}, 5.35-MeV protons; a drift length between first collimator and lens of 1.80 m; a drift length between lens and sample of 0.10 m.

sity is typically 4–5% of the beam intensity. For focusing four quadrupole lenses are used with an effective length l = 18.05 cm and an aperture $2r$ = 3.84 cm each. This arrangement is capable of producing an orthomorphic image of the first collimator (Table III), in good agreement with the theoretical work of Dymnikov *et al.* (1965b). A very critical procedure

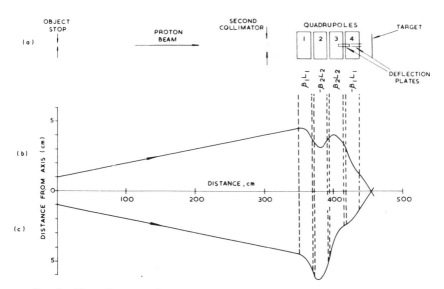

FIG. 6. Harwell proton microprobe. (a) The layout of the focusing system; (b) calculated trajectory in the horizontal plane for a ray starting 1 cm from the axis with 0.01 radian divergence; (c) calculated trajectory in the vertical plane.

TABLE III

FOCUSING PROPERTIES OF THE HARWELL PROTON MICROPROBE[a]

Object aperture (μm) $x = y$	Divergences (mrad) $x' = y'$	Singlet 1	2	3	4	Beam size $x \cdot y$ (FWHM) in the target plane (μm^2)
19	0.23 1.33	x foc	x defoc	x foc	x defoc	$2.2 \pm 0.2 \cdot 3.2 \pm 0.2$[b] $2.9 \pm 0.5 \cdot 3.7 \pm 0.5$[b]
168	1.33	x foc	x defoc	x foc	x defoc	$32.2 \cdot 32.2$[c]
381	1.33	x foc	x defoc	x foc	x defoc	$71.4 \cdot 71.4$[c]

[a] From Cookson and Pilling (1970).
[b] Obtained with a scanning method.
[c] Obtained with an optical microscope.

is the mechanical adjustment of such a system consisting of four singlets; a rotation around the beam axis of one quadrupole by only 0.1°, for example, increases the beam spot by more than 10 μm. This focusing system has a relatively poor phase-space acceptance (see Table IV); but in connection with a one-stage accelerator current densities of 10 pA μm^{-2} in the target plane can be obtained easily.

2. The Zurich Microprobe

The Zurich microprobe represents yet quite a different type of setup (Fig. 7). A similar device is described by Cho *et al.* (1974). Here, focusing

TABLE IV

PHASE-SPACE VOLUME FOR THE DIFFERENT PROTON MICROPROBES
CALCULATED WITH COMPUTER CODE ION BEAM[a,b]

System	Distance Object (m)	Image (m)	Maximum acceptance parameters $\pm x_0$	$\pm y_0$	$\pm \alpha_0$	$\pm \beta_0$	Phase-space volume/4π (μm$^2 \cdot$ mrad^2)
Harwell	3.5	0.21	8.5	8.5	0.62	0.4	18
Zurich	8.8	0.48	43	6.6	0.24	0.43	29
Heidelberg	1.84	0.11	7	40	0.70	0.39	76
Karlsruhe	2.66	0.15	3.46	43.6	1.17	0.47	83

[a] From Heck and Kasseckert (1976).
[b] For comparison the same final spot size of 3 × 3 μm and image aberrations ≤1 μm are assumed.

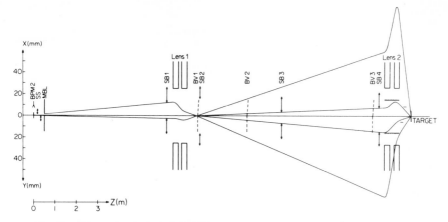

FIG. 7.   Schematic view of the Zurich microbeam facility. The two x, y beam profiles shown to the right of BV1 are those defined by the emittance of an accelerator (outer profile) and by the acceptance of the second quadrupole doublet lens (inner profile) (BPM, beam scanner; SS, stabilizing slits; MBL, object aperture; SB, movable high-precision horizontal and vertical apertures; BV, beam viewer).

is accomplished in two steps, and consequently the collimators can have rather wide apertures without slit scattering contributing significantly to a halo. This arrangement, however, needs a very long drift length, the resulting instability, residual gas scattering, and the influence of the magnetic field of the earth detracting from the lateral resolution. Moreover, calculations by Heck (1978a) show that aberrations increase drastically in such an arrangement.

In fact, in one direction the desired resolution of 10 μm cannot be obtained with this microprobe. The first collimator (Fig. 7) has a square opening of 1 mm side length. This square is to be focused in two steps to 10×10 μm². The first focusing step consists of a quadrupole doublet with an effective length $l = 25.4$ cm and an aperture $2r = 5.1$ cm of each singlet. The lenses in the second step have an effective length $l = 23.5$ cm and an aperture $2r = 5.1$ cm for each singlet. This setup of rather weak focusing lenses causes the very long drift length of ~ 17 m between the first collimator and target. The resulting influence of parasitic magnetic fields on the beam of charged particles has to be compensated for by three pairs of Helmholtz coils. The lateral resolution (FWHM) achieved so far is 11 μm and 26 μm in the x and y directions, respectively (Bonani et al., 1978). The reported current density ranges from 1 to 2 pA μm⁻². The system is capable of focusing protons as well as heavy ions and might thus be used for analytical work as well as for deep implantation of heavy ions.

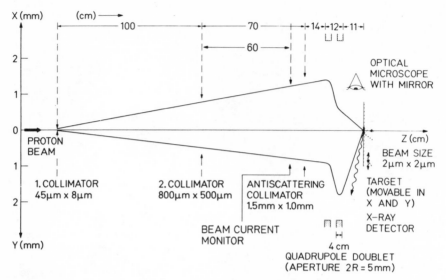

FIG. 8.   Profile of the Heidelberg proton microprobe.

3. The Heidelberg Microprobe

In the construction of the Heidelberg microprobe system (Fig. 8) the above guidelines were applied.* A collimator is used with which the geometric emittances ϵ_x and ϵ_y can be adjusted from < 10 μm $\times$ 0.01 mrad to 100 μm $\times$ 2 mrad. Since crossed slits are used for adjusting the area as well as the divergences, the horizontal and vertical emittances can be regulated separately. The aperture for adjusting Collimator 1 consists of two piezoelectrically driven slits, similar to the arrangement described by Nobiling et al. (1975) (Fig. 9). Due to the limited range of tension of the piezoceramic drivers a lever transmission was chosen to enhance the variability of the slit width. Such drivers were installed into one slit, having identical calibrations performed with a Michelson Interferometer. In the completely assembled slits the calibration was then checked with an optical microscope. The neutral points of the calibration are rechecked from time to time during measurement periods for possible deviations.

For the front edges of the slits Widia metal (tungsten carbide) was used. The peak-to-valley height at the surfaces attainable with this material is of the order of 0.05 μm. In this way slit scattering is diminished. The actual angles and sizes of the front edges in use at the Heidelberg microprobe are given in the caption to Fig. 5. The width of the slits can be

* Nobiling et al. (1977).

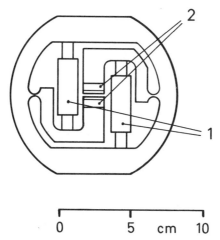

```
┌─────────┬─────────┐
0         5   cm    10
```

Fig. 9. Drawing of a variable slit used for the first collimator in the Heidelberg micro-probe. The slit width is controlled by the tension of the piezoceramic drivers (1) with a variable high voltage. The ring is made out of V4A antimagnetic steel, the inner parts of the slits (2) of tungsten carbide. Since steel and the piezomaterial have different coefficients for thermal expansion, aluminum cylinders connect both to compensate for this.

regulated precisely by varying the high voltage. The construction shown in Fig. 9 achieves a maximum slit width of 120 μm by means of an active piezolength of 40 mm, the voltage for this extension being 1.5 kV.

One meter behind this aperture, four single-slit edges are installed that may be adjusted separately with micrometer screws to vary the divergences from 0.01 mrad to about 2 mrad. With this arrangement the horizontal and vertical divergences can be controlled independently to adjust the emittance of the collimator. Even for inconventional applications, for example, a greater focal depth, an optimal adjustment can be achieved.

The beam is focused using a short quadrupole doublet. From a comparison between a doublet and a triplet having nearly the same field gradients it can easily be seen (Table II) that for a fixed drift length between first collimator and the image plane and for a given distance between lens and sample the former yields the highest demagnification. The other well-known advantages of the triplet (Regenstreif, 1967) have thus been neglected.

The lens was designed for focusing particles with momenta up to 300 MeV c^{-1}. That is, a maximum field gradient of 400 T m^{-1} is needed in the geometry described in Table II. Such a high gradient may be obtained by means of the very narrow aperture of 5.0 mm in diameter. Quadrupole lenses, however, especially in combination with narrow apertures, are afflicted with seemingly unsurmountable parasitic aberrations. "The problems posed by parasitic aberrations are frustrating ones, which each experimentalist must solve for his particular system; they probably form the most formidable obstacle to the widespread use of quadrupoles at the present time" (Hawkes, 1970, p. 65).

Some special provisions were made in the construction and performance to keep these parasitic aberrations small. Naturally, the narrow aperture requires great precision in machining the iron parts of the lens; tolerances of about ±5 μm were achieved. Equally important is the symmetry of the magnetic return path between pole pieces and yoke to avoid field asymmetries from distrubances in the magnetic circuits (Hardy, 1967; cited in Hawkes, 1970). Moreover, the choice of material for the iron parts as well as its treatment are essential. The iron parts are made out of Vacoflux 50* with a saturation of 2.3 T. The material is hot-rolled for better homogeneity. The pole pieces and yokes are then milled and turned on a lathe, respectively. Thereupon they are annealed to attain magnetic properties and to remove mechanical and magnetic stress. In the last step of fine grinding the material is kept at room temperature to preserve the magnetic properties. To improve the quality of the quadrupole field the coils are wound as close as 4 mm to the aperture (Taylor, 1965).

A completely assembled singlet is shown in Fig. 10. To produce a proper quadrupole field the iron parts near the aperture (Fig. 11) have the following properties. For practical reasons the profile of the pole tips was chosen cylindrical simply because such a profile can be manufactured with sufficient accuracy (±5 μm); it has been shown theoretically and experimentally (Shukeilo, 1959; Dayton et al., 1954, Banford, 1966) that a cylindrical profile provides a constant field gradient (±1%) within 80% of the aperture. For the iron profile parallel to the z direction a profile similar to a Rogowsky (1923) profile was chosen to reach a uniform magnetization of the iron and to avoid edge saturation (Braams, 1964).

Further details on the Heidelberg lens design are given in Fig. 11. On account of the very accurate machining the parasitic abberations were kept at such orders of magnitude that the imaging properties given in Table V were accomplished.

Both singlets are installed in a support with which mismachining can be compensated by means of mechanical adjustments by shifting the singlets relative to each other in the x and y directions and by tilting them in the x', y', and z' directions. In practice, however, it was only necessary to rotate the first quadrupole in the z direction and to improve the alignment of the whole lens relative to the collimator axis. Apparently, the

---

* 50% iron, 50% cobalt; trademark: Vacuumschmelze, Hanau.

0   5   cm   10

FIG. 10.   Photograph of a quadrupole singlet with a 5-mm aperture used in the Heidelberg microprobe. The lens design is similar to the one of the short lenses in the UNILAC
accelerator at Darmstadt (Langenbeck, 1973). The vacuum tube is made out of antimagnetic
steel (V4A), the coils out of enamel copper wire with a rectangular cross section (1 mm²).

very accurate machining causes the mechanical axis and the magnetic
axis of both singlets to coincide with an accuracy sufficient for achieving
spot sizes of 1–2 μm.

To monitor the beam spot and its shape and size during the focusing
procedure the fluorescence light emitted from a plastic scintillator is observed with an optical microscope. For better accuracy this scintillator
should be about 10–20 μm thick. Neither scintillators that stop the protons nor quartz can be used for beam diagnostics in the micrometer
region. Especially with quartz the scintillation patterns exceed the beam
diameter by more than 10 μm. Quantitative measurements of the beam
profile were performed as follows. A polished edge of a copper foil with a
thickness of 10 μm was used as target. It was moved with a step motor
within the image plane through the beam. The K_α and K_β counts of Cu
were recorded for every step. Two pieces of information may be extracted from such measurements: the beam diameter can easily be calculated from the number of steps in the falling or rising part of the measurement, as well as the halo of scattered particles from the ratio
$counts_{in}/counts_{out}$ since the copper foil area is some square millimeters
and hit by half the scattering halo. Typical halo intensities ranged from

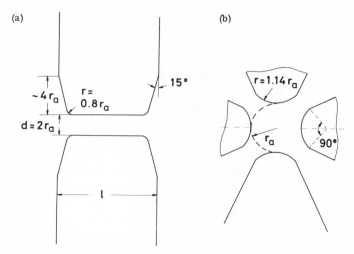

FIG. 11.   Profile of the iron parts of the lens (a) parallel to the beam axis and (b) perpendicular to the beam axis. The radius r_a of the aperture depends on the maximum field gradient with which one wishes to work. For two reasons apertures with $2r_a < 4$ mm are not recommended: the mechanical accuracy becomes more critical and a narrower tube (<3.5 mm) within the aperture causes a poor vacuum. Two examples, both with $1 = 4.5$ cm, are given: (1) $2r_a = 10$ mm: for $B = 1$ T at the pole tip follows for $B'_{max} = 2$ T/cm with 2000 AT (ampere $\times$ turns); (2) $2r = 5$ mm (actual dimensions of the lens in use at the Heidelberg microprobe): $B'_{max} = 4$ T cm^{-1} with 1000 AT.

TABLE V

FOCUSING PROPERTIES OF THE HEIDELBERG PROTON MICROPROBE

Slit width (μm)		Divergences (mrad)		Singlet		Beam size in the target plane (μm^2)
x	y	x'	y'	1	2	
90 ± 3	16 ± 2	0.3	0.3	x defoc x foc	x foc x defoc	$4.5 \cdot 4 \pm 1^a$ $<1 \cdot 23 \pm 1^a$
30 ± 3	8 ± 2	0.4	0.4	x defoc	x foc	$1.1 \cdot 1.3 \begin{Bmatrix} +0.5 \\ -0 \end{Bmatrix}$ FWHM $1.8 \cdot 1.9 \begin{Bmatrix} +0.5 \\ -0 \end{Bmatrix}$ 99% width^b

^{a} Radiation damage on a plastic scintillator measured with an optical microscope.

^{b} Measured by a slow scanning procedure. A copper foil of about 1 mm^2 in size with a well-polished edge was glued on a plastic scintillator and moved by means of a step motor through the beam. The yield of the copper K_α line was recorded in dependence of the target position.

10^{-4} to 10^{-3} of the beam intensity. These values had been expected from slit scattering and residual gas scattering, and apparently lens aberrations do not contribute significantly to this halo. Some results from such scans are given in Table V. A typical current density obtained is $5-10$ pA μm^{-2}.

4. The Karlsruhe Microprobe

The same principle of one-stage focusing in connection with adjustable slits as described in Section II,D,3 is utilized in the device described by Heck (1976). The proton beam is focused with a quadrupole doublet with an effective length $l = 10$ cm and aperture $2r = 5$ cm. The smallest beam diameter obtained so far is of the order of 2.5 μm; the beam current density achieved is 60 pA μm^{-2}, the highest value reported for a microbeam system up to now; the halo-to-beam-intensity ratio is $1:2500$.

Concluding, good collimators and a simple arrangement of carefully manufactured strong lenses in connection with standard electrostatic accelerators constitute a facility that may perform either scans or point analyses with both good lateral resolutions and sensitivities. The following section illustrates the analytical application of the proton microprobe.

III. SELECTED FINDINGS

The PIXE technique is most often applied in the investigation of solid samples, preferably as thin foils containing 10–15 elements in amounts of 10–0.01 ng. The experimental methods developed during these investigations are summarized in a review article by S. A. E. Johansson and T. B. Johansson (1977). Another field of interest is the determination of the trace element content in solutions. The most common case is that of water solutions (Johansson et al., 1972; van Rinsvelt, 1974; Lochmüller et al., 1972, 1974). However, biological and medical samples also have been investigated by the PIXE method with proton beams several millimeters in diameter (Johansson and Johansson, 1977).

In order to demonstrate the characteristic properties of a proton microbeam, for example, lateral resolution and detection sensitivity, and to show what kind of studies can be performed with such a probe, we present here some of the projects that were carried out with the proton microprobe at the Max-Planck-Institut für Kernphysik, Heidelberg.

In connection with the lunar program of the institute the proton microprobe was used to determine the trace elements in mineral grains of a lunar basalt (Apollo 17, Sample No. 75015) whose compositions had been determined previously with the electron microprobe. Two mineral grains, *ilmenite* (FeTiO$_3$) and *baddeleyite* (ZrO$_2$) were chosen for the search for trace elements that had not been detected by the electron microprobe. The qualitative analysis was carried out with the electron microprobe at 15 and 30 keV, respectively, using a Si(Li) detector to identify the elements. No elements other than those measured qualitatively could be detected. In agreement with the results of previous electron microprobe investigations (El Goresy *et al.*, 1974) we found that the Zr in the Apollo 17 ilmenites is below the detection limit for the electron microprobe. The insets of Fig. 12 show the electron microprobe spectra of an ilmenite grain measured at an excitation energy of 15 keV. The same grain was then analyzed with the proton microprobe at an excitation energy of 2 MeV with the results given in Fig. 12. The K_α and K_β lines of Y, Zr, and Nb are well developed in the spectra of ilmenite 3. Note the absence of the L lines of these elements in the spectra taken at 15 keV due to the high bremsstrahlung background (inset of Fig. 12). Table VI displays the elements measured with the proton microprobe that were not traced with the electron microprobe. The results disclose the ability of the proton microprobe to identify trace elements in solids that cannot be detected, even qualitatively, with the electron microprobe.

To demonstrate the applicability of the proton microprobe as a scanning device we show the analysis of a pollen tube of *Lilium longiflorum* (Fig. 13). These pollen tubes are classical examples of tip growth with

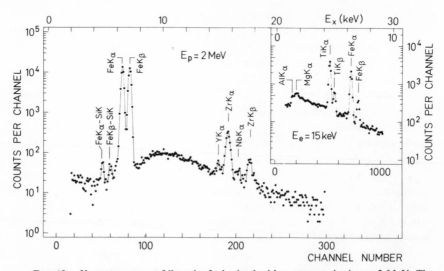

Fig. 12. X-ray spectrum of ilmenite 3 obtained with proton excitation at 2 MeV. The inset is the spectrum taken with the electron microprobe at 15 keV for the same grain. The K spectra of Y, Zr, and Nb are well developed in the proton probe spectrum.

TABLE VI

CALCULATED CONCENTRATIONS OF Zr, Y, AND Nb AS MEASURED WITH THE
PROTON MICROPROBE IN ILMENITE 3 IN LUNAR SAMPLE NO. 75015

Element	Concentration (ppm)
Zr	1600 ± 300
Y	60 ± 20
Nb	40 ± 15

oriented exocytotic secretion (Rosen, 1968; Schnepf, 1969; Franke *et al.*, 1972; Morré and Vanderwoude, 1974). It is speculated that the Ca^{2+} ion plays an essential role in pollen tube growth (Herth, 1978). This is induced from the fact that Ca^{2+} is the dominant agent for the exocytosis of animal secretory cells (Foreman, 1973; Allison, 1974; Dahl and Gratzl, 1976). The calcium concentration along the pollen tube (100 μm long) thus being of interest we scanned a cell with a 2-MeV proton beam. The P, S, and Ca X-ray intensities per step were recorded simultaneously with a multi-scaling device. An example is given in Fig. 13. The scans showed Ca gradients along the pollen tube, the concentration of which depended on the

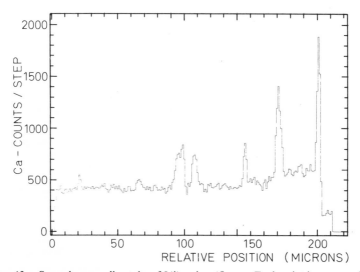

FIG. 13. Scan along a pollen tube of *Lilium longiflorum*. Each point is measured for the same accumulated charge. All counts of Ca-characteristic X rays (K_α and K_β) are recorded. After each measured point an advance of the sample of 1 μm was performed by a stepping motor.

preparation method of the pollen cells. The absolute amount of Ca in one of the investigated samples was 0.016 pg.

These studies demonstrate that the difficulties in the investigation of biological samples are not caused by the microbeam facility but rather by the preparation of the samples.

IV. Future Developments

By modifying and developing various aspects of the high-energy ion microprobe the analytical potential can be altered. We first have to consider possible improvements of the focusing technique. Constructing lens systems with higher demagnification factors will improve the lateral resolution of existing facilities. Maintaining lateral resolutions of 1–2 μm such lenses also render possible the construction of a setup that is much more compact. But such a lens system, for example, a multiplet with an intermediate focus between the lenses, will introduce additional aberrations that exceed those of a simple doublet by far. More accurate studies of lens systems, mainly of aperture aberrations, will be performed.

By improving the stabilization of the accelerators, chromatic aberrations may become smaller than aperture aberrations. In addition, the energy spread of the beam accepted by the collimating system is smaller than the energy spread of the beam from a standard Van de Graaff accelerator. This may be proved by simple geometric considerations.

For microprobes with a lateral resolution of not less than 0.1 μm the present technologies of ion sources and accelerators are suited well since the current densities obtainable ($\sim$60 pA μm^{-2}) (Heck, 1978b) are most always sufficient and for some samples even too high. For instance, mica samples analyzed with proton beams of 2-MeV energy and $\sim$10 pA μm^{-2} current density suffered severe heat damage. Improving the lateral resolution by means of a higher beam current density may thus impose additional requirements on the sample stability.

The difficulties encountered when investigating samples *in vacuo* may partly be alleviated by analyzing the targets in air using external beams. For such experiments the sample is mounted outside the vacuum system, the ion beam traversing a thin foil acting as window between vacuum system and atmosphere (Horowitz and Grodzins, 1975; Cookson and Pilling, 1976; Shroy *et al.*, 1978). In this respect one might also want to consider analyzing biological samples *in vivo*. Unfortunately, however, this is not possible since the cell structures as well as the cell membranes will most probably be damaged by the bombarding ions within the very first seconds of the analysis, leading to an instantaneous diffusion of elements within the cell and the surrounding medium. The cells have to be fixed by shock freezing or similar methods, possibly transferred into vacuum, and then analyzed without introducing artifacts. Analyzing samples in the deep-frozen state (Kaufmann and Echlin, 1978) is believed to be the best method.

The analytical potential of a microbeam facility can also be expanded by using detectors other than the Si(Li) detector. As shown (Nelson and Courtney, 1977), combining a detector for backscattered particles with an X-ray detector will open new possibilities for the detection of elements with $Z \le 12$. A detector for nuclear γ rays will yield information on certain elements or isotopes.

The resolution of X-ray lines can be improved by using a crystal spectrometer. If heavy ions instead of, for example, protons or α particles are used as projectiles, this might open a new approach to the element analysis: detecting the X-ray satellite lines after heavy-ion collisions additional information on the ionization state may be extracted (Watson et al., 1977). Although the use of a crystal spectrometer connected to a microbeam facility is generally difficult because of the space between the target and the last quadrupole and because of poor counting rates, this detector system may still be of interest. For instance, in analyzing the biological samples discussed above we are not only interested in the presence and distribution of different ions; it is of equal importance to learn about the ion configuration in order to understand their function in a biological cell. We are currently trying to distinguish among different states of the ions by varying the preparation methods of the samples. In some cases, a crystal spectrometer might give such information more directly.

In conclusion, high-energy ion microprobes excel the electron microprobe not only in detection limit but might open up new analytical methods as well.

REFERENCES

Allison, A. C., and Davies, P. (1974). Symp. Soc. Exp. Biol. 28, 419.
Armstrong, D. D., and Wegner, H. E. (1971). Rev. Sci. Instr. 42, 40.
Augustyniak, W. M., Betteridge, D., and Brown, W. L. (1978). Nucl. Instr. Meth. 149, 669.
Bambynek, W., Craseman, B., Fink, R. W., Freund, H.-U., Mark, H., Swift, C. D., Price, R. E., and Venugopala Rao, P. (1972). Rev. Mod. Phys. 44, 716.
Banford, A. P. (1966). "The Transport of Charged Particle Beams." Spon, London.
Bonani, G., Suter, M., Jung, H., Stoller, C., and Wölfli, W. (1978). Nucl. Instr. Meth. 157, 55.
Bosch, F., El Goresy, A., Martin, B., Povh, B., Nobiling, R., Schwalm, D., and Traxel, K. (1978a). Science 199, 765.

Bosch, F., Martin, B., Nobiling, R., Povh, B., and Traxel, K. (1978b). *Microsc. Acta Suppl. II*, 331.

Braams, C. M. (1964). *Nucl. Instr. Meth.* **26**, 83.

Brune, D., Lindh, U., and Lorenzen, J. (1977). *Nucl. Instr. Meth.* **142**, 51.

Burge, E. J., and Smith, D. A. (1962). *Rev. Sci. Instr.* **33**, 1371.

Cho, Z. H., Singh, M., and Mohabbatizadeh, A. (1974). *IEEE Trans. Nucl. Sci.* **21**, 622.

Cho, Z. H., Singh, M., and Melvin, J. (1975). Scanning ion microprobe: An alternative to the scanning electron microscope, Int. Rep., Lab. Nucl. Med. Radiation Biol., UCLA.

Cookson, J. A., and Pilling, F. D. (1970). *Harwell Rep.* **AERE-R** 6300.

Cookson, J. A., and Pilling, F. D. (1973). *Thin Solid Films* **19**, 381.

Cookson, J. A., and Pilling, F. D. (1976). *Phys. Med. Biol.* **21**, 963.

Cookson, J. A., Ferguson, A. T. G., and Pilling, F. D. (1972). *J. Radioanal. Chem.* **12**, 39.

Dahl, G., and Gratzl, M. (1976). *Cytobiology* **12**, 344.

Dayton, I. E., Shoemaker, F. C., and Mozley, R. F. (1954). *J. Sci. Instr.* **25**, 485.

Dymnikov, A. D., Fishkova, T. Ya., and Yavor, S. Ya. (1965a). *Sov. Phys. Tech. Phys.* **10**, 592.

Dymnikov, A. D., Fishkova, T. Ya., and Yavor, S. Ya. (1965b). *Sov. Phys. Tech. Phys.* **10**, 340.

El Goresy, A., Ramdohr, P., Medenbach, O., and Bernhardt, H.-J. (1974). *In Proc. 5th Lunar Sci. Conf.* **1**, Suppl. 5, 627.

Folkmann, F. (1975). *J. Phys. E: Sci. Instr.* **8**, 429.

Folkmann, F., Gaarde, C., Huus, T., and Kemp, K. (1974). *Nucl. Instr. Meth.* **116**, 487.

Foreman, J. C., Mongar, J. L., and Gomperts, B. D. (1973). *Nature* **245**, 249.

Franke, W. W., Herth, W., Vanderwoude, W. J., and Morré, D. J. (1972). *Planta* **105**, 317.

Garcia, J. D., Fortner, R. J., and Kavanagh, T. M. (1974). *Rev. Mod. Phys.* **45**, 111.

Geraskin, E. V., Grebinnik, V. G., Zhukov, V. A., Malyaev, V. Kh., Manych, A. P., and Selivanov, G. I. (1973). *Int. Rep. P13-7297*, Joint Inst. of Nucl. Phys., Dubna.

Glaser, W. (1952). "Grundlagen der Elektronenoptik." Springer, Wien.

Goulding, F. S., and Jaklevic, J. M. (1973). *Ann. Rev. Nucl. Sci.* **23**, 45.

Hardy, D. F. (1967). Combined magnetic and electrostatic quadrupole electron lenses. Dissertation, Cambridge University.

Hawkes, P. W. (1970). Quadrupoles in electron lens design, *Adv. Electron. Electron Phy. Suppl. 7.*

Heck, D. (1976). *Kernforschungszentrum Karlsruhe KFK Rep.* **2379**, 108.

Heck, D. (1978a). Private communication.

Heck, D. (1978b). *Kernforschungszentrum Karlsruhe KFK Rept.* **2668**, 115.

Heck, D., and Kasseckert, E. (1976). *Kernforschungszentrum Karlsruhe KFK Rep.* **2379**, 130.

Herth, W. (1978). *Protoplasma* **96**, 275.

Horowitz, P., and Grodzins, L. (1975). *Science* **189**, 795.

Horowitz, P., Aronson, M., Grodzins, L., Ladd, W., Ryan, J., Merriam, G., and Lechene, C. (1976). *Science* **194**, 1162.

Johansson, S. A. E. (1977). *Nucl. Instr. Meth.* **142**, 1.

Johansson, S. A. E., and Johansson, T. B. (1976). *Nucl. Instr. Meth.* **137**, 473.

Johansson, T. B., Akselson, R., and Johansson, S. A. E. (1972). *Adv. X Ray Anal.* **15**, 373.

Kaufmann and Echlin, eds. (1978). Microprobe Analysis in Biology and Medicine, Microscopica Acta, Suppl. II. Hirzel Verlag Stuttgart, West Germany.

Langenbeck, E. (1973). *GSI Rep. 1973/1*, 9.

Larson, J. D. (1971). *IEEE Trans. Nucl. Sci.* **NS-18**, 3 1088; *Optic II*, unpublished.

Lochmüller, C. H., Galbraith, J., Walter, R., and Joyce, J. (1972). *Anal. Lett.* **5**, 943.

Lochmüller, C. H., Galbraith, J. W., and Walter, R. L. (1974). *Anal. Chem.* **46**, 440.
McKenzie, C. (1978). Private communication.
Martin, F. W. (1978). *Ann. N.Y. Acad. Sci.* **306**, 262.
Mayer, J. W., and Ziegler, J. F. (eds.) (1974). "First International Conference of Ion Beam Analysis, Yorktown Heights, U.S.A., 1973." Elsevier Sequoia, Lausanne.
Meyer, O., Linker, G., and Käppeler, F. (eds.) (1976). "Second International Conference of Ion Beam Analysis, Proceedings." Plenum, New York.
Morgan, D. V. (1975). *Contemp. Phys.* **16**, 221.
Morré, D. J., and Vanderwoude, W. J. (eds.) (1974). *Proc. Symp. Soc. Develop. Biol. 30th.*
Nelson, J. W., and Courtney, W. J. (1977). *Nucl. Instr. Meth.* **142**, 127.
Nobiling, R., Civelekoğlu, Y., Povh, B., Schwalm, D., and Traxel, K. (1975). *Nucl. Instr. Meth.* **130**, 325.
Nobiling, R., Traxel, K., Bosch, F., Civelekoğlu, Y., Martin, B., Povh, B., and Schwalm, D. (1977). *Nucl. Instr. Meth.* **142**, 49.
Pierce, T. B., and Huddleston, J. (1974). *Nucl. Instr. Meth.* **144**, 231.
Regenstreif, E. (1967). In "Focusing of Charged Particles" (A. Septier, ed.), Vol. I. Academic Press, New York.
Rogowski, W. (1923). *Arch. Elektrotech. (Berlin)* **12**, 1.
Rosen, W. G. (1968). *Ann. Rev. Plant Physiol.* **19**, 435.
Scherzer, O. (1936). *Z. Physik,* **101**, 593.
Schnepf, E. (1969). "Protoplasmatologia VIII/8." Springer, Wien, New York.
Septier, A. (1960). *Nucl. Instr. Meth.* **7**, 217.
Septier, A. (1967). In "Focusing of Charged Particles" (A. Septier, ed.), Vol. II, p. 123. Academic Press, New York.
Shroy, R. E., Kraner, H. W., and Jones, K. W. (1978). *Nucl. Instr. Meth.* **157**, 157.
Shukeilo, I. A. (1959). *Sov. Phys. Tech. Phys.* **4**, 1123.
Singh, M., Melvin, J., and Cho, Z. H. (1976). *IEEE Trans. Nucl. Sci.* **NS-23**, 657.
Taylor, E. A. (1965). *Proc. Int. Symp. Magnet Technol., Stanford,* 208.
Uemura, Y. J., Kuno, Y., Koyama, H., Yamazaki, T., and Kienle, P. (1978). *Nucl. Instr. Meth.* **153**, 573.
Valković, V. (1977). "Nuclear Microanalysis." Garland, New York.
van Rinsvelt, H. A., Punnam, F. E., Russel, J. P., and Bolch, W. E. (1974). *Proc. 3rd Conf. Appl. Small Accelerators, 1974* **I**, 148.
Watson, R. L., Leeper, A. K., and Sonobe, B. I. (1977). *Nucl. Instr. Meth.* **142**, 311.
Wilde, H. R., Roth, M., Uhlhorn, C. D., and Gonsior, B. (1978). *Nucl. Instr. Meth.* **149**, 675.
Woköck, H.-D. (1977). *J. Phys. E: Sci. Instr.* **10**, 973.
Wolicki, A. E., Butler, J. W., and Treado, P. A. (1978). *Nucl. Instr. Meth.* **149**, 1.

Index

A

Aberration, 45–47
 correction, 109–132
  Darmstadt high-resolution project, 132–140
  foil lenses and space charge, 109–118
  high-frequency lenses, 118–121
  lens combinations, 105–109
  mirror correctors, 128–132
  quadrupoles and octopoles, 121–128
  system optimization, 91–109
 equations of motion, 49–51, 53–55
 field ion guns, 289–294
 ion microprobe, 327–328, 335, 338, 344
 ion microscopy, 264–268, 270
 scanning systems, 102–103
Aberration coefficient, 46–47, 49, 59–90, 127–128
 computer algebra systems for calculation of, 82–90
 extrema, 91–94
 ion microscopy, 266, 268
 lens combinations, 105
 matrix techniques for calculation of, 71–78
 microwave cavity lens, 119
 scanning system, 103
Accelerator, 161–162
 microprobe technology, 324–325, 344
 trajectory tracing, 59–60
Achromat lens, 134
Algebra language, for computer programming, 82–90
Anisotropic aberration, 65–66
Anisotropic aberration coefficient, 105
Aperture aberration, 67–68, 134, 137
Aperture lens, 5
Aplanatic lens, 134–138
Apochromat lens, 134–135
Argon, field ionization, 273, 275, 277, 301
Astigmatism, 64–65, 67, 69, 135, 137, 139
Asymetrical lens, 95

B

Asymptotic aberration coefficient, 60–63, 66, 86
Auger electron microscope, 116–117
Automation, of beam emittance measurement, 235–240
Axial field curve, for lens, 41–42

Backscattering, 321–322
Backstreaming secondary electrons, in beam measuring devices, 248
Beam brightness, 159–259
 basic definitions, 176–184
 brightness–current curve, 229
 intensity–brightness curve, 195, 197, 211–214
 invariance, 179–182
 measurement of, 201–235
 relation to emittance, 186–187
 scanning ion microscopes, 264–265, 268–289, 320
 specific brightness, 264–265
 symbols and conventions, 252–254
Beam emittance, 159–259
 basic definitions, 184–186
 coupling due to magnetic field, 187–189
 ellipse, 183, 185–186
 improvement of concept of, 192–194
 intensity-emittance characteristic curve, 194–198
 invariance, 184–185
 measurement of, 201–248
  automation and continuous display, 235–240
  possibilities and limitations of various methods, 250–251
  systematic errors, 240–248
 in quadrupole lens, 128
 relation to brightness, 186–187
 root-mean-square emittance, 198–200
 symbols and conventions, 252–254

349